D0267765

Elementary Textiles

Julia Southard Lee, Ph.D.

Professor of Home Economics
New Mexico College of Agriculture and Mechanic Arts

Elementary Textiles

1 9 5 3

Prentice—Hall, Inc.

New York

Preface

ECONOMICS AND TECHNOLOGY largely determine which textile fibers are available. It is only after the consumer understands the advantages and limitations of the various fibers and fabrics that wise selections can be made for clothing and household fabrics. The combined information of producer and consumer-buyer is often needed to assure a selection which will give satisfactory service.

Market research has shown, however, that the average customer is only vaguely conscious of type of fiber or construction of fabric, but he does want appearance, wearability, cleanability (launder or dry clean), color fastness, and a suitable hand—all of this at a favorable price. The specific things asked for can be summarized by saying that attractive and serviceable fabrics are wanted in every price range. So much progress has been made in producing new fibers and finishes that many luxuries of a decade ago are in common use today. The increasing variety of textile materials emphasizes the need for consumer information on the performance of fibers, fabrics, and finishes.

The many aspects of the subject—cultural, economic, and technological, the aesthetic and the practical—are considered in the following pages, which should lead to a general understanding and appreciation of:

(*a*) Sources of materials from which fabrics are made.

(*b*) Properties which adapt fibers and fabrics to specific uses.

(*c*) Methods by which the beauty or usefulness of fabrics are increased.

v

(*d*) Methods by which standards of fabrics are improved or controlled.

(*e*) Procedures by which the useful life of household fabrics and garments are prolonged.

(*f*) The interchangeability of fibers in end uses.

(*g*) The place of fibers in the economic lives of people and nations.

The reader will find worthwhile information in *Elementary Textiles*. Facts are given on the history, production, properties, and consumption of fibers from which clothing and household fabrics are made. The importance of the industrial uses of both fibers and fabrics in everyday life is indicated. Both the consumer and the professionally interested should gain factual knowledge which will help them in the selection, use, and care of clothing and household fabrics.

Maps and figures have been used to supplement the text. It is hoped that the footnotes will not only serve as documentation for the text but will familiarize the reader with names of the people who have made fundamental contributions to one phase or another of one of the world's most diversified, oldest, and largest industries—textiles.

Elementary Textiles is divided into two parts. Part One is a study of the present or potential value of fibers in world commerce. In some instances, the primary reason for including a fiber in this study is for its potential value or for its scientific interest. World maps show areas in which production of each fiber is important, and figures illustrate comparisons of some properties of fibers. The natural fibers are considered first, for two reasons: They are the oldest by centuries, and they still constitute about nine-tenths of the world's supply of fibers.

The manufactured fibers are considered second. Those made from natural fibrous materials are of potential value as a means of using to advantage surplus materials or by-products. The opportunities for development of synthetic fibers are great. It is conceivable that, within another century, synthetic fibers may as adequately satisfy needs for fabrics as synthetic dyes satisfy the need for color today.

Part Two is a study of fabrics and the procedures by which they are constructed, dyed, finished, and cared for. The factors contributing to their deterioration are also discussed. Included in the study are some of the problems of the consumer-buyer as he tries to find and interpret labels and other information on the serviceability of fabrics and garments. Apropos of the consumer's difficulties, there is a description of several agencies working in his behalf and contributing to the improvement or standardization of fabrics.

The Appendix includes a glossary of terms, indexes commonly used for reference in the library, a list of textile books, a list of textile journals and magazines, a list of abstracts, for speed in reference work, an inventory of textile resources of the United States, and a conversion table.

The fabrics of each age reflect not only the technological progress but also the social and economic life of its people. We have emphasized those aspects, historically and in contemporary living. The fibers and fabrics of today are presented for the study and appreciation of an important phase of modern life.

Sincere appreciation is expressed to each who has contributed in any way by encouragement or assistance. Special thanks are extended to Professor Rosalie V. Rathbone whose early encouragement made this task seem possible; to John Hoye, who gave valuable help and criticism on the original outline; to Robert Wright and Steve Allured, who prepared the figures; to Elvira Lindquist, whose special contribution was the preparation of Chapters Fifteen, Sixteen and Seventeen; to Mary Eliason and Mason E. Miller, who read the entire manuscript; to Professor M. E. Ensminger, who read and made helpful suggestions on Chapter Seven; and to Professor Jessie V. Cole, who read and made constructive suggestions on Chapter Twenty-two.

JULIA SOUTHARD LEE

Contents

PART ONE, FIBERS

PART TWO, FABRICS

Part One

Fibers

Chapter One

Introduction to Fibers

MOST CONSUMERS think textiles consist of only fibers and fabrics used for clothing and household purposes. Industrial uses should not, however, be overlooked, as they are of growing importance in consumer products such as automobile upholstery, stuffings, and tire fabrics. This book will therefore cover fibers and fabrics commonly used for industrial purposes as well as for clothing and household furnishings.

TERMINOLOGY IN FIBERS

In order that terminology may be clear, some textile terms will be described. Terms basic to all fibers and fabrics are, for the most part, well defined. Vagueness exists chiefly when textile materials or their performances are not well understood or are too new to have become established in the pattern of things. *Fiber* will be described here; other terms will come later.

Fiber. Fiber has been defined as a unit of matter in which the length is at least 100 times the diameter.[1] Although fibers are abundant throughout plant and animal life, only a few of them have the requisites that make them valuable as textile fibers. A minimum length of 5 mm., pliability, cohesiveness, and sufficient strength are essential.[2] Other fiber properties of more or less value for specific uses are elasticity, fineness, uniformity, durability, and luster.

[1] A.S.T.M. Committee D-13, *A.S.T.M. Standards on Textile Materials.* (Philadelphia: American Society for Testing Materials, 1949).
[2] A.S.T.M., *op. cit.*, 1950.

3

Textile fibers are either *staple fibers* or *filaments* and are the fundamental units used in textile fabrication. They can be spun into yarns or made into fabrics by a variety of methods. Yarns are always used in weaving, knitting, lacemaking, and some other methods of fabric construction.

Staple fibers. If fibers are short and have to be spun to make them into yarns, they are called staple fibers. In the case of natural fibers, the length of the staple is a measure of quality. The quality of manufactured fibers is not, however, related to length. Long staple cottons, such as Egyptian and Pima, command a premium on the market. On the other hand, fine, expensive wools have a shorter staple than do cheaper and coarser wools. Length, in itself, as an indication of high quality depends upon the fiber in question.

Filaments. When the length is indefinite, as it may be in the case of silk and manufactured fibers, the fibers are called filaments and may be twisted together or laid together to form yarns. Manufactured fibers and silk may also be cut into staple lengths and spun into yarns.

CLASSIFICATION OF FIBERS

Fibers may be classified in a number of ways. Any one method will depend upon the aspect of fibers under consideration. Three general classifications are based upon:

a) composition—organic or inorganic
b) method of production—natural or manufactured
c) use—apparel, household, or industrial

There is broad overlapping in the last classification.

Composition. In composition, fibers may be divided into two groups: organic and inorganic. The organic fibers include a wide variety of both natural and manufactured fibers. All fibers in this class contain carbon atoms, regardless of how widely their composition or structure may differ otherwise. The natural fibers, with few exceptions, are of either plant or animal origin. The plant fibers are chiefly cellulose (a plant-building material). The animal fibers are chiefly protein (an animal-building material). The manufactured organic fibers are made either from fibrous or fiber-forming materials from plants or animals or from small molecules which have to be built into long ones. The inorganic fibers are comparatively few. They do not contain carbon atoms. Probably the most familiar of the inorganic fibers are asbestos, Fiberglas, and aluminum. Asbestos occurs as a fibrous rock in nature. The other two are manufactured fibers.

The following classification based upon composition is only one of a number which might be given to aid in clarifying the relationships between fibers:

I. Cellulose and related products
  A. Natural fibers
    1. Seed hairs—cotton, milkweed, kapok
    2. Bast—flax, hemp, ramie
    3. Root—palmetto
    4. Hull—coir
    5. Leaf—henequen, sisal, abacá
  B. Manufactured fibers
    1. Regenerated cellulose, rayon [3]
      a) Viscose
      b) Cuprammonium
    2. Cellulose derivatives (made from cellulose)
      a) Estron,[4] cellulose acetate
      b) Modified celluloses
    3. Algenates, from seaweed (related to cellulose)

II. Proteins and protein derivatives
  A. Natural fibers
    1. Animal hair and wool
    2. Silk fibroin
  B. Manufactured fibers
    1. Animal proteins, casein, albumen, keratin, fibroin
    2. Plant proteins, zein, peanut, cottonseed, soya

III. Synthetic fibers [5]
  A. Nylon
  B. Vinyon and Saran
  C. Orlon and Dynel
  D. Dacron
  E. Others

IV. Inorganic fibers
  A. Natural: Asbestos
  B. Manufactured
    1. Glass
    2. Metal

Production. From the standpoint of production, fibers may be considered as belonging to either of two large groups, natural or manufactured. Natural fibers still furnish approximately 91 per cent of the total world supply, the manufactured fibers about 9 per cent.[6] The natural fibers used in fabric manufacture include a large variety of materials of plant and animal origin. The *World Fiber Surveys* of 1947 and 1948 consider nine fibers of major economic importance. Cotton, wool, jute, flax, hemp, silk, abacá, sisal, and henequen are the natural fibers which

---

[3] *Rayon* is a generic term for filaments or staple fiber composed of regenerated cellulose.

[4] *Estron* is a generic term for filaments or staple fiber composed of one or more esters of cellulose.

[5] *Nylon* is a generic term for linear polyamides. Vinyon, Saran, Dacron, Orlon, and Dynel are trademarked names.

[6] *World Fiber Review* (Washington, D. C.: Food and Agriculture Organization of United Nations, 1948).

constitute 91 per cent of the world's supply. The rayons and estron
which account for 8.8 per cent, are of minor importance from the standpoint of the total quantity of fibers produced. About 0.2 per cent of
total fiber production is nylon. The manufactured fibers are gaining
so rapidly in relative importance that some estimates claim they may
eventually equal or exceed the production of natural fibers.[7]

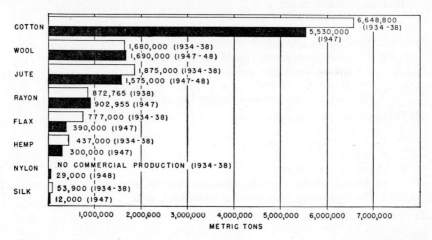

**Fig. 1.1. World production of some textile fibers for selected periods, 1934–38 and
1947–48.** *Source:* WORLD FIBER REVIEW *(Washington: Food and Agriculture Organization of the United Nations, 1948).*

The period 1934–1938 is considered a normal period in fiber production before World War II. It is used frequently in this book for purposes of comparison, since that was the last prewar period for which
sufficient data are available on a comparative basis. The production of
fibers was seriously disrupted by the war. Data on total production
during the war are difficult or impossible to obtain and are largely estimates.

The changes which occurred during that period were far-reaching.
Some centers of fiber production will probably never attain the leadership
held prior to the war; for example, sericulture in Japan, jute production
in India, and wool production in the United States.

Natural fibers. Natural fibers include all plant fibers, all animal fibers,
and asbestos. The plant and animal fibers form an important part of
agricultural output in such nations as India, Japan, Australia, and the
United States. Of more than 300 different plant fibers, only seven
(cotton, flax, hemp, jute, abacá, sisal, henequen) are of commercial importance. Other plant fibers, however, are not unknown in commerce.

---

[7] J. H. Dillon, "Problems Accompanying the Introduction of the Newer Synthetic
Fibers," *American Standards for Testing Materials,* A.S.T.M. Bulletin No. 184 (Philadelphia: September 1952), 56–61.

Twenty-three have been listed as being in use but of minor importance in the United States.[8] Wool and silk are the only animal fibers of commercial importance, but others are valuable though their quantity is limited. The specialty hair fibers are generally included with wool unless specifically named. Rayon and estron (manufactured fibers) together are ninth in volume of the commercially important fibers.

Plant fibers. Plant fibers may be classified according to the part of the plant that produces the fiber. Seed hairs are one-celled fibers which develop from the epidermis of the seed of certain plants. Cotton is the only member of this group which is of commercial importance, but kapok and milkweed fibers serve useful purposes. The United States produced 52 per cent of the world supply of cotton in 1948–1949 and exported about 30 per cent of her production. Long staple cottons and fine cotton manufactures are imported by the United States. Shifts in the relative importance of fibers were produced by World War II. In 1948, prices for American cotton as well as Australian Merino wool (very fine) were about three times prewar prices. The rise in the costs of natural fibers, especially cotton and wool, is in sharp contrast to the cost of rayon fibers, which were only 20 per cent above the prewar average. Jute and the hard fibers increased much more sharply in price during World War II than did even wool or cotton.

Bast fibers are multicelled fibers which result from differentiation of cells in the inner bark of the stems of certain plants. Flax, hemp, and jute are of commercial importance. Ramie is an exceptionally beautiful fiber, but production problems still limit interest in the fiber and its commercial value. Thirty per cent of the total Indian exports in 1946–1947 were jute and its manufactures. More than half of the world's jute-processing industry is located in India. The remainder has been heavily concentrated in the United Kingdom and western Europe. Seed hair and bast fibers are the soft fibers.

Leaf or hard fibers (abacá, sisal and henequen) are multicelled fibers which result from differentiation of cells in the vascular system of the leaf. They are coarse, hard, and stiff compared to the fibers produced by the seeds or stems of plants. The hard fibers and hemp are of commercial value for cordage.

Hull, root, and latex fibers are found in commerce, though they are of minor value. The hull fibers, *coir,* are multicelled and result from differentiation of cells in the inner part of the outer hull of the coconut. Root fibers are obtained from plants such as the palmetto. Latex is obtained from the milk of the rubber tree.

Animal fibers. Animal fibers are protein fibers. Silk and wool are well-known for clothing and household uses.

Silk is spun by the silkworm as two continuous filaments of fibroin

[8] A.S.T.M., *op. cit.,* 1948.

held together with a silk gum called sericin. Silk is produced by both wild and cultivated silkworms. During 1934–1938, Japan produced 78 per cent of the world's supply of silk. By 1947, production in Japan had dropped to about half the world supply, which in itself was less than one fourth the prewar figure. The sale of Japanese raw silk was drastically reduced by the high prices in the United States markets after the war, as well as by the increased competition from nylon and rayon filament yarns. Silk production, like the production of other natural fibers, involves a good deal of hand labor, a commodity which is becoming increasingly dear. A program was drawn up after World War II to develop and stabilize the silk industry in Japan at a level to meet her needs for foreign exchange.

Wool is fiber from the fleece of sheep. The Federal Trade Commission includes the hair or so-called "specialty" fibers in its administration of the Wool Products Labeling Act. Hair fibers include fibers from angora and cashmere goats, camels, llamas, the alpacas, and vicunas. Other animal fibers of value are obtained from angora rabbits, ordinary rabbits, cows, and horses. Wool is more widely produced than the other animal fibers. Australia produced over 36 per cent of the wool entering international trade in 1947–1948.

Inorganic fiber. The inorganic natural fiber of most importance at present is asbestos.

Manufactured fibers. Manufactured fibers constitute approximately one tenth of the world's total supply of commercially important fibers. It is this group of fibers, however, which is expected to grow in number, in volume, and in value. Production of these fibers resumed a strong upward trend after World War II. The relative costs of natural and manufactured fibers leave much to be desired from the standpoint of the country dependent upon exporting natural fibers in exchange for either goods or money. Wide fluctuations in price of natural fibers are a disadvantage in trade.

The manufactured fibers are being made from a growing number of raw materials. Animal and vegetable proteins, as well as other raw materials of organic and of mineral origin, are being used in increasing amounts. With the advance of technical knowledge and with the desirability of finding uses for agricultural by-products and surpluses, government laboratories have led in developing fibers from both animal and vegetable proteins. At present, fibers from casein, zein, feathers, egg white, waste hair, silk, soybeans, and peanuts are primarily of scientific interest only.

Natural fibrous materials. The natural products, such as those listed above, provide vast resources upon which to draw for raw materials.[9] Suitable long-chain protein molecules may be obtained from both

[9] A.S.T.M., *op. cit.*, 1950, pp. 14–23.

plant and animal sources. Cellulose is obtained from a number of plants. Rayons include the regenerated cellulose fibers, cuprammonium and xanthate (viscose) rayons. There are also other modifications. Rayons and estron (cellulose acetate) are made from the cellulose of wood pulp or cotton linters, both of which are plant products. The rayons and estron form the bulk of manufactured fibers and make up approximately 9 per cent of the world's supply of commercial fibers.

Nonfibrous molecules. Small nonfibrous molecules are being used to build the synthetic fibers, which seem destined for a bright future. The synthetic fibers are being developed to meet specific needs. Some are water soluble; some have very low melting points; some are highly resistant to alkali, acid, weathering, and oxidation. None is attacked by moths. All are resistant to the action of microorganisms. Some absorb almost no water; others dissolve in water. Many of these fibers will find their only uses in industry or other highly specialized fields. Of the present group, nylon is of greatest commercial value in wearing apparel. Others, such as Orlon, Dynel, and Dacron, are being welcomed for properties which adapt them to special uses.

Rubbers, fibers, and plastics are closely related members of the rapidly growing group of synthetic substances; in many instances, the chief difference is in physical form and not in composition. Synthetic fibers are emerging from the laboratories in such numbers that it is not safe to predict their relative importance, number, or uses for the future. Present indications are that the synthetic fibers will gain in importance. The answers will depend upon economic, technological, and political factors.

Uses. Social, economic, and geographic factors determine the uses the various nations of the earth make of fibers. Uses of textile fibers may be classified as follows:

a) mainly apparel and household fibers: cotton, wool, silk, flax, rayon and nylon
b) mainly industrial fibers: hemp, jute, abacá, sisal, and henequen

Such a classification has many exceptions, that would be seen if the volumes of fibers and their uses were compared.

Estimates differ on the percentage of fibers going into each of the big use classes. This is not surprising, since there are broad overlappings in use. For example, a cotton print cloth may be finished in a manner suitable for chintz window drapery (a household use), for a dress (an apparel use), or for a feed sack (an industrial use). In the past, the Indians of the Northwest used large quantities of the fibrous inner bark of cedar trees in the construction of their clothing. In some lands, grasses are used. These same materials may be used in baskets (an industrial use) or in floor coverings (a household use). Most fibers at one time or another are used for industrial purposes. Cotton is being consumed in increasing quantities in industry. Some fibers are used exclusively by industry.

The fibers in Fig. 1.2 would present an entirely different picture if presented according to value instead of volume. The relative values

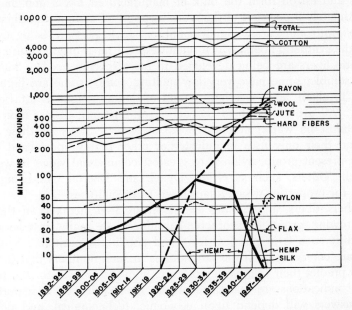

Fig. 1.2. World production of major fibers and fiber groups. *Source: Gerda Blau,* WORLD FIBER SURVEY *(Washington: Food and Agriculture Organization of the United Nations, 1947), 3.*

of fibers, as well as the volumes produced, vary with changes in economic and technological conditions (Fig. 1.3).

Clothing and household fabrics. Clothing and household fabrics consume about two thirds of the world's fibers. Human requirements for apparel fibers have not been measured with precise and objective standards; nor do we have a measure of the extent to which the various fibers satisfy social, physiological, and economic requirements. Such requirements are very real, and serious deficiencies constitute a danger to health and to the more intangible factors of morale and self-respect. Climate, age, and occupation affect the amount and kind of clothes needed. Income and availability limit the amount and kind that can be obtained. Apparel fibers provide warmth and protection, are essential for hygiene and comfort, satisfy conventional standards of modesty, taste, and fashion, and thus enable people to conform to the dictates of tradition and social environment.

The world's requirements for clothing fibers are, at best, an estimate.

The most practical approach to date is an analysis of actual clothing consumption patterns of the peoples of various nations under the different social and economic conditions in which they live. This procedure for measuring requirements is in error to the extent that the peoples of the earth lack adequate clothing at the time a study is made.

The consumption of major clothing fibers per person in 1934–1938 in the United States bore a definite relationship to the estimated real income. Fashion is so powerful a factor in the consumption of clothing that conspicuous consumption is known at every income level. As incomes increase, the actual cost of clothing consumed increases far more rapidly than the actual amount of the fibers concerned. Quality, not quantity, increases most rapidly.

Consumption of the three major apparel fibers—cotton, rayon and

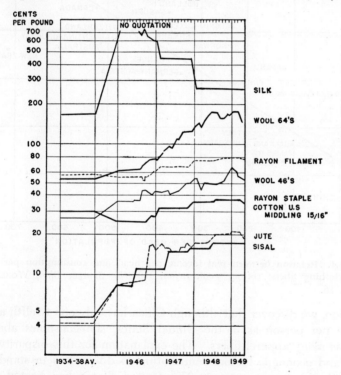

Fig. 1.3. **Prices of major fibers, average 1934–38 and monthly averages to 1949.**
Source: WORLD FIBER REVIEW *(1947, 1949).*

wool—has been related to income per person for different parts of the world (Figs. 1.4, 1.5, and 1.6).

There has been a great increase in the level of fiber consumption in the United States, Latin-American countries, and the British Dominions. Europe and the Far East are the major raw fiber importing areas.

They have not yet reached the prewar level of production of textile
products. Shortage of foreign exchange, cost of producing natural
fibers, and need for food production contributed to the slow recovery of
world fiber trade after the war. Overproduction of fibers feared by
many, especially for cotton and wool, did not develop in world markets.

Taking the United States and China as extremes in income and con-

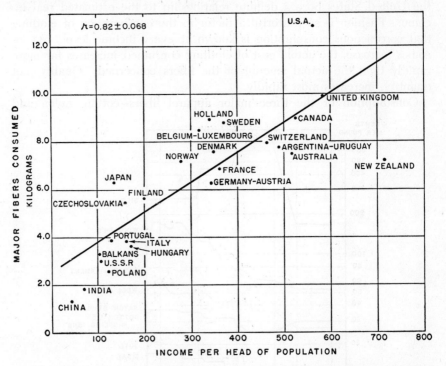

Fig. 1.4. **Relation between real income per head and consumption per head of
major clothing fibers: cotton, wool, rayon, 1934–38.** *Source: Blau,* World Fiber
Survey, *16.*

sumption, we discover that although China has only one twelfth as much
income per person as in the United States, she consumes about one
ninth as many apparel fibers. The explanation for this disparity lies in
social and economic factors contributing to differences in standards of
living in the two countries. The United States has heated houses,
heated public buildings, and heated cars, but China has to wear clothes
to keep warm. It has been shown that about 18.5 per cent of the
world's population consumes more than 50 per cent of the world's fibers.
The high-level consuming areas are the United States, United Kingdom,
Argentina, portions of western Europe, and three of the British Dominions. The greatest textile deficiencies in the postwar world were found
in continental Europe, China, Japan, southeast Asia, Russia, and Africa.

The need for more clothing in many parts of the world is enhanced by inadequate dwellings, lack of fuel for home heating, food shortages, and limited soap and laundering facilities.

Industrial fabrics. Industrial uses demand about one third of the world's fibers for fabrics such as automobile upholstery, burlap bags, protective coverings for merchandise, wrapping for cotton bales, bags for citrus fruit and other produce. The industrial use of fibers is necessary for the welfare of people in our society. The dividing line be-

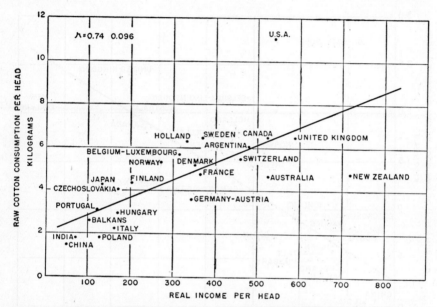

Fig. 1.5. **Relation between real income per head of population and consumption of cotton per head.** *Source: Blau, loc. cit.*

tween apparel and industrial uses for fibers is broad and indistinct. There are, however, certain fibers which are used chiefly or entirely for industrial purposes. Likewise, certain fibers are used chiefly for clothing and household purposes.

Soft fibers. The soft fibers from the seeds and stems of plants are generally useful in clothing, household, or industrial fabrics. Cost and specific physical and chemical properties normally determine the use of these fibers in industry; fashion and custom usually determine their use in household and clothing fabrics. During war, availability often determines the uses of fibers. Jute, cotton, rayon, and hemp are the soft fibers most commonly used for industrial purposes. The synthetic fibers may be made soft or hard as desired. They will be more widely used as they are developed.

The movement to market of much of the world's agricultural com-

modities has been in jute bags, but political events in India have curtailed the output of jute. The major portion of the world's output of
jute is produced in a 300-mile radius of Calcutta. That probably represents the world's most highly concentrated textile industry. Bengal
was divided between Pakistan, which includes the jute-producing centers, and India, which controls the jute-manufacturing plants of the
world, together with the marketing and exporting facilities. Trade wars
which then developed between Pakistan and India accelerated the use

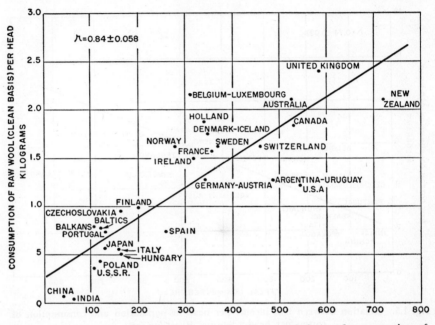

Fig. 1.6. Relation between real income per head of population and consumption of
wool per head. *Source: Blau, loc. cit.*

of paper and cotton in bagging and the use of bulk shipping. Jute accounts for about 30 per cent of India's total exports. It is easy to see
that fibers and fiber manufactures exert a vital influence upon the welfare of many nations.

Cotton has been losing ground to rayon, estron, and nylon in apparel,
household, and industrial uses. The replacement of cotton by rayon in
tire cord fabric is extensive.

Hemp production and consumption are centered in Europe. Russia
is both the greatest producer and the greatest consumer of this fiber.

Hard fibers. The hard fibers (abacá, sisal and henequen) are used
almost entirely for industrial purposes. Since they are used chiefly in
cordage, they will not be discussed in detail. The Philippines and East
Indies produce all of the abacá and most of the sisal of commercial im-

portance in the world markets. Most of the henequen is produced in Mexico.

During periods of stress, such as World War II, people and countries find themselves cut off from normal sources of supply. As a result, they turn to available materials and adapt them to their needs. In recent years, new fibers have been tried and in many cases found to have properties equal or preferable to those of the natural fibers. In many instances, however, development costs must still be written off before new products can compete pricewise in free markets.

Chapter Two

Cotton

COTTON, genus *Gossypium,* a member of the Mallow family, is the world's most abundant fiber. It is discussed here in considerable detail because of its great importance.

HISTORY

Compared to wool and silk, cotton is a relative newcomer; yet it is not a new fiber. Cotton was apparently grown and made into cloth before recorded history and was in widespread use at an early date. For example, evidence of its use in 3000 B.C. in the "City of the Dead" in India has been found. Cotton fabrics were uncovered in the graves of men who lived in Peru before the Inca Indians. Excavations in Utah gave evidence of the prehistoric growth of cotton in North America. Early in history the Chinese were known to have raised cotton as a decorative house plant. It is believed that cotton was brought to the Mediterranean area about 300 B.C., probably from India or Egypt. By 800 A.D. the plant had been introduced into Japan from India. However, it was not until the Crusades (1096–1270) that cotton was introduced into Europe. Columbus found cotton growing on the Bahama Islands in 1492. Magellan, after his trip around the world about 1519, reported finding cotton in Brazil. Where it came from is not known.

By 1500, the British woolen industry had begun to feel the growing popularity of cotton and by 1700 secured the passage of a law forbidding the use of cotton in England. A second law was soon passed penalizing everyone who wore dyed or printed cotton. This was to discourage the

16

use of cotton and to favor the use of the home-grown wool. There was no law against wearing dyed or printed wool. However, cottons were so popular with the English that the law was disregarded, and, as the demand grew, England became world famous for her cotton fabrics.

Colonial America. Cotton was produced in comparatively small amounts by the colonists who used chiefly wool and flax, both of which could be prepared and made into cloth more easily than cotton. The colonists imported the first Negro slaves and began to cultivate cotton in 1619, but it was well over 100 years before they had enough to export to England.[1]

The first cotton export on record in the United States was in 1764. Eight bags were sent from Carolina to Liverpool. From this small beginning, the cultivation of cotton has been extended until today it has become one of our most important items of international trade.

The beginning of a cotton industry. The biggest fiber industry the world has ever known had its real beginning in the Industrial Revolution of the eighteenth century. The invention of the cotton gin by Eli Whitney, in 1793, foretold the beginning of the new industry. In Pawtucket, Rhode Island, in 1790, Samuel Slater built the first successful cotton goods mill in America. Before the invention of the cotton gin, the real bottleneck had been the slow hand process of removing lint from the seed. But mechanical means for removing the fiber from the seed, as well as for spinning and weaving the cloth, put the price and quantity of cotton fabrics within the reach of the masses of people.

The discovery of synthetic dyestuffs by Sir William Perkins, in 1856, made it possible to dye cotton fabrics to beautiful fast colors at small cost. Today purchasers in every income class in the United States ask for and get colored cottons of increasing beauty and variety.

Cotton in present-day America. Through war and peace, the cotton industry grew to become the country's largest fiber industry, with the production, manufacture, and distribution of cotton goods in the United States providing a way of living for about one tenth of the population.

However, the industry is declining in relative importance. Some of the unfavorable factors facing domestic cotton production are:

    a) increased foreign output
    b) increased trade restrictions
    c) manufactured fibers at home and abroad
    d) government restrictions on planting

The price and quality of lint determine the extent to which American cotton can compete in foreign markets. Some of the factors which help to improve the price and quality of lint are:

[1] M. D. C. Crawford, *The Heritage of Cotton* (New York: G. P. Putnam's Sons, 1924).

a) good methods of harvesting and handling
b) more seed of a variety to produce well in a given locality
c) control of insects and plant diseases
d) better organization and management adapted to size and type of farm
e) better ginning methods to handle machine-picked cottons

It is a startling fact that many of the people, who toil to produce the greatest quantity of fibers in the world, harvest and sell their crop without knowing the quality and relative value of the product they sell. A study of the marketing of cotton in producers' local markets has brought out a number of reasons for the uneconomic production of cotton in the United States.[2] Comparative data for 1935–1936 and for 1947–1948 reveal that the cotton farmer was seldom able to classify his own cotton as to standard grade, and frequently, he was not told the grade when he sold it. Therefore, he did not know whether or not he was paid according to the quality he sold.

There are, however, signs of improvement as indicated by the improved financial position of the cotton producer. Comparatively few farmers today have to sell their cotton at the going price to meet debts. Thus, they can hold the crop for a while to await better prices.

Factors other than production and marketing methods are affecting the position of cotton. Synthetic fibers are providing more fibers to choose from, and many of those are specifically adapted to their uses. Research on the manufactured fibers, however, has provided information which has been useful in improving and modifying the natural fibers. Cotton, the most versatile and widely used fiber in the world, has benefited from these studies. New finishes have increased both its uses and its usefulness. Because of the importance of cotton, efforts will continue to be made to improve and to promote its production and use.

PRODUCTION

Most of the world's cotton is grown between 35° north and 25° south latitude (See Fig. 2.1) because cotton requires a frost-free growing season of 200 days, a minimum of 20 inches of annual rainfall or 7 to 8 inches during the growing season, a hot summer, and a fairly dry harvesting season.[3] At present, these limitations, coupled with requirements for soil fertility, skill, and science applied to production, materially limit areas in which cotton can be produced profitably.

The man-hour requirements are tending to reduce the competitive position of cotton (Table 2.I). In 1939, 21 per cent of the man-hours

[2] R. C. Soxman, *Marketing of Cotton in Producers' Local Markets* (Washington, D. C.: Production and Marketing Administration, Cotton Branch, United States Department of Agriculture, 1949).

[3] Gerda Blau, *World Fiber Survey* (Washington, D. C.: Food and Agriculture Organization of United Nations, 1947), 47.

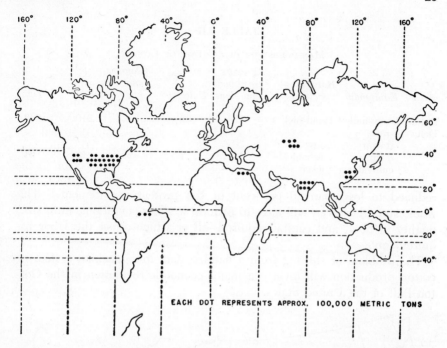

Fig. 2.1. The world's major cotton producing areas. *Source:* WORLD FIBER REVIEW
  (*Washington: Food and Agriculture Organization of the United Nations, 1948*).

spent on crops in this country were spent on cotton production. Mechanized procedures now being introduced in the United States repre-
sent the first great advance since the invention of the cotton gin over a
century and a half ago.

TABLE 2.I

MAN-HOURS FOR PRODUCTION OF SOME MAJOR FARM CROPS

Crop	Millions of man-hours	Area	Value $1,000
Cotton	2,198	1	2,294,543
Wheat	461	2 x 1	3,288,905
Corn	2,480	4 x 1	5,432,785

Source: Gerda Blau, *World Fiber Survey* (Washington, D. C.: Food and
  Agriculture Organizations of United Nations, 1947), 47 and Agricultural Statistics, 1948.

In Egypt, where about one third of the nation's irrigated land is in
cotton, labor requirements are five or six times that of any other crop.
A significant comparison of labor requirements has been presented by
Langsford of the United States Department of Agriculture (Table 2.II).
Those figures indicate that by further mechanization man-hours could be

TABLE 2.II

MAN-HOURS FOR PRODUCTION OF COTTON

Area	Equipment	Harvesting method	Prepare seed bed and plant	Cultivate	Chop and hoe	Pick	Total
					Man-hours		
Delta	1-row-mule	Hand-pick	25	32	81	210	348
Delta	4-row tractor & flame cultivator	1-row mechanical picker	12	7	32	10	61

reduced to less than 20 per cent of the present requirements. The whole story, however, will have to include weather conditions, farm size, quality of fiber, and capital required—all of which affect the labor requirements.

The problem of shifting from a hand system to a machine system of cotton production will involve a major economic revolution in the Cotton Belt of the United States.

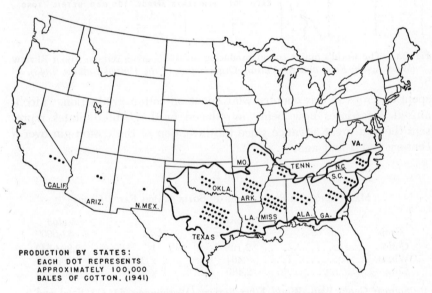

PRODUCTION BY STATES:
EACH DOT REPRESENTS
APPROXIMATELY 100,000
BALES OF COTTON. (1941)

Fig. 2.2. Cotton belt of the United States.

World War II took many people from the rural to the urban areas where war industries were located. This accelerated social and economic changes already under way. A new mode of living has been evolving in the South as machinery is developed to do the hand labor long considered primarily the work of poor Negroes and white sharecroppers.

Cotton is grown in the following regions, defined by the Department of Agriculture:

SOUTHEAST REGION: Alabama, Georgia, North Carolina, South Carolina, Virginia

MIDSOUTH REGION: Arkansas, Louisiana, Mississippi, Missouri, Tennessee

SOUTHWEST REGION: Oklahoma, Texas

FAR WEST REGION: Arizona, California, New Mexico

Some varieties are better suited to certain purposes and to certain regions than to others. The long staple (1½ to 2½ in.) cottons such as Sea Island and Pima, the latter grown under irrigation in the southwest, have evolved from the same species as Egyptian cotton. The long fine staple cottons are a small percentage of the total cotton crop. The upland cottons are the short staple (¾ to 1½ in.) cottons and constitute the greater proportion of commercially important cottons. The most important varieties of upland cotton grown in the United States are: [4]

Deltapine, fairly fine staple
Stoneville 2B, fairly fine staple
Coker 100, average staple
Acala 4–42, average
Hibred, coarse staple
Rowden, coarse staple
Wilds, long fine staple

The first three varieties listed account for over half of the cotton produced. New varieties are being developed to meet better the conditions of production or to provide fibers of improved properties. The growing custom of buying cotton according to variety provides the mills with raw material of comparatively uniform properties. Yield, economy, and suitability for spinning are the factors which determine the commercial value of any variety of cotton.

Grading and Marketing. Much more efficient grading and marketing procedures than have been followed in the past are now coming into use in the United States. The official grade standards (Table 2.III) divide cottons into nine grades, which are subdivided according to color: white, extra white, spotted, tinged, yellow stained, or gray.

The percentage of each grade produced in 1944–1946 shows the biggest yield to be Grade No. 6, strict low middling. Eighty-six to 90 per cent of the cotton produced in the United States is white or extra white (Table 2.IV).

[4] P. M. Thomas, "Cotton Varieties," *Textile World*, 98-10 (1948), 107–122.

TABLE 2.III

OFFICIAL GRADE STANDARDS

Grade No.	White Grade name	Abbre-viation	Extra white	Spotted	Tinged	Yellow stained	Gray
1	Middling fair ...	MF					
2	Strict good middling	SGM					
3	Good middling ..	GM	GMEW	GMSp	GMT	GMYS	GMG
4	Strict middling ..	SM	SMEW	SMSp	SMT	SMYS	SMG
5	Middling	M	MEW	MSp	MT	MYS	MG
6	Strict low middling	SLM	SLMEW	SLMSp	SLMT		
7	Low middling ..	LM	LMEW	LMSp	LMT		
8	Strict good ordinary	SGO	SGOEW				
9	Good ordinary ..	GO	GOEW				

Source: P. M. Thomas, "Cotton Varieties," *Textile World*, 98-10 (1948), 107–122.

TABLE 2.IV

PRODUCTION BY GRADE
(Percentage of total crop)

Grade (all lengths)	1944	1945	1946
Middling fair	None	None	None
Strict good middling	Less than 0.05	Less than 0.05	Less than 0.05
Good middling	0.1	0.4	0.5
Strict middling	6.3	7.0	12.0
Middling	34.5	30.9	36.6
Strict low middling	37.8	35.1	35.1
Low middling	13.5	14.5	9.8
Strict good ordinary	3.6	5.3	3.5
Good ordinary	1.9	3.9	1.7
Gray (all grades)	1.2	0.7	0.6
Below	1.1	2.2	0.2
Descriptive grade			
White and extra white	90.1	86.7	87.3
Spotted	7.4	10.3	11.8
Tinged	0.2	0.1	0.1
Yellow stained	Less than 0.05	Less than 0.05	Less than 0.05
Gray	1.2	0.7	0.6
Below	1.1	2.2	0.2

Source: P. M. Thomas, "Cotton Varieties," *Textile World*, 98-10 (1948), 107–122.

Cotton in the 1947–1948 period was marketed through the following buyers: [5]

[5] R. C. Soxman, *Marketing of Cotton in Producers' Local Markets*, Production and Marketing Administration, Cotton Branch, United States Department of Agriculture, Washington, D. C., 1949.

Buyers	%
Ginner	33
Independent local	36
Cotton merchant	11
Cooperatives	6
Factors	12
Other	2

A large amount of the cotton is sold on sample, 62 per cent on actual sample and 20 per cent on classification by U. S. Department of Agriculture standards. The prices at which the growers sold in 1947–1948 were chiefly (93 per cent) based on the New York futures market; 4

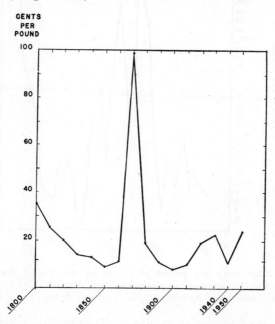

Fig. 2.3. **Average price of New York spot cotton by decades, 1800–1940.** *Source: Merritt J. Matthews,* Textile Fibers, *5th ed. (John Wiley & Sons, Inc., New York, 1947), 183.*

per cent sold according to prices of the nearest central market.[6] New York and Chicago commodity exchanges deal in cotton futures. New York and New Orleans have spot markets. Spot markets provide prices and an opportunity to trade in commodities which are at the time available and ready for delivery. On the other hand, futures' markets provide prices for trading in commodities which will not be available for delivery until some specified time in the future. Average spot prices on cotton since 1800 show only one "wild flight." New Orleans provides the greatest spot market for cotton in the world.

[6] *Ibid.,* 6.

The average price per pound of cotton in the United States has fluctuated widely. This price factor adds to the financial hazards of cotton production. Partly because of the very high price paid for cotton in

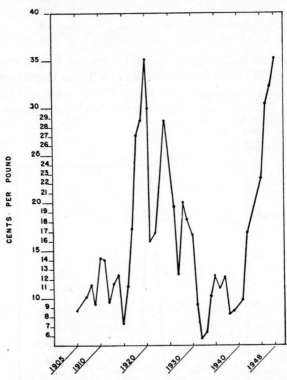

Fig. 2.4. Average price per pound of cotton in the United States, 1905–1948. *Data from* COTTON PRODUCTION AND DISTRIBUTION, *Bulletin No. 177 (Washington: United States Department of Agriculture, 1942), 45 and* WORLD FIBER REVIEW *(1948).*

1947–1948, most growers insured their unsold cotton.[7] Cotton which was unsold at the time of ginning was stored as follows:

Per cent	Place
72	Public warehouses
24	Gin yards
2	Public cotton yards
1	Farms
1	Weighing platforms

Progressive marketing procedures are more generally used in the Far West and Southwest than in the traditional Cotton Belt.

Trends in Production. Labor shortage, war, famine, need for increased food production, inflation, and transportation shortages have all

[7] *Ibid.*, 6.

contributed to a reduction of the world supply of cotton. But cotton is so large a percentage of the total supply of fibers that it still sets the pattern of the world fiber supply. From 1903–1913 the United States produced 61 per cent of the world's supply of cotton. From 1934–1938 she produced only 42 per cent and by 1947–1948 still less. The important postwar cotton-producing countries of the world besides the United

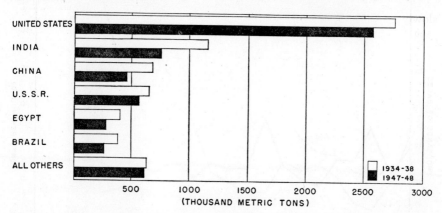

Fig. 2.5. Cotton production by major producing countries, 1934–38 and 1947–48.
Source: WORLD FIBER REVIEW *(1948), 17.*

States are India, China, Russia, Egypt, and Brazil. The trend is toward a reduction of the importance of cotton in the United States. Since 1937, the production of cotton in this country has been declining, and the price has been increasing. The actual number of bales of cotton produced in the United States in 1946–1947 was less than the 1934–1938 average. The United States' reduction of cotton from the 1909–1913 average yield is much greater than for the other major cotton-producing countries (Table 2.V).

TABLE 2.V

COTTON, MAJOR PRODUCING AREAS

Country	1909–13	1934–38 1000 bales *	1946–47
United States	13,033	12,712	8,640
India	3,785	4,619	3,000
China	1,500	3,127	1,930
U.S.S.R.	682	2,967	2,240
Egypt	1,453	1,846	1,210
Brazil	387	1,793	1,575
Others	660	2,811	2,905
World Production	21,500	29,875	21,500

* Bale weighs 216.8 Kg. net.

Source: Gerda Blau, *World Fiber Survey* (Washington, D. C.: Food and Agriculture Organization of the United Nations, 1947).

Mechanization and increased yields should go far toward reversing the present trends. Mechanization in cotton production must come slowly in order that varieties may be developed which are best suited to mechanized procedures.[8] Some of the problems may be illustrated

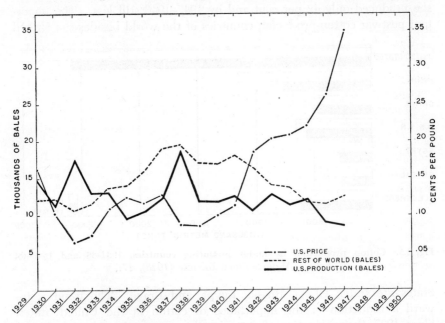

Fig. 2.6. U. S. production, world production, and U. S. price of cotton. *Data from P. M. Thomas, "Cotton Varieties."*

by a few examples. Coarse fibers need to be developed because mechanical picking machines and the subsequent cleaning processes damage the long fine fibered varieties such as Wilds. Spinning qualities must be maintained while developing other qualities. Instead of hairy leaves which cling to the cotton bolls, smooth leaves need to be developed in order to facilitate cleaning procedures.

A defoliation process, which consists of dusting the cotton plants with a chemical at just the right stage in development, causes the leaves to drop, leaving the bolls undamaged. This process not only allows cleaner picking of cotton but also makes it possible for the sun to reach all of the bolls and thus permit more uniform ripening. The cotton field may be picked only once instead of two or three times. During wet seasons, the bolls on the lower branches will mature instead of rot.[9] Also, army worms and pink bollworms cause little damage if the leaves are shed.

Bigger yields of a number of crops have been obtained by treating

[8] Thomas, "Cotton Varieties," 107–122.
[9] *For Instance*, No. 19 (New York: American Cyanamid Co., 1946).

their seed before sowing or by spraying the plants in the fields. Chemicals dusted on cotton plants during the flowering period resulted in a large increase of cotton per acre.

Complete modernization of cotton production may revolutionize the industry. Certain areas of the world such as the United States should lead in modern production methods. At present, the cost of hand labor makes it difficult for American cotton to compete in world markets. Better varieties of cotton, bred for special qualities, combined with machine planting, cultivation, and harvesting are factors which tend to insure a continuing place for cotton production in American life.

By-products. An industry's profit or loss can be affected materially by its by-products. For 80 years after cotton became the most important crop in the South, the cottonseed, except for planting purposes, was considered a waste product. The seed now ranks about tenth or eleventh in farm income among all farm products in this country. The oil is the most valuable part of the seed. It is used for vegetable shortening, margarine, soaps, paints, and in artificial leathers. The meal is a source of protein which can be used for feed, protein fibers, or amino acids. The hulls are used for feed and packing. The linters, the short fibers left on the seeds after ginning, are an excellent source of a very pure form of cellulose. Cellulose acetate, cuprammonium rayon, and high-tenacity viscose rayons are manufactured from the cellulose from linters. The linters may also be used for padding. The proportion of linters to lint (the cotton fiber) is about 1 to 10. The various products obtained from the cotton plant can scarcely indicate the great variety of consumer goods made from those products.

Origin and Structure. The origin and structure of cotton fibers are much more complex than they are generally thought to be. Cotton fibers are single-celled outgrowths of epidermal cells of the seed coat. On the day the flower appears, there also appears a swelling on the outer wall of certain epidermal cells of the seed.

The swellings develop into tubular outgrowths which elongate rapidly for 20 to 30 days.[10] During elongation, the seed hair has only a thin primary wall to hold the protoplasm. After the elongation ceases, cellulose is laid down in layers. The cavity (vacuole) holding the protoplasm grows smaller and smaller as the layers of cellulose are laid down until the boll opens, after which no more cellulose is deposited. The cell then dies and dries up but remains attached to the seed. Fibers from any one seed vary in degree of maturity, since the fibers develop at different rates from different areas of the epidermal layer of the seed.

The fibers are from 1200–4500 times as long as they are wide. They appear under a low-power microscope as flat ribbons with from 20 to

[10] R. F. Nickerson, "Cotton Fibers: Constitution, Structure and Mechanical Properties," *Industrial and Engineering Chemistry*, 32-11 (1940), 1454–1461.

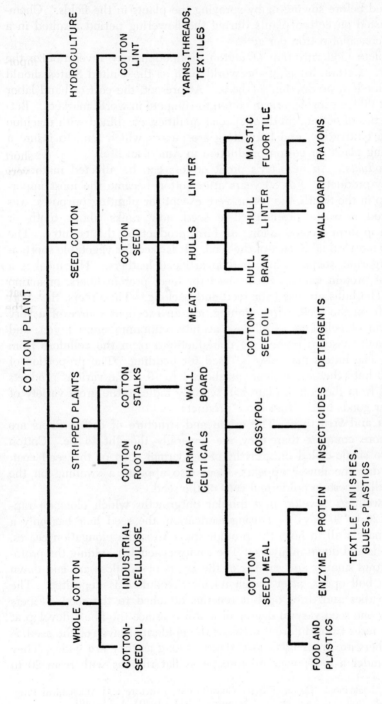

Fig. 2.7. **Products of the cotton plant.** *Source: G. R. Merrill, A. R. Macromac, and H. R. Mauersberger,* AMERICAN COTTON HANDBOOK *(New York: Textile Book Publishers, 1941).*

100 half convolutions per centimeter. The convolutions or "twists" in the cotton fibers are explained by inequalities among fibrils in the fiber wall, by the ratio of width to thickness of the cell wall, and by irregularities in the crystalline structure, the orderly arrangement of fiber molecules.

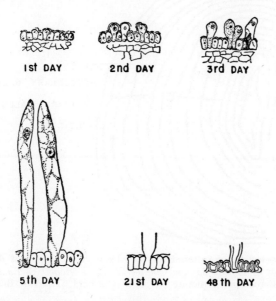

1st DAY   2nd DAY   3rd DAY

5th DAY   21st DAY   48th DAY

Fig. 2.8 Stages of growth of cotton fibers: 1st–21st day shows stages of elongation; 48th day shows cell wall thickened by secondary cellulose wall. *Source: Gordon G. Osborne,* "Micro-analysis of Textile Fibers," TEXTILE RESEARCH, *5-6 (1934–35), Part III,* "Observations on the Structure of Cotton," *275–297.*

The mature cell is a cottonseed hair or cotton fiber and consists of these parts: outside cuticle, primary wall, secondary wall, and lumen (vacuole) with its dried cell contents. The cuticle is of a waxy nature which protects the fiber from wetting until it is removed. The primary cell wall is composed of cellulose strands which form a network around the fiber. As stated above, these cellulose molecules or strands are only about one half as long as those in the secondary wall. When fibers are greatly swollen, this outer wall splits transversely since it does not stretch. Cellulose is not thought to be the chief constituent of the primary wall, since minerals, waxes, and pectic substances have also been observed. The lumen contains waxes and pectic substances together with varying amounts of the residue of the protoplasm which is found in all plant and animal cells.

The secondary wall is laid down during the second half, 20–30 days, of fiber growth. This wall consists of alternate layers of dense and less dense cellulose. Each 24 hours, two layers, one dense and one less dense, are laid down. The less dense layer is laid down in daylight.[11] Fibers grown in continuous light and uniform temperature have no "growth rings." Temperature and light both affect the structure of the

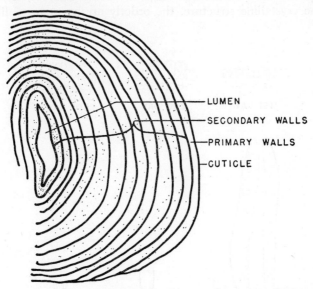

LUMEN

SECONDARY WALLS

PRIMARY WALLS

CUTICLE

Fig. 2.9. Cross-section of cotton fiber showing alternate layers of dense and less dense cellulose or lamallae. *Source: Charles W. Hock, Robert C. Ramsay, and Milton Harris,* "Microscopic Structure of Cotton Fiber," Textile Research, *11-4 (1940), 200–218.*

cell wall. Except for experimental purposes, cotton is grown with variations of both light and temperature, and thus the fiber walls do have variations in density.

The entire cotton fiber seems to be a very porous structure. Air spaces apparently extend from the outer surface to the lumen. English workers have reported 32 to 41 per cent of the fiber volume to be pore space. The fact that fine cottons are less porous than thick-walled is consistent with other physical data such as fiber strength, amount of water absorbed, and ease of dyeing. The fine cottons dye less readily and hold less moisture.

Properties. The widespread use of cotton is in part a result of the useful set of properties with which it is endowed.

Physical properties. The service qualities of cotton fabrics depend largely on the physical properties of the fibers from which they are made. In any determination of cotton fiber quality, physical properties such as length, diameter, density, thickness of cell wall, degree of twist, and orientation of fibrils (groups of cellulose chains) within the fiber

[11] Donald Anderson and Thomas Kerr, "Growth and Structure of Cotton Fibers," *Industrial and Engineering Chemistry,* 30 (1938), 48–54.

wall are considered important.[12] With cotton fibers, as with any other biological material, there is great variability. Even so, a degree of uniformity of qualities exists in any one variety of fiber.

The value of cotton depends for spinning qualities upon the shape or contour of the individual fibers. Stronger yarns can be made from fibers with crimp, convolutions, and rough surfaces than from smooth fibers, provided the fibers are not too rough to spin smoothly. Some surface friction is necessary in the production of yarns from all staple fibers.

The length of a staple fiber is of special importance. Cotton fibers, lint, range in length from about ¾ to 2½ inches or longer. The texture and strength as well as the length are in general characteristic for the different types of cottons (Table 2.VI).

TABLE 2.VI

WORLD COTTONS

Type	Staple length	Texture	Fiber strength
Asiatic	Short	Coarse	Medium
Peruvian	Short to long	Coarse to medium	Weak to medium
American Upland	Short to long	Medium to fine	Weak to strong
Egyptian	Medium to long	Medium to fine	Medium to strong
Sea Island	Long	Fine	Strong

Source: P. M. Thomas, "Cotton Fibers," Textile World, 98-10 (1948), 107–122.

Over a necessary minimum length for spinning, the length of cotton fibers is of special importance because of other properties associated with length in the fiber, namely, strength, length of molecular chains (degree of polymerization), and their orderly arrangement (crystallinity).

The strength of cotton fibers is important because it is associated with desirable service qualities. Breaking strength of a fiber may be expressed either as tenacity or as tensile strength.[13] Tenacity is the breaking strength per unit of fineness.[14] Data show that the shortest fibers weigh the most (Table 2.VII). In other words, the short fibers are coarser than the long fibers, assuming that the cell walls have the same density in both cases. Fineness in weight per inch of cotton fibers varies from 1.23 for Sea Island, a long fine fiber, to 2.65 for Rowden, a short coarse fiber. The relationship of fiber length to strength shows that in general the longer, finer fibers are also stronger (Fig. 2.10).

[12] Carl M. Conrad, "Cotton Quality Determination," Textile Research, 7-4 (1936–37), 165–174.

[13] James N. Grant and Ora W. Morlier, "Relation of Specific Strength of Cotton Fibers to Fiber Length and Testing Method," Textile Research Journal, 18-8 (1948), 481–487.

[14] Fineness as used here refers to mass per unit length or linear density and may be expressed in grams per 10,000 meters for grex or in grams per 9,000 meters for denier. Grex and denier are used to describe the fineness of fibers as well as yarn numbers.

TABLE 2.VII

WEIGHT FINENESS OF INDIVIDUAL FIBERS,
DETERMINED ON CENTER SECTION OF FIBERS

Length Group (1/16 in.)	Rowden (Grex)	Weight Fineness Stoneville 2B (Grex)	Wilds 13 (Grex)	Sea Island (Grex)
11	2.65	...	...	...
13	2.58	...	...	...
15	2.49	1.96	1.47	1.28
17	2.26	1.95	1.75	1.24
19	2.04	1.90	1.66	1.23
21	2.13	1.85	1.68	1.31
23		1.87	1.64	1.28
25			1.57	1.37
27			1.43	1.38
29				1.30
31				1.24
33				1.29

1 Grex = 2.54 micrograms/inch of fiber

Source: James N. Grant and Ora W. Morlier, "Relation of Specific Strength of Cotton Fibers to Fiber Length and Testing Method," *Textile Research Journal,* 18-8 (1948), 481–487.

Tensile strength is the breaking strength per unit of fiber cross section and is dependent to a large degree upon the amount of cellulose per unit of cross-section area of the fiber. The tensile strength of cotton fibers varied from 66–82 psi for some southeast varieties to 84 to 89 psi [15] for one mid-South variety.[16] Density and thickness of fiber walls vary in a measure with variety, region of growth, and maturity. Such qualities help to determine the service which the fiber gives in clothing and household fabrics.

The amount of moisture held by cotton fibers affects physical properties such as breaking strength, hand, and ease of ironing. In addition to the regular pore spaces, the cotton fiber wall has cracks and fissures which appear diagonally located, possibly in line with the spiral structure of the outer wall.[17] The cracks afford additional surface for moisture absorption and chemical attack.

Polymerization is one means by which nature and man make certain small molecules combine to form long-fiber-forming molecules. The degree of polymerization of cellulose determines the length of the molecules which in turn help to determine the service qualities of the fabric in which it is used. Length is an essential property of the molecule if

[15] *psi* is the abbreviation for "thousand pounds per square inch" of fiber cross section, a calculated value.

[16] Thomas, "Cotton Varieties," 107–122.

[17] Edward R. Schwarz, "Textile Fibers in the Light of Modern Science," *Textile Research,* 7-8 (1937), 310–327.

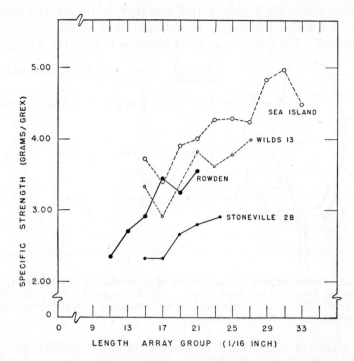

Fig. 2.10. Strength and fiber length for Stoneville 2B, Rowden, Wilds 13, and Sea Island cottons. Specimen length ¼ inch. *Source: James N. Grant and Ora W. Morlier,* "Relation of Specific Strength of Cotton Fibers to Fiber Length and Testing Method," TEXTILE RESEARCH JOURNAL, *8-8 (1948), 481–487.*

it is to qualify as a fiber molecule. The degree of polymerization of cellulose in cotton fibers varies with:

a) variety
b) different locations in the cotton boll
c) different areas on the cottonseed
d) different portions of the fiber wall itself
e) the degree of maturity of the boll when harvested [18]

Fig. 2.11. Cracks and faults in cotton fiber as they appear under a high-power microscope lens. Such irregularities contribute to the variability of textile materials. *Source: Schwarz,* "Textile Fibers in the Light of Modern Science."

[18] Lyle E. Hessler, George V. Merola, and Earl E. Berkley, "Degree of Polymerization of Cellulose in Cotton Fibers," *Textile Research Journal,* 18-10 (1948), 628–634.

Rowden, Stoneville, Tashkent, Half and Half, and Sea Island were the
varieties for which the degree of polymerization of the cellulose has
been studied.   The cellulose in fibers from the base of the seed has the

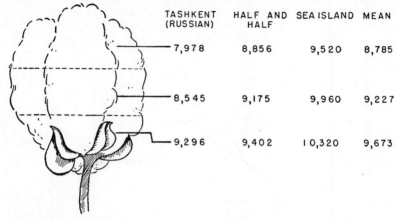

	TASHKENT (RUSSIAN)	HALF AND HALF	SEA ISLAND	MEAN
	7,978	8,856	9,520	8,785
	8,545	9,175	9,960	9,227
	9,296	9,402	10,320	9,673

**Fig. 2.12. Outline of open boll and degree of polymerization of cellulose in 3 areas
of the boll for 3 varieties of cotton.** *Source: Lyle E. Hessler, George V. Merola, and
Earl E. Berkley,* "Degree of Polymerization of Cellulose in Cotton Fibers," TEXTILE
RESEARCH JOURNAL, *8–10 (1948), 628–635.*

longest chains or molecules; that from the tip of the seed has the shortest.   The cellulose from the fibers at the base of the cotton boll has the
longest molecules.   The cellulose chains are about twice as long in the
secondary or main fiber wall as those found in the outer or primary wall.

	ROWDEN	STONEVILLE 2B	SEA ISLAND	MEAN
	7,627	8,840	9,100	8,522
	8,603	9,462	9,520	9,195
	9,112	9,500	10,240	9,617
	8,958	9,630	10,200	9,563

**Fig. 2.13. Outline of cotton seed and degree of polymerization of cellulose for 3
varieties of cotton.** *Source: Hessler, Merola, and Berkley, ibid.*

The long chains of cellulose have the highest degree of polymerization.
   Crystallinity of a fiber is a measure of orderliness of the molecular
chains within the fiber.   The degree of orderliness which exists in the
arrangement of cellulose chains within a fiber in part determines the

magnitude of certain physical properties such as strength, elongation, stiffness, toughness, elasticity, and resilience. In general, an increase in crystallinity increases stiffness and strength but decreases resilience.

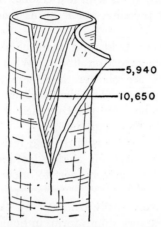

Fig. 2.14. Diagram of cotton fiber with primary wall peeled back, showing degree of polymerization of 5,940 for primary wall and 10,650 for secondary wall. *Source: Hessler, Merola, and Berkley, ibid.*

Serviceability studies on fabrics made from fibers for which specific physical and chemical data are known should be of value. Some such studies are being carried out under the direction of the Bureau of Human Nutrition and Home Economics.

Chemical properties. The composition and general behavior of cotton fibers are of considerable importance in its use and care.

Composition of cotton fibers varies with different investigators, as reported in their findings. This is probably caused in part by differences which exist between one variety of cotton and another. The data in Table 2.VIII have been reported by Nickerson from selected references.

TABLE 2.VIII

COMPOSITION OF COTTON FIBERS

Constituent	Raw cotton per cent	Kier boiled cotton per cent
Cellulose	80.0–85.0	99.1 –99.5
Wax, fatty acids	0.4– 1.0	0.15– 0.01
Ash	0.8– 1.8	0.75– 0.05
Pectate	0.4–11.1	— —
Nitrogen as protein	1.2– 2.5	0.5 – 0.1
Pigment, resins, etc.	3.0– 5.0	—
Water	6.0– 8.0	—

Source: R. F. Nickerson, "Cotton Fibers: Constitution, Structure and Mechanical Properties," *Industrial and Engineering Chemistry*, 32–11 (1940), 1454–1461. Reprinted by permission.

The *general behavior* of cotton is primarily that of cellulose, its chief constituent. Cotton fibers do not dissolve in water; yet they absorb large amounts. They are easily cleaned by laundering with soap and water. Cotton is readily dyed with fast colors. It is not easily scorched in ordinary ironing or pressing; yet it burns readily. It does not melt under a hot iron.

When exposed to heat, light, and some chemical reagents, it seems relatively easy to damage cotton fibers. When molecular chains are broken, the molecules are shorter, and new active end groups are formed on the broken pieces. The increased number of new end groups causes the molecule to be more reactive than it was originally; that is, it is more sensitive to further degradation.

The primary wall of the fiber is fairly acid resistant, but the secondary wall is very sensitive to inorganic acids. Cotton is quickly hydrolyzed by inorganic acids but is relatively inert to organic acids under ordinary conditions.

Cotton is comparatively easily oxidized by chlorine bleaches, which often are used, but in a very dilute form, in home and commercial laundries. Bleaching under carefully controlled conditions does not unduly reduce the service qualities of cotton fabrics, even though it has been estimated that the molecular chains of cellulose in bleached cottons are only about one half as long as in the native cotton. Cotton has fair resistance to weathering.

Alkaline solutions such as concentrated sodium hydroxide are used under controlled conditions to mercerize cotton fabrics. Mild alkaline solutions, such as are found in soap solutions, are desirable for laundering cellulose fibers. Very few of the associated substances found in raw cotton remain after treatment in hot sodium hydroxide solutions under pressure at 120 C for a few hours (a kier boil). Much rinsing in dilute acid removes the alkali, thus leaving the cotton fiber 99.1 to 99.5 per cent pure cellulose.

Consumption and Uses. Today's consumption and uses of cotton exceed those of any other fiber the world has ever known. Around 1800, when the cotton textile industry was being established in the United States, cotton was consumed chiefly in clothing and household fabrics. Recently it has been estimated that at least 40 per cent of the cotton is going into industrial uses, about 40 per cent into clothing, and 20 per cent for household fabrics.

According to an analysis of cotton consumption by areas, the United States has increased her consumption percentage-wise.

Only four of the major areas produced a surplus of cotton in 1947–1948. Only two of the four had a surplus sufficient to be of material help to the countries whose needs were far in excess of their production, e.g.,

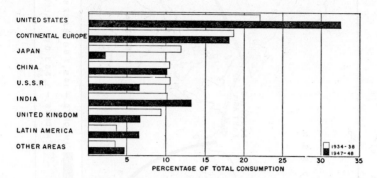

Fig. 2.15. Consumption of cotton for major areas, 1947–48. *Source:* WORLD FIBER REVIEW *(1948).*

Europe. When and where money is scarce, food is purchased, not clothing. When food is eaten, it is gone, and when food is the greater need, clothing and household fabrics can always be used a little longer. Much of the world today has no surplus of either food or clothes.

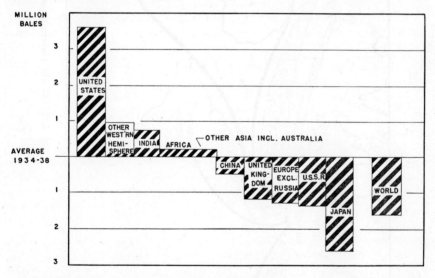

Fig. 2.16. World consumption of raw cotton by areas, showing change from 1934–35 average. *Source: Gerda Blau,* WORLD FIBER SURVEY *(Washington: Food and Agriculture Organization of the United Nations, 1947), 72.*

The world movement of cotton shows that the United States produces and exports most of the world's crop as well as imports large amounts of long staple cotton produced elsewhere.

An estimate has been made of the quantities of cotton consumed in the manufacture of 10 specified fabrics for selected years (Table 2.IX).

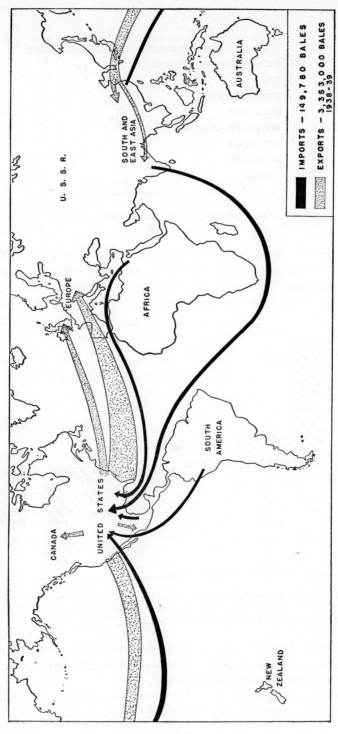

Fig. 2.17. World movement of cotton.

IMPORTS — 149,780 BALES

EXPORTS — 3,353,000 BALES
1938–39

TABLE 2.IX

ESTIMATED QUANTITIES OF COTTON CONSUMED IN THE MANUFACTURE
OF 10 SPECIFIED FABRICS FOR SELECTED YEARS

| Fabric | *Estimated number of bales of cotton consumed in manufacture of fabric in:* | | | | |
	1935	1939	1941	1947	1948
Plain print cloth	595	668	709	572	622
Wide sheeting	208	377	493	479	500
Narrow sheeting	475	552	787	853	679
Denim	247	268	370	349	392
Drill	135	213	284	197	185
Duck	103	136	195	162	161
Osnaburg	137	214	176	220	187
Carded broadcloth	116	149	200		164
Combed broadcloth	88	138	116		129
Lawn and organdy	68	71	85	67	73
Total	2,172	2,786	3,415	3,163	3,092

Source: William J. Martin and Joe H. McLure, *Market Outlets for Cotton in Some of
the Principal Cotton Fabrics.* (Washington, D. C.: Production and Marketing Administration, Cotton Branch, United States Department of Agriculture,
1950.)

The increase in demand for these fabrics from 1935 to 1948 represents
in part the increased per capita consumption and in part the increase
in the population. The years 1941 and 1947 reflect the war years.

Regardless of efforts to extend the uses of all fibers, there has remained a relatively constant figure on consumption from 1904 to 1939—
41 pounds of all textile fibers per person per year in the United States.
With the coming of World War II, this figure jumped to 55 pounds, but
in 1947 it was down to 47 pounds per person. Of this amount, 26.7
pounds were cotton and 6.4 pounds were rayon. By 1952, the Presi-
dent's Materials Policy Commission reported that of the 39 pounds of
fiber per person consumed in this country, 20.2 pounds were cotton,
16.6 pounds were manufactured fibers, and 2.2 pounds were wool.
These figures emphasize the trends in fiber production and consumption; however, cotton still sets the pattern of total fiber consumption
because it is so large a part of the whole.

The uses of cotton are legion. There is at least one government bulletin which lists only *uses for cotton*. Most of the "work clothes" of the
world are made of cotton. That means not only hard service for the
fibers, but it frequently means they must withstand rigorous methods of
cleaning. Even so, the uses which can be made of cotton are growing
with improvement in quality and kinds of finishes which can be applied
to the fibers or the fabric. Cotton has an excellent combination of
properties in its own right, but specific finishes will often enable it to
compete for specialized uses. Evans has pointed out that the "markets

go to the product which gives the consumer the most for his money." [19] Since the Industrial Revolution, cotton has been the fiber which had the most to give for the money, but if it is to continue to lead in world markets it has a worthy but rugged fight ahead, as is indicated by the rapid development of rayon and the synthetic fibers.

A great variety of woven fabrics over 12 inches in width (except tire fabrics) which are made from cotton shows a large increase in total quantity from 1939 to 1946 (Table 2.X).

TABLE 2.X

WOVEN GOODS MADE FROM COTTON
(Goods over 12 in. in width except tire fabrics. All in
grey except blankets and blanketing.)

	1939 (1000 yds.)	1946 (1000 yds.)
Total	8,287,249	9,111,002
Cotton duck	173,979	234,456
Narrow sheeting and allied fabrics	1,585,034	2,190,678
Print cloth	2,999,356	2,880,806
Napped fabrics (total)	451,412	450,586
Flannel, moleskin, and duvetyn	313,346	294,513
Blankets, except crib (total)	74,774	43,411
All cotton	58,407	37,924
Not jacquard	45,452	
Jacquard	12,955	
Part wool	16,367	5,487
Crib blankets	10,750	20,635
Blanketing	5,507	
Other napped goods	47,035	92,027
Colored goods	683,659	616,773
Fine goods (all combed or part combed, or combed or synthetic decorative yarns)	1,036,206	1,272,273
Towels, toweling, terry fabrics	482,641	413,217
Wide cotton fabrics	557,475	562,020
Specialties and others	317,487	490,193

Source: P. M. Thomas, "Cotton Varieties," Textile World, 98-10 (1948), 107–122.

These fabrics are used for industrial, household, and clothing purposes. Only part of the fabrics produced are finished. The remainder is used as grey goods, primarily in industry.

Clothing and household uses. About 60 per cent of the production goes into clothing and household uses. A great amount of the increasing quantity of knit goods is made from cotton. Woven cotton goods classified by kind of finish (bleached, dyed, or printed and finished) constitute about half our cotton woven goods and are used chiefly for clothing and household purposes. The quantities of cotton goods fin-

[19] Robert B. Evans, *Synthetic Fibers and Paper as Competitors of Cotton.* AIC *217* (New Orleans: Southern Regional Research Laboratory, December, 1948).

ished for 1949 were much above the 1939 quantities (Table 2.XI). Rayon
and nylon are at present the most formidable competitors.

TABLE 2.XI

FINISHED COTTON GOODS
(Woven cotton goods over 12 in. in width, except tire fabrics—
bleached, dyed, and finished.)

	1939	1946 Prelimi-
Total	(*1000 yds.*)	nary (*1000 yds.*)
Bleached, dyed or printed	5,050,065	6,941,348
Bleached and white-finished	2,174,352	3,380,226
Plain dyed and finished	1,431,938	1,883,361
Printed and finished	1,443,775	1,677,761

Source: P. M. Thomas, "Cotton Varieties," *Textile World*, 98-10 (1948), 107–122.

Industrial uses. Cordage, bags, twine, beltings, and tire cord are typical of the industrial uses which consume about 40 per cent of the production of cotton. More cotton is used for tire cord than for any other
single use. Rayon is beginning to replace cotton for this use. Jute,
paper, rayon, nylon, Vinyon, and Fiberglas are among cotton's competitors. The manufactured fibers are as yet in their infancy and promise
greater competition for cotton in the future; however, fibers which meet
highly specialized needs do not have qualities which make for the kind
of satisfactory general usage given cotton. Paper is a formidable competitor and is displacing cotton in such products as draperies, towels,
napkins, handkerchiefs, lamp shades, and bags.[20] Bags, of course, have
usually been the first or second most important uses of cotton. Paper
bags, however, are replacing both cotton and jute. The comparisons
made on costs do not, however, always point out the fact that a paper
bag does not have the same re-use value as cotton and jute bags.

To a very large extent, the uses for cotton will depend upon satisfactory applications of finishes and finishing materials which modify and
adapt the fabric to new uses or enable it to serve the old uses better.
Cotton is our most versatile fiber since cotton fabrics form an excellent
foundation for many kinds of finishes which adapt the fabrics to innumerable uses.

Cotton's future. Vast sums are being spent for research on production,
properties, and uses for cotton lint, linters, and cotton by-products.
Some researches follow fibers of known history from harvesting, through
processing, yarn making, weaving, finishing, and garment construction
through carefully controlled wearing and laundering procedures, until
the garment is no longer serviceable. The research on fiber properties
is of special interest, since such properties as color, length, fineness, ma-

---

[20] Evans, *Synthetic Fibers and Paper as Competitors of Cotton.*

turity, strength, absorptivity, and elasticity are related to wearing qualities and uses of cotton fabrics.

There has been little change in the weaving process since the power loom was invented over 150 years ago. Many phases of the cotton industry are antiquated and costly from the standpoint of modern concepts of production, processing, and marketing. It is estimated that 50 per cent of the cost of cotton fabrics is for processing alone. Modernization of machinery and procedures should produce greater speed in production of cotton fabrics, more uniformity of quality, and lower costs.

At present, a yarn reflects only about 20 per cent of the strength of the fibers from which it is made. Better cohesion between fibers may be achieved by chemical or mechanical means, or both. Finishes for fabrics have proved to be a fruitful approach to improving the service qualities of cotton fabrics. Another factor to consider is about a 10 per cent waste factor in cotton, against practically no waste in rayon production. This can result in loss of ground price-wise.

It always has to be kept in mind that appearance and hand of a fabric for clothing and household uses are usually more important than durability and, in some income levels, price.[21] The reverse is true for industrial uses of fabrics. Durability is of prime importance in a large proportion of the uses, and cost is either first or second, depending upon the specific use. The problems facing production, distribution, and consumption of cotton are as vast as the multitudes who produce and use it. Technological progress and economics will decide whether or not cotton will be "fashionable" for the future consumer.

[21] *Women's Preferences among Selected Textile Products,* Misc. Pub. No. 641 (Washington, D. C.: United States Department of Agriculture, 1947).

Men's Preferences among Selected Clothing Items, Misc. Pub. No. 706 (Washington, D. C.: United States Department of Agriculture, 1949).

Chapter Three

Flax

THERE ARE TWO TYPES OF PLANTS in the flax family, Linaceae. One is a branching type which is grown mostly for seed but which also produces fiber. The other type, *Linum usitatissimum* (genus, *Linum;* species, *usitatissimum*), is nonbranching and is grown especially for fiber. Flax is one of the oldest known fibers. It is, however, of minor importance today in the United States.

HISTORY

The history of flax is one of the most interesting of all textiles. Before the invention of the cotton gin in 1793, flax was the most commonly used plant fiber.

Early History. According to one historian, records of the early cultivation of flax are lost in the obscurity of the Stone Age.[1] Flax seed and remnants of linen cloth found both north and south of the Mediterranean prove that flax was cultivated, spun, and woven before 2500 B.C., within the later European Stone Age. Emil Vogt, the eminent Swiss archaeologist, has been quoted as saying that no textile fabrics of the Stone Age are known which were not made of flax.

The Bronze Age saw a great decrease in the use of flax because of the large amount of hand labor required. Sheep raising had greatly increased. It was much more economical of time and effort to dress in wool.

---

[1] Gustav Schaefer, "On the History of Flax Cultivation," *Ciba Review,* 5-49 (1945), 1762–1778.

In the Orient, flax processing reached the highest perfection. Linen fabric was used in costly garments for the nobility.

In Egypt, the use of linen became symbolic and was required in many religious activities. Linen was used for mummy wrappings from 2500 to 1700 B.C. Before that, woolen wrappings were used. When the dead were embalmed, it was the custom to encircle the body with long pieces of linen fabric. The fineness of fabric which was used differed in accordance with the rank of the deceased person and was sometimes as much as five feet wide and 60 feet long.

At Augsburg, in 1499, a decree ordered that all children who died be sewed into linen cloth for burial. This custom prevailed until linen rags became scarce for making paper. After that, a decree prohibited the use of linen for burial purposes.

At a very early date, feeling developed that linen cloth should be worn next to the skin. By the end of the first century of the Christian Era, Plutarch wrote of linen, "It provides the wearer with a smooth and always clean attire, does not burden man with its weight, is fitting for all seasons, and is avoided by troublesome vermin."

During the Middle Ages, flax spinning was one of the most common occupations of women, regardless of class or rank. Among the ancient Hebrews, it was the custom for women to do all the working and dressing of flax for ropes, strings, lamp wicks, belts, and clothing.

Unlike the air-conditioned rooms in use today, early working conditions for linen making were very poor. Work in damp caves made it possible to spin finer yarns, because the damp fibers were more manageable than dry, brittle ones. The laborers rarely saw sunlight and were continually exposed to dust. The primitive horizontal looms were attached to four posts driven into the ground.[2] Vegetable dyes were used exclusively.

Through the years, flax remained the most widely used plant fiber until 1768 when Richard Arkwright invented the spinning frame, a machine on which cotton yarns could be made as strong as linen threads. Then cotton began its climb to supremacy as a textile fiber. The consumption of flax dropped but has never disappeared.

Colonial America. Considerable quantities of flax were raised in the colonies for hand spinning in the homes. It was the most important fiber for clothing and household use until after the middle of the nineteenth century, when flax cultivation almost disappeared with the spinning wheel.

With the decline in importance of flax went fortunes in Holland, Belgium, and France. The American Civil War (1861–1865) brought some relief because of world shortage of cotton, but the flax industry did not revive. In 1892, the Dutch government was paying high subsidies to

2 Alfred Leix, "The Land of Linen," *Textile Colorist,* 61-8 (1939), 728.

flax producers but was not able to save the industry. Switzerland found dairy and stock farms more profitable, France the cultivation of turnips.

FLAX PRODUCTION

Today flax is grown chiefly in Europe and Russia. Russia, France, and Belgium, in that order, are the three largest producers; the Netherlands, Poland, and Czechoslovakia come next.

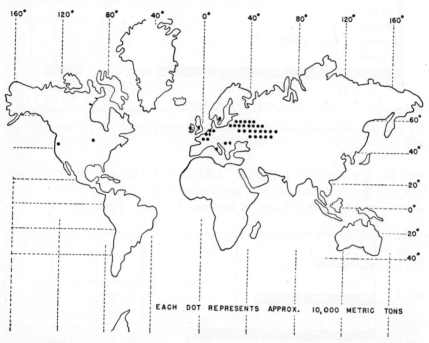

Fig. 3.1. **The world's major flax producing areas.** *Source:* WORLD FIBER REVIEW *(Washington: Food and Agriculture Organization of the United Nations, 1948).*

Before World War II, fiber production in Europe had been improving, apparently because of better seed selection, increased use of fertilizer, and mechanization. By 1940, there were 10,000 pulling machines, 800 complete threshing machines, and over 640 scutching machines in Europe. Fiber production was disrupted by the war as shown in a comparison (Fig. 3.3) of flax production for 1934–1938 and 1947–1948.

There has been considerable effort to use tow (the coarser flax fibers) to replace cotton in eastern Europe where a large part of the population traditionally wears coarse linen clothing and uses linen for most household fabrics. Before the war, Russia consumed all of her own flax crop except about 10 per cent which was exported to the United Kingdom, Belgium, and France. Flax holds an important place in the agriculture

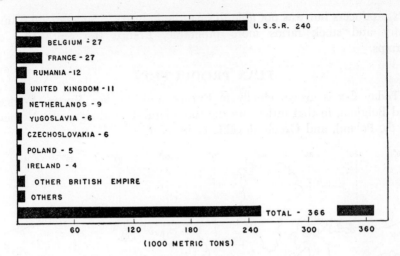

Fig. 3.2.   **Flax fiber, estimated production by countries, 1947.** *Source:* WORLD FIBER
REVIEW *(1948), 123.*

and foreign trade of Lithuania, Latvia, and Estonia. Most of their
flax, which constitutes about 10 per cent of their total foreign trade, went
directly to the linen industry of northern Ireland. France has long had

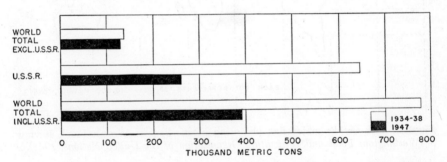

Fig. 3.3.   **Flax production for selected periods, 1934–38 and 1947–48.** *Source:* WORLD
FIBER REVIEW *(1948).*

a well-established linen manufacturing industry. The United Kingdom
is the chief importer of flax fiber and the chief exporter of linen manufactures. The United States is the chief consumer of finished linen
goods.

After years of research and experiment, a fiber flax industry, the first
of its kind in western Canada, is in sight for Manitoba. The Dominion
government opened a pilot plant for fiber flax manufacture at Portage
la Prairie.

The production of flax in this country is small and is consumed entirely at home. The high costs of labor for cultivating, harvesting, and preparing the fiber have limited its production.[3] If the costs can be brought within the reach of average incomes, there should be a good market because linen fabrics have long been especially prized for household

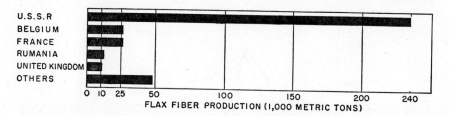

U.S.S.R
BELGIUM
FRANCE
RUMANIA
UNITED KINGDOM
OTHERS

0 10 25   50   100   150   200   240
FLAX FIBER PRODUCTION (1,000 METRIC TONS)

Fig. 3.4. Flax production, Russia and the world, 1934–38, 1947. *Source:* WORLD FIBER SURVEY (*Washington: Food and Agriculture Organization of the United Nations, 1947), 123.*

uses. On the other hand, patterns of consumption change as new products are developed and new patterns of living are established.

Flax will grow over most of the United States, but production is limited chiefly to Minnesota, the Dakotas, Kansas, California, and Oregon. In all of these states except Oregon, flax seed is the primary product, and the fiber is secondary.

Oregon has an especially favorably climate in the Willamette Valley for growing fiber flax. This section of the United States; Puget Sound, Washington; and the Great Lakes region are the only sections with good fiber flax climate. Oregon produces 80 per cent of the domestic flax fiber crop which amounts to 400–500 tons annually. The flax is tank retted; this provides a more uniform quality product than pool or stream retting. The Oregon flax is of good quality and is used chiefly for thread and twine, though some fabrics are produced for household use. In 1939, the crop was worth about $200,000; imports amounted to about 40 million dollars worth of linen fabric and two to three million dollars worth of fiber. In other words, less than 1 per cent of the total amount consumed was produced here. Economic and political conditions have led to a rapid decline in the production of flax since 1942.

Minnesota has a two-step process which produces a long, strong fiber with controllable characteristics and eliminates the necessity for the centuries-old process of enzyme retting. It is believed that this could bring linen down to the price range of high-quality cottons. Appar-

[3] *World Fiber Survey* (Washington, D. C.: Food and Agriculture Organization of the United Nations, 1947).

ently, however, neither fine cottons nor linen are able to compete with manufactured fibers in mass markets.

The varieties of flax grown in Minnesota and the Dakotas are chiefly for seed. At one time, it was thought that seed flax could not produce fiber. However, Minnesota's chemical method of retting seed flax straw produced usable fiber.[4] The fiber was spun and woven into fabrics

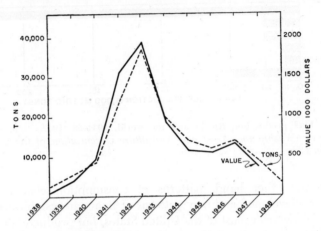

Fig. 3.5. Oregon flax production. *Source:* AGRICULTURAL STATISTICS *(Washington: U. S. Dept. Agriculture, 1948).*

which compared favorably with commercial crash. The fiber bleached to a satisfactory white.

The School of Technology at Atlanta, Georgia, has demonstrated that flax straw can be stapled, decorticated, and cleaned in one continuous process. The decorticated fiber is then degummed in a kier, transferred to a washing machine and washed, then dried in another continuous process.[5] From the drier, the fibers go to cotton-opening equipment and on through the regular textile operations.

There were only 15 flax spinning mills in the United States in 1940. It is conceivable that with a better understanding of fiber production and manufacture flax growing may be on the increase even at present. Improved varieties, machinery for much of the hand work of old, and an understanding of the chemistry of retting may be the means of reviving an industry which has practically disappeared in the United States.

Factors Affecting Yield. The areas where production of flax is profitable are limited, not only by climate but also by soil, seed, growth, fibers, and preparation of the plant for industrial conversion.

[4] Ethyl L. Phelps, "Linen Fabrics from Seed Straw Flax," *Rayon Textile Monthly,* 29-8 (1948).

[5] Harold Bunger, J. L. Taylor, and C. A. Jones, "Domestic Flax," *American Dyestuff Reporter,* 30-25 (1941), 673.

Soil type influences the yield and the quality of the fiber in the flax straw. A medium heavy soil which is well drained is best. It should contain ample quantities of available plant food materials.

The preparation of the seed bed is important. The seed bed should be smooth and fine in order to secure a uniform stand of plants. It is well to rotate flax with a cultivation crop in order to kill weeds. When there are too many weeds in flax, it has to be used for upholstery tow.

The seed for the varieties of flax produced in the United States are usually imported from Russia or the Netherlands every three or four years. It seems to be difficult to secure pure strains of seed in this country. The varieties are named for the regions from which they come; e.g., Blue Blossom Dutch comes from the Netherlands. Sometimes varieties are named for people or exporting companies.

Planting time is one of the important factors to consider, since early plantings usually result in better straw which, in turn, results in better fiber. Each inch in height of the stem is important.

The manner of planting also affects the stand. Formerly the seeds were broadcast by hand. Today the best results are obtained by planting with a drill and covering with soil by dragging.

The growing season ranges from 85 to 100 days. The plants bloom when 55 to 65 days old. Blue blossom varieties of flax produce a finer fiber and mature six to ten days earlier than the white blossom varieties.

Time of harvesting must be controlled. The fiber flax is harvested at an earlier stage of development than seed flax. If flax is harvested too early, the fibers are silky and fine but lack strength. If it is harvested too late, the fibers are coarse, harsh, and do not spin well.[6] The flax is usually pulled by hand in Europe, but there would not be much of an industry if machinery were not available in this country. Upholstery tow is obtained from flax seed straw which is always mowed, never pulled.

Processing. A summary of the steps in preparation and processing of flax includes:

- *a*) pulling (Europe) or cutting (U.S.A.)
- *b*) rippling to remove seed capsules
- *c*) retting in tanks or fields to release the long fibers from the inner stem and the outer bark
- *d*) drying
- *e*) breaking to extract the fiber from the stem
- *f*) scutching to remove shives (portions of the bark)
- *g*) combing to prepare for the spinning mills

Pulling or *cutting* is the first step in harvesting fiber flax. In Europe, the stems are usually pulled out by the roots whereas in the United States

[6] B. B. Robinson, *Flax, Fiber Production,* U. S. Department of Agriculture, Farmers' Bulletin No. 1728 (Washington, D. C.: Government Printing Office, 1934).

machinery is used to cut the stems. In either case the degree of maturity of the stem is of critical importance.

Rippling or *threshing* of flax stems removes the leaves and seed capules.

Retting processes are of two kinds: *dew retting* or *tank retting*. Field or dew retting is a slow process and likely to produce variations in fiber quality. Several tons of straw can be retted in a tank at one time, and more control can be exercised over tank or chemical retting than over field or dew retting. To release the flax fibers, the retting processes first attack the cambium layer, then the thin-walled cells of the cortex of flax and related bast fibers such as hemp, jute, and ramie, all of which have a similar origin and structure.[7] After retting, the stems are placed under sheds until time for breaking and scutching.

A comparison of the results of dew retting and tank retting indicates that the chemical (tank) retting procedures compare favorably with dew (field) retting for a number of bast fibers (Table 3.I).

TABLE 3.I

RETTING METHODS COMPARED FOR SOME BAST FIBERS

	RETTING METHOD				
	(dew)	(tank)	(control)		
	Weath-	Ammonium	Water		Length of
Species	ered	Oxylate	Stem	Bark	fiber in cm
Apocynum cannabinum					
Indian hemp	S*	S	S	S	2– 8
Cannabis sativa					
Marihuana hemp	O**	U***	S	S	2– 87
Asclepias syriaca					
Common milkweed	O	S	U	U	13–230
A. sullivantii					
Smooth-leaf milkweed	O	S	U	U	13–167
A. verticillata					
Whorled milkweed	O	S	S	U	2– 45
Gonolobus laevis					
Climbing milkweed	S	U	U	U	5– 45
Polygonum scandens					
Climbing buckwheat	O	U	U	U	0

Source: Harriette Brita Hanson, "Structure, Properties, and Preparation of Certain Bast Fibers," *Iowa State College Journal of Science*, 20-3 (1946), 365–383.

  * satisfactory
  ** dew retting is satisfactory for some uses only
  *** unsatisfactory

Drying of the retted stems is necessary in order that the woody material in the stem may be easily broken away from the fiber.

Breaking is a process by which the fiber and bark are separated from the rest of the stem.

[7] Charles W. Hock, "Microscopic Structure of Flax and Related Bast Fibers," *Journal of Research of National Bureau of Standards*, 29-41, Research Paper 1482 (Washington, D. C., 1942).

Scutching frees the fiber from the last portions of bark called shives. Combined breaking and scutching machines and large combine-type scutching machines exist, the latter enabling men to increase their output from about 70 pounds per day to two to four times as much of better-quality fiber. Mechanized procedures are replacing the old hand processes with a general improvement of fiber quality.

Combing or *hackling* pulls the fibers through successively finer combs to separate the valuable line, the long fibers, from the less valuable tow, the short fibers.

PROPERTIES

The properties of flax fibers are in general those of other bast fibers of value as textile fibers. Bast fibers grow from root to tip of certain plant stems and are located between the outer bark and the cambium layer. *phloem cells*

Physical Properties. The long, fine flax fibers are called *line;* the short coarse fibers are known as *tow.* The cells in each are similar.

The multicelled fiber bundles are found in the inner bark of the stem. Long bundles of varying size grow down the entire length of the stem. A diagram of a section of a fiber bundle (Fig. 3.6) will illustrate the compact manner in which the individual cells are arranged. A diagrammatic sketch of a cross section of a flax stem, fiber, cell, and serial

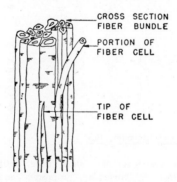

CROSS SECTION
FIBER BUNDLE

PORTION OF
FIBER CELL

TIP OF
FIBER CELL

Fig. 3.6. Flax cells in fiber bundles. *Source: Gordon G. Osborne,* "Micro-analysis of Textile Fibers," TEXTILE RESEARCH, *5-10 (1934–35), 448.*

cross sections of a cell (Fig. 3.7) will demonstrate the location of fiber bundles in the bark and the variety of sizes of cross sections of cells to be found at any one point on a flax stem. This variety of cross sections results from the fact that the cells overlap each other in such a way that tapering ends of some cells fit along the wider parts of other cells.

The length and fineness of the fiber depend upon the degree of purification which has been carried out.   Fibers from the more finely divided bundles are shorter than those from the less finely divided bundles.

The cell structure of flax fiber is typical of that found in other stem fibers.   Each fiber may be one or several cells in diameter (Table 3.II).

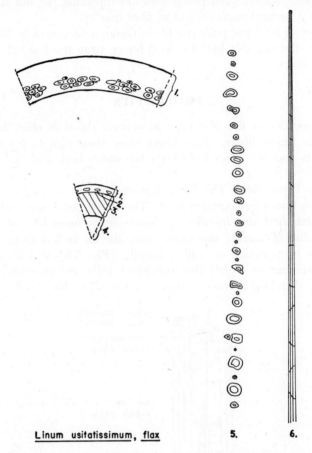

Linum usitatissimum, flax   5.   6.

Fig. 3.7. Diagrammatic sketch of flax stem, fiber, cell, and cell cross-sections. *Source: Harriette Brita Hanson,* "Structure, Properties, and Preparation of Certain Bast Fibers," IOWA STATE COLLEGE JOURNAL OF SCIENCE, *20-3 (1946), 365–383.*

The finer fibers have fewer cells in the cross section.   Serial cross sections of stems of plant fibers were studied by Osborne who isolated cell bundles.[8]   He found them to vary from 1 to 20 inches in length and to have 4 or 5 to 30 or 40 cells in a bundle or fiber.

A study of individual flax cells was made by Hock who was able to isolate the individual cells by mounting the fibers on a microscope slide

[8] Gordon G. Osborne, "Micro-analysis of Textile Fibers," *Textile Research,* 5-8 (1935), 351.

TABLE 3.II

PHYSICAL CHARACTERISTICS OF BAST FIBER CELLS OF CERTAIN SPECIES

Species	No. cells	Diameter		Length cm	Ratio Length/Diameter	Cell wall %	Length Taper mm	Bulge width μ	Cross marks	Twist
		fiber μ	lumen μ							
Apocynum cannabinum, Indian hemp	1–78	23.7–395.0	7.9–71.1	1.8–3.0	570– 970	52.8–92.1	1.2	none	yes	left
Cannabis sativa, Marihuana hemp	1–68	15.8–434.5	7.9–27.7	.8–3.1	475–1266	82.4–95.9	0.9	23.7	none	left
Asclepias syriaca, Common milkweed	1–230	23.7–474.0	7.9–47.4	.0–3.5	601–1139	69.7–91.5	1.2	79.0	yes	left
A. sullivantii, Smooth-leaf milkweed	8–175	47.4–790.0	7.9–79.0	.5–2.5	632–1055	58.2–92.9	1.2	47.7	yes	right
A. verticillata, Whorled milkweed	2–24	23.7–418.7	7.9–39.5	.5–1.2	316–1519	74.6–94.6	1.0	23.7	none	none
Gonolobus laevis, Climbing milkweed	1–30	13.3–197.5	3.8–31.6	.9–1.7	570–1013	80.7–91.2	1.03	none	none	right
Polygonum scandens, Climbing buckwheat	1–17	15.8–316.0					1.2			
Linum usitatissimum, Commercial flax			11.9–63.2	1.5–2.5	791–1681	52.2–91.2	1.2	none	yes	right

Source: Harriette Brita Hanson, "Structure, Properties, and Preparation of Certain Bast Fibers," *Iowa State College Journal of Science,* 20-3 (1946), 365–383.

and treating them with a suitable reagent.[9] The fibers were attacked by the reagent first at the surface markings (Fig. 3.8) which are only fissures

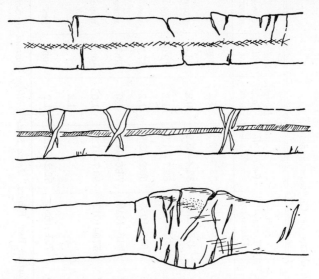

Fig. 3.8. Diagram of flax cells with fissures and "cross-markings." *Source: Osborne, op. cit., Part IV,* "Observations on the Structure of Flax, Manila, and Jute," *431– 460.*

in the fiber. The microscopic appearance (Fig. 3.9) of the fibers showed the transverse markings (fissures) or nodes as dark areas or lines. When the cellulose in the flax cell was dissolved, it left:

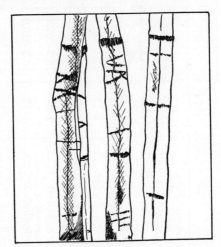

Fig. 3.9. Sketch of microscopic appearance of flax fibers.

[9] Hock, "Microscopic Structure of Flax and Related Bast Fibers."

a) residue of intercellular substances
b) primary cell wall
c) lumen wall
d) part of the secondary wall

The pectic substances in cotton seem to be in the primary wall, but in flax they seem to be in narrow lamellae or layers especially noticeable around the lumen of the cell. The lamellae were from 0.1 to 0.2 microns thick.

The cells of the bast fibers are similar in a number of ways to those of the cotton fiber. Length is the striking difference. Similarities are to be expected. Both are plant cells. Both have primary and secondary cell walls. The primary cell wall constitutes the surface of the cell. The secondary wall is composed of cellulose fibrils, some of which wind in one direction and some in the other (Fig. 3.10). More layers of fibrils are found in the cells at the base of the plant stems than are found

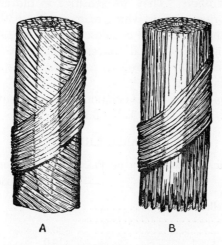

A   B

Fig. 3.10. Schematic diagram of arrangement of fibrils in the cells of flax and related bast fibers: A. Flax and ramie; B. Hemp and jute. *Source: Charles W. Hock,* "Microscopic Structure of Flax and Related Bast Fibers," RESEARCH PAPER 1482 *(Washington: National Bureau of Standards, 1942).*

toward the tip where the cells are still growing.

Flax and ramie differ from jute and hemp in physical properties partly because of differences in the way the fibrils wind around the cell walls in the two groups of fibers. In flax and ramie, the direction of twist of the fibers [10] seems to be determined by the bulk of fibrils which appears to make an S twist.[11] In hemp and jute, the parallel orientation of most

[10] *Ibid.*
[11] A.S.T.M. Committee D-13, *A.S.T.M. Standards on Textile Materials,* Designation: D 508-43, (Philadelphia: American Society for Testing Materials, 1950).

of the fibrils does not influence the fibers to twist at all.   In these fibers, the Z twist in the outer layer appears to be the determining factor.

Measuring the fiber length of mature unbroken fibers helps distinguish between ramie, which is 60 to 260 mm long, and flax, which is 10 to 50 mm long.   Some of the differences between flax and other bast fibers are hard to distinguish.   Microscopic identification is frequently uncertain.

The sizes of the cells are of considerable interest since modified methods of handling bast fibers were introduced to avoid the slow retting process.   It is necessary that a fiber be 5 mm in length to be spinnable.[12] Flax fiber cells have been found to vary from 15 to 25 mm in length, and from 11.9 to 31.6 mu in diameter.[13]   It is generally stated that a fiber, to be spinnable, must be 100 times as long as it is wide.   Many of the single cells are of spinnable length.

Chemical Properties.   The behavior of flax fibers is generally characteristic of all bast fibers.   They are sensitive to the action of even extremely dilute inorganic acids which react readily with the pectic substances between the cells.   The cellulose is more sensitive to the action of acids than of alkalis of equal concentration.   Bleaching agents, unless their use is carefully controlled, cause rapid deterioration to any fabrics made of flax fiber.

The composition of flax-straw components has been reported by the Georgia School of Technology (Table 3.III).

TABLE 3.III

CHEMICAL COMPOSITION OF FLAX-STRAW COMPONENTS

	PERCENTAGE		
Chemical constituent	*Cortex*	*Fiber*	*Shive*
Cellulose and hemicellulose	65.0	72.0	60–70
Lignin		24.0	20.3
Pectin	20.0	2.5	
Wax	10.0	1.0	1.0
Rosin			1.5
Coloring matter	5.0	0.5	1.0

Source: Harold Bunger, J. L. Taylor, and C. A. Jones, "Domestic Flax," *American Dyestuff Reporter,* 30-25 (1941), 673.

Great care is necessary in chemical processing because of the close similarity in the chemical compositions of shives and fibers.[14]   It is desirable to remove only a portion of the pectic matter, since that seems to form part of the binding or cementing material between cells.   Before

[12] A.S.T.M. Committee D-13, *A.S.T.M. Standards on Textile Materials,* Designation: D 123-48 (Philadelphia: American Society for Testing Materials, 1950).

[13] Harriette Brita Hanson, "Structure, Properties, and Preparation of Certain Bast Fibers," *Iowa State College Journal of Science,* 20-3 (1946), 365–383.

[14] A. J. Turner, "The Structure of Textile Fibers, VII: the Structure of Flax," *Journal of the Textile Institute,* 40-9 (1949), P857–P868.

the seeds have matured, the green flax plants have less lignin associated with the fibers.   Lignin is a woody substance.

The composition of flax fibers is similar to that of raw cotton (Table 3.IV).

TABLE 3.IV

COMPOSITION OF FLAX FIBERS

Constituent	Unretted flax	Retted flax	Cotton (raw)
Cellulose	56.5	64.1	82.7
Hemicellulose	15.4	16.7	5.7
Pectin	3.8	1.8	0.0
Lignin	2.5	2.0	0.0
Flax and wax	1.3	1.5	0.6
Water solubles	10.5	3.9	1.0
Moisture (water)	10.0	10.0	10.0

Source: A. J. Turner, "The Structure of Textile Fibers, VII: the Structure of Flax," *Journal of the Textile Institute*, 40-9 (1949), P857–P868.

The structure and properties of the chief constituents of flax fibers are related.[15]   Cellulose, which forms the greater part of the fiber, is the most inert.   Hemicellulose is more sensitive to alkali than cellulose, but is closely related.   Pectin is related to cellulose and exists in a number of forms in flax fibers.   Pectin is the acid sensitive binding material which holds the cells together in the fiber bundles and is also thought to be located around the lumen.   In the very young plant, the pectic substances are chiefly water soluble.   In the mature plant, pectin exists as complexes which are converted to acids by retting.   Lignin is not found in cotton but is about 2 per cent of the flax fiber.   Lignin increases as the fiber matures and is found in largest amounts in over-mature stems.

The coloring matter in flax consists chiefly of chlorophyll, a green plant material; xanthophyll, a yellow plant material; and associated products found in the outer layers (bark) of stems of many plants.

CONSUMPTION AND USES

The consumption and uses of flax have always depended upon its relative economy of production.   The United States has used large quantities of fine linens in the past.   The flax imports for 1946–1947 and 1947–1948 were primarily from Canada and the United Kingdom.

IMPORTS IN 1000 LB.

	1946–1947	1947–1948
Canada	1,429	705
United Kingdom	779	17
Total	2,208	722

[15] *Ibid.*

Flax is a useful fiber for clothing, household, or industrial fabrics, but today it is a luxury fiber. It has been replaced by cotton in many of its household and industrial uses. At present, jute has replaced flax in many industrial uses. The cost of linen fabrics keeps them out of mass markets.

There are at present two distinct markets for flax. One is for fine dress and handkerchief linens, chiefly consumed in the United States, and the other for sewing thread, twines of many kinds, carpet warp, fishing lines, fishing nets, and other uses where strength and durability are of importance. Tow finds a large market as upholstery stuffing.

The history of the handkerchief alone is a story of the finest linens. The history of customs, of usage, and of kinds of handkerchiefs illustrate but one small phase of the linen industry.[16]

By-products. The by-products of flax raising are quite valuable. Seeds yield oil for paints and varnishes. Linseed cakes are fed to livestock. Upholsterer's tow is obtained from seed flax. Fine paper, such as cigarette paper, uses flax fibers. The shives are used for fuel, since it affords about 9,200 Btu[17] per pound.

The markets for flax straw are few in the United States. There are no quotations on flax fiber in this country, since our prices for flax fiber are largely controlled by the Russian and Belgian markets.

Future of Flax. The future use and consumption of flax products will depend in part upon the success of the industry in developing and adapting modern methods of production and processing of the fiber.

Two developments have been used with a degree of success. One is the elimination of the slow retting process and the substitution of a decorticating or breaking process used on green stalks. The coarse, drab, green cloth made from the unretted fibers filled many of the uses for which strong flax fibers were needed with much less expenditure of time and money than is necessary to produce retted flax. Another development involves breaking up the fibers by a series of chemical and mechanical processes into short staple lengths to mix with other fibers. Time and money are saved, but the fibers do not have, to the same degree as formerly, the much-prized qualities of softness, flexibility, durability, and fineness.

In prewar years, Belgium sold approximately 50 per cent of her linen to the United States, and she hopes to regain her chief customer. To that end, in March, 1948, representatives of the governments concerned held a meeting in Washington, D. C., in an effort to:

    a) re-establish relations with government officials and business men
    b) determine the present characteristics of the United States market

---

[16] M. Braun-Ronsdorf, "The History of the Modern Handkerchief," *Ciba Review*, 8-89 (1951), 3203.
[17] British thermal units, a measure of heat required to raise one pound of water 1 F.

Some of the hindrances to re-establishing trade are:

a) increased competition from other textiles, old and new
b) occasionally poor quality of the linen
c) too high price
d) lack of efficient merchandising

The flax industry is faced with the problem of cutting costs of production and of reducing the amount of hand labor needed. The uses of flax fibers and by-products might well be extended to the benefit of the industry if costs could be brought to a competitive level.

Chapter Four

Ramie and Hemp

RAMIE

RAMIE is a stingless nettle of the family Urtica, subdivision *Boehmeria*. There are two varieties: *Boehmeria nivea*, the white-leafed ramie; and *Boehmeria tenacissima*, the less hardy tropical green-leafed plant sometimes called rhea.

History. Like cotton and flax, ramie has a long history. Mummy cloth of ramie was used to wrap the dead in Egypt in the 15th dynasty.[1] China has cultivated ramie for centuries. Ramie has been used thousands of years in the Orient but was not taken to Europe until about 1845, which seems to be about the time it came to America.[2] Since then, large sums and much attention have been allocated to efforts to produce the fiber on a sound economical and technological basis. The strong, beautiful fibers obtained by hand processes in the Orient have been the will-o'-the-wisp which has led people to continue to hope that the same soft, silky staple may sometime be prepared by less laborious methods.

Production. The production of ramie, like other bast fibers traditionally has been a hand process but is undergoing mechanization.

Centers of production. To a certain extent production of ramie has been limited by the requirements for its growth: soil, rainfall, and labor. It grows best on a light loamy soil, in a warm climate, with about 40 inches of rainfall per year. Among the many types of plants tested in

---

[1] J. W. Brown, "Ramie Fibers," *Textile Colorist,* 63 (1941), 532 and 565.
[2] *Ibid.*

the Florida Everglades, ramie has been found to be best adapted to the
soil, climate, and agricultural pattern.[3]   Great effort has been made to
produce the fiber on a commercial basis in both Florida and Mississippi.
Before World War II, China had provided practically all of the ramie

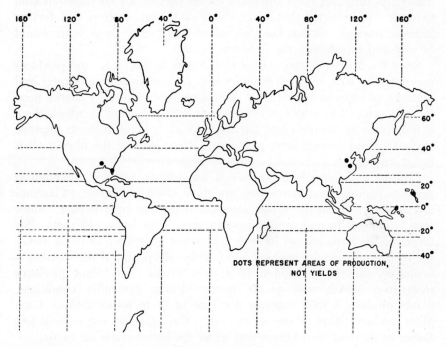

Fig. 4.1. The world's ramie.

in the world markets. The green-leafed variety has been produced
chiefly in China, India, and Formosa. The white-leafed variety, which
is most prized commercially, has been grown chiefly in Formosa and
Malaya.[4]

Other countries which produce ramie are: the Philippines, Sumatra,
Brazil, West Africa, Cuba, and Australia. Australia established a ramie
industry about 1940, since it was thought that technical and mechanical
improvements were such that little hand labor would be necessary.

Technical difficulties. At present, the number of areas which can
profitably produce ramie is limited by technical difficulties.

The Philippine ramie interests (government and private) feel that they

[3] J. R. Neller, *Culture, Fertilizer Requirements, and Fiber Yield of Ramie in the
Florida Everglades,* University of Florida Agricultural Experimental Station Bulletin
No. 412 (Gainesville, Fla., 1945).

[4] A. J. Turner, "The Structure of Textile Fibres VIII: the Long Vegetable Fibers
(1) Bast Fibers, Jute, Hemp, Ramie, Sunn Hemp (2) Leaf Fibres, Sisal, Manila,
Phormium," *Journal of the Textile Institute,* 40-10 (1949), P972–P984.

have devised suitable decorticating machinery.[5] A new chemical process for degumming the fiber has been developed which apparently does not destroy the desirable properties of the fibers. These two improvements, in addition to being able to harvest four crops per year, may make it possible for the Philippines to put part of her uncultivated land to work. It is hoped that by-products of the ramie crop will further increase revenue. It has been estimated that two or three years would be required to establish the industry.

Since the fiber will grow in the Gulf States in the U. S., and produces exceptionally well, research is under way to mechanize the industry and improve varieties in order that it can compete pricewise. Varieties need to be developed in which all stems mature at once and in which there is uniformity of strength and fineness. Work is being done to improve harvesting and decorticating machines. The nature of the fiber itself is being studied.

Planting and harvesting. Ramie is not difficult to grow, although at present, planting and harvesting are done chiefly by hand. Plantings are usually made in the spring after the danger of frost is past. Since seed is difficult to use, ramie is grown from 3- to 5-year-old roots. Six inches of the roots are set in rows 3 to 4 feet apart and 18 to 24 inches in the drill. These are covered 1 to 2 inches deep, and, if the weather is favorable, the shoots emerge in 2 to 3 weeks. The plant produces roots from which new plants sprout. Under favorable conditions, plants produce 3 to 6 cuttings per year of 6- to 8-foot stems. Each plant produces 20 to 50 stems per year. The canes are cut when a few inches at the root turn brown and when the leaves come off easily.

The fiber constitutes about 5 per cent of the gross green weight of the plant. About 27 to 45 tons of green matter are removed from an acre per year. Attempts are being made to leave most of that in the field when the fiber is harvested. The portable Short Machine was developed in Florida to decorticate the fibers in the fields. At present, this results in lower quality of fibers because machine harvesting has to take all the stems, mature and immature.

Processing. Ramie is processed in a manner similar to that of other bast fibers. The difficulties in harvesting and preparing the crop for market have kept the fibers out of the price range of most customers. Fibers may be separated from either green or dry stems. The procedure in India is to collect the mature stems, cut, crush, and clean the fibers by hand. The Chinese hand strip the fiber ribbons from the green stalk and hand scrape the outer bark from the fibers. One man produced 2 to 6 pounds of crude fiber per day by scraping the ramie

[5] J. G. Schnitzer, *World Trade in Commodities, Textiles and Products,* Vol. VI, Part 19, Nos. 26 and 27 (Washington, D. C.: U. S. Department of Commerce, Office of Internal Trade, 1948).

fiber free of the green stem.[6] Such a hand process could scarcely clothe America! Even so, before the war about 100,000 pounds annually were produced in China.

Extraction of the fiber includes (a) decortication, which is the separation of the fiber from the rest of the stem; and (b) degumming which removes the gums, waxes, and pectins from the fiber. Sometimes bleaching and softening are added. Decortication of green stalks has so far proved to be the most successful procedure. The gums and other connecting substances have not hardened, and removal is much easier than in the mature stalks. Less damage is done to the fiber. So far, mechanical methods of decorticating are more successful than chemical methods, including bacterial retting. The decorticated fiber, before it is degummed, is sometimes sold to this country as China grass. Canton linen and Chinese linen are names sometimes given the fabric.

The degumming process removes about one third of the weight of the fiber. Many degumming procedures have been developed, but none as yet is completely successful, because most chemicals which attack the gum attack the fiber. A recent process consists of subjecting the ramie stems to steam under pressure and crushing the dried stems to remove the woody portion in order to produce a clean degummed fiber. The method causes no loss of fiber or luster. Proper degumming eliminates much of the undesirable brittleness which results in a fabric of poor wearing qualities.

One difficulty in processing ramie in this country is that the long fibers require flax spinning equipment, although it can be handled on worsted machinery if cut to 5 or 6 inches in length. Cutting the long fibers in order to spin on cotton machinery loses part of the value of long fibers.

Cost estimates indicate that in 1945 the decorticated fiber cost the farmer about $0.04 per pound. About 1 to 5 pounds of degummed fiber is realized from each 100 pounds of green plant.

Properties. The properties of ramie fibers are in general those of other bast fibers. The fiber bundles extend the entire length of the plant stem and are found between the cambium and the cortex. They are held in place by gums, waxes, and pectins. It is much more difficult to extract ramie than flax, hemp, or jute.[7] This has limited the production. The potentialities of the fiber, however, have kept it under investigation.

Physical properties. Its physical properties give ramie fibers special value. Apparently the fibers possess extremes of properties, some of

[6] Department of Agriculture, *Letter from Secretary of Agriculture on Regional Research Laboratories,* Senate Document 65, 76th Cong., 1st sess., 1940 (Washington, D. C.: Government Printing Office, 1940).

[7] Turner, "The Structure of Textile Fibers, VIII: the Long Vegetable Fibers," P972–P984.

which are very bad, and some very good. The best quality is strength (Table 4.I). It resists rot, will bleach to snowy whiteness, and the lustrous fibers can be separated to almost the fineness of silk. The poor qualities of ramie are its brittleness and low torsional (twisting) and bending strength. It is thought that the fiber could be softened by *complete* degumming.

TABLE 4.I

PHYSICAL PROPERTIES OF SELECTED FIBERS

Fiber	Breaking strength, gm/denier	Extension at break, per cent
Ramie	6.7	3.74
Flax	6.1	3.01
Japanese silk	4.4	23.40
Jute	3.5	1.80
American cotton	2.8	7.60

Source: William B. Dall, "Ramie," *Textile World*, 95-12 (1945), 3.

The cells of ramie fibers are sometimes about 3,000 times as long as they are wide. When the long fibers are broken down to single cells, the cells are found to vary in length from 1 to 12 inches and are from 0.002 to 0.003 inches in diameter. The cells have a lumen and thick walls. A microscopic examination of cross sections of the cells shows great fissures (Figs. 4.2 and 4.3) both inside and outside the walls.[8]

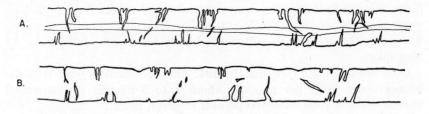

Fig. 4.2. Diagram of ramie fiber showing cracks and fissures in fiber wall. *Source: Osborne, op. cit. Part II, "Observations on Ramia," 5 (1934–35), 75–91.*

Apparently there are few unbroken fibrils in the cell.

If the fissures are the result of mechanical action, the fiber may give more satisfactory service in such uses as drapery fabrics, which do not require the resistance to physical deformations necessary in the use and care of clothing and most other household linens.

The crystalline structure of cellulose in ramie has been of special interest in fiber structure studies. It probably has the most orderly ar-

[8] Gordon G. Osborne, "Micro-analysis of Textile Fibers, II: Observations on Structure of Ramie," *Textile Research*, 5 (1934–1935), 75–91.

rangement of molecules of all plant fibers, whereas flax and hemp are considered more complex and the single-cell cotton fiber probably the most complex of all.[9]

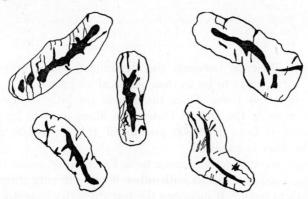

Fig. 4.3. Diagram of cross-section of ramie cell, showing cracks and fissures extending outward from the lumen and in outside wall. *Source: Osborne, loc. cit.*

The cellulose walls of a ramie fiber cell are built up of fibrils, as in cotton fibers and flax cells, except in the case of ramie the cellulose chains are approximately parallel to the length of the fiber but tend to be arranged in left-hand spirals. Ramie and flax always have an S or clockwise twist when drying. Jute and hemp have a Z or counterclockwise twist when drying. The extremely orderly arrangement of cellulose within the ramie fibrils contributes to the high tensile strength and high luster on the one hand and to its brittleness, low extensibility, and lack of flexile strength on the other.

Chemical properties. The chemical properties are similar to those of flax, since the intercellular substances are similar though not exactly alike. All the differences are not known. The cellulose is the same chemically, but according to some comparative figures the cellulose molecules of ramie are longer than those of cotton and manila hemp.

Fiber	Degree of polymerization of cellulose
Ramie	2,660
Cotton	2,020
Manila hemp	1,990

The composition of ramie is similar to that of flax. Therefore, it is sensitive to acids, alkalis, and bleaches. The same precautions should be used in caring for fabrics made from ramie as for those made from flax.

[9] Martha A. Morrow, "Old Fiber Has New Uses," *Science News Letter*, 51-11 (1947), 170.

Constituent	Per cent
Cellulose	68.6
Hemicellulose	13.1
Pectin	1.9
Lignin	0.6
Water solubles	5.5
Fat and wax	0.3
Moisture	10.0

The chief difference between the degummed fibers of ramie and other bast fibers seems to be in their physical properties.

Consumption and Uses. Since there is as yet little commercial production of ramie in the United States, the fibers have to be imported. Imports dropped from 2,000,000 pounds in 1919 to 50,000 pounds in 1937. Some fiber is exported.

Aside from novelty uses and some table linen, ramie seems to be most satisfactorily used as a blend with other fibers. It cuts shrinkage and adds strength to wool. It increases the wet strength of rayons. It gives linen-like properties to cottons. It has been tried as a structural element in plastics. Ramie has been suggested for use in operating rooms, in sail cloth, cords, and nets.[10] Experimental work has been done in which fabrics of ramie were used for summer wearing apparel, table fabrics, draperies, upholstery material, and kitchen towels. In addition, industrial uses include canvas, seat covers for automobiles, tape, cordage, and packing.[11] Ramie is frequently mixed with wool and mohair because of its luster and long staple. One of ramie's chief domestic uses is as a stern tube packing for ocean-going vessels.

HEMP

Hemp is a soft bast fiber from the *Cannabis sativa* plant, a member of the Moraceae family.[12] This variety of hemp is also called true hemp, tree hemp, American hemp, or Kentucky hemp. In addition to *Cannabis sativa*, certain other soft fiber plants, such as Indian hemp (dogbane) and sunn hemp, and some hard fiber plants, such as Manila hemp (abacá) and sisal hemp, are commonly known as hemp.

History. Hemp became known much later than flax. The Egyptians, the Phoenicians, and the Swiss lake dwellers knew nothing about hemp. Possibly as late as the Iron Age, the plant was unknown. It is believed that hemp originated near the Caspian Sea and spread from there to

[10] A. C. Whitford, "The Present Situation in Ramie Fiber," *Rayon Textile Monthly*, 23 (1942), 459.

[11] James L. Taylor and H. T. Coss, "Georgia Research on Ramie," *Rayon and Synthetic Textiles*, 29-11 (1948), 55.

[12] Department of Agriculture, *Letter from Secretary of Agriculture on Regional Research Laboratories*, Senate Document 65, 76th Cong., 1st sess., 1940 (Washington, D. C.: Government Printing Office, 1940).

Russia and Siberia.[13] In India and China, hemp appeared at an early date. The fibers were used for paper making about 105 A.D. by the Chinese. Japan considers hemp her oldest textile fiber. By 100 A.D., the Romans were using hemp rope to hang prisoners. However, the Romans preferred esparto grass for general use, although hemp grew well in Italy.

By the Middle Ages, flax was much more popular for clothing than was hemp, use of which was considered a mark of poverty. Hemp was used chiefly for ropes for rigging on sail ships. By the sixteenth and seventeenth centuries, Russia planted large areas in hemp and gradually came to dominate the market.

Production. Hemp is a sturdy plant and will grow at altitudes up to about 8,000 feet. It requires a longer and hotter growing season than

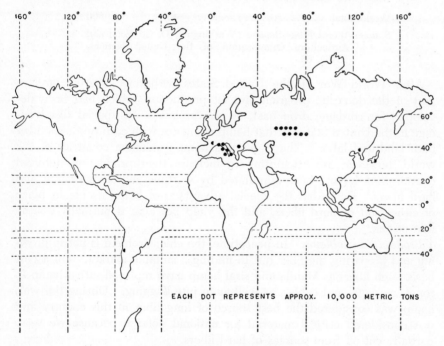

Fig. 4.4. The world's hemp.

flax but has much less exacting growing conditions. Hemp may be planted in April and harvested in August and September. No cultivation is required. If the plants are close together, a much better quality of fiber is produced.

[13] Gustav Schaefer, "Flax and Hemp," *Ciba Review,* 5-49 (Basle, Switzerland: Society of Chemical Industry, 1945).

Production centers. Although grown mostly in Russia, hemp is raised also in Poland, France, India, China, and South America, as well as Italy, where the best fiber is grown.[14] Since hemp is adaptable to a wide range of growing conditions, it is scattered over many temperate countries (Table 4.II).

TABLE 4.II

HEMP PRODUCTION

Country	1934–38 1000 lbs.	1947 (Prelim.) 1000 lbs.
Europe (excl. U.S.S.R.)	192	170
North America, U.S.A.		2
U.S.S.R.	203	100
South America, Chile	5	4
Asia (excl. China)	37	24
World total	437	300

Source: World Fiber Review (Washington, D. C.: Food and Agriculture Organization of the United Nations, 1948), 63.

After World War II, the United States withdrew government support of the domestic program and let production, which had been developed for cordage, drop back to prewar levels. A special disadvantage in the United States is that hemp competes with corn production for both land and labor. The traditional hemp-producing countries of the world, however, are attempting to increase their production, internal consumption having been stimulated by wartime shortages of jute and hard fibers. Hemp has the special advantage of being usable in place of either soft or hard fibers, and the yield per acre is normally double that of flax.

Production problems. In peacetime, the chief problem is not in growing and preparing the fiber but in finding a suitable market. On a cost basis, such fibers as Manila and sisal hemp have replaced sativa hemp in ropes, cordage, and cables, as well as in jute bagging. During the war, hemp was considered the best source of long fiber in this country and was considered critical material for national defense because we were partially cut off from sources of hard fibers.

There are, however, numerous and serious problems in its production. A variety is needed in which all plants mature at one time, in which no narcotic drug is produced, and in which the fiber is not destroyed if the seed matures. The variety best adapted to growth in this country is known as Kentucky or American hemp and is of Chinese origin.[15]

In the present varieties, the male plant dies before the female plant,

[14] Turner, *op. cit.*
[15] B. B. Robinson, *Hemp*, U. S. Department of Agriculture Farmers' Bulletin No. 1935 (Washington, D. C.: Government Printing Office, 1943).

one situation which produces fibers of a mixed degree of maturity. The male plant produces good fiber but needs to be pulled early. In addition to fiber, the female plant produces seed which need to mature fully before harvesting, thus reducing fiber quality.

Processing. Either of two procedures may be used: cottonization or retting. The wartime development of cottonization, which especially applied to flax and hemp, breaks the green fibers by a series of chemical and mechanical processes into short staple lengths. The green fibers may be used in the cottonization process, or, as they are harvested, they may be put through a decorticating or breaking process in place of the slow retting process which requires more experience and skill. Both hemp and flax fibers produced by the above processes lack the softness, flexibility, and fineness produced by conventional retting and are considered poor substitutes for cotton and rayon.

Generally in the United States, hemp is cut by machine and allowed to dew ret on the ground. A most important step in processing the fiber is to stop the retting at the proper time. The stems should be retted, not rotted. The disintegrated stalks are then collected in stacks and sold to the hemp mill, where the stalks are dried and put through a *hemp brake* in order to remove the fiber from the stalk.

Properties. The properties of hemp are similar to those of flax.

Physical properties. The fiber cells of *C. sativa,* hemp, are grouped in comparatively small irregular aggregates throughout the bark (Fig. 4.5). The inner rows of aggregates of secondary origin are produced by the cambium during the growing season, and are less mature than the first row when harvested.[16] This characteristic of the cambium, together with the differences in maturity of the male and female plants, accounts for the great variations in maturity of hemp fibers in commercial production. Longitudinal views of single cells showed bulges on six out of ten fibers. A cross section of the stem at any one point shows a variety of cell shapes at various places in the cell. The variation is in part caused by the manner in which cells overlap in the fiber bundles.

Hemp fibers, together with other bast fibers, are distinguished by cross markings and swellings. Osborne has described the nature of cross markings as being fissures in the walls of the fibers.[17] The fissures were increased with increasing mechanical manipulations during manufacturing processes. As the fissures were increased, the tensile strength of the fiber was lowered. The fissures are admittedly points of weakness for chemical attack not only in hemp but in any fiber having such breaks in the cell walls. The actual origin or cause of the points of weakness

---

[16] Harriette Brita Hanson, "Structure, Properties and Preparation of Certain Bast Fibers," *Iowa State College Journal of Science,* 20-3 (1946), 365.

[17] Osborne, "Micro-analysis of Textile Fibers," 458.

is not known, but there is some evidence that they arise from mechanical imperfections in the structure of the fiber itself. This theory can be tested but has not been as yet.[18]

The fiber cells range from 5 mm to 55 mm in length and average about 20 mm.[19] The cells range in width from 0.016 mm to 0.05 mm and aver-

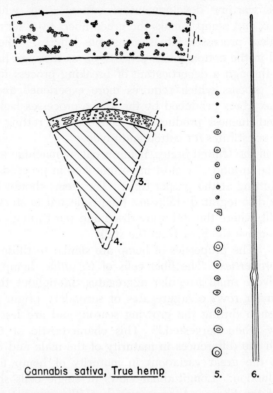

Cannabis sativa, True hemp

Fig. 4.5. Diagrammatic sketch of stem of hemp, showing fiber bundle, cell, and cross-section. *Source: Harriette Brita Hanson,* "Structure, Properties and Preparations of Certain Bast Fibers," Iowa State College Journal of Science, *20-3 (1946), 365–383.*

age 0.022 mm. The ratio of length to diameter is about the same as flax, 1,000 to one.

As stated before, the fibrils in hemp have a Z twist, which gives it a characteristic counterclockwise direction of twist when drying.[20]

Chemical properties. The properties of hemp are those of bast fibers in general. The composition of hemp is similar to that of jute and

[18] Hanson, "Structure, Properties and Preparation of Certain Bast Fibers," 365.

[19] Turner, "The Structure of Textile Fibers, VIII: the Long Vegetable Fibers," P972–P984.

[20] A.S.T.M. Committee D-13 *A.S.T.M. Standards on Textile Materials* (Philadelphia: American Society for Testing Materials, 1950), 76.

ramie.[21] As a result, these fibers behave similarly toward wear and deteriorating agents.

Constituent	Per cent
Cellulose	67.0
Hemicellulose	16.1
Pectin	0.8
Lignin	3.3
Water solubles	2.1
Fat and wax	0.7
Moisture	10.0

Consumption and Uses. In 1947, the United States imported large quantities of bast fibers from Great Britain (see Fig. 4.6). Hemp, ramie, and especially flax were third in value of imports from Britain. Whiskey and wool ranked first and second respectively. Most of the fiber is used for cordage, although attractive and useful household fabrics may be made from hemp. The seed are valuable for oil and for bird food, but they are much less valuable than flax seed. Future developments in genetics, chemistry, and pharmacology may well warrant an extension of the hemp production in the United States.

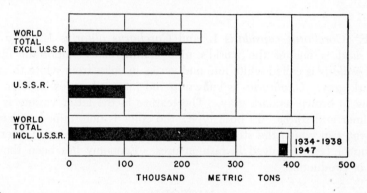

Fig. 4.6. **Estimated production of hemp, 1934–38, 1947.** *Source:* WORLD FIBER RE-VIEW (*Washington: Food and Agriculture Organization of the United Nations, 1948*).

Hemp has many competitors in its various uses: jute, abacá, sisal, flax, henequen, and cotton. Even though hemp has superior qualities for various uses, it is also expensive. Recently some of the synthetic fibers have joined the list of competitors of hemp. Ropes, cables, and coarse cordage are made chiefly from hard fibers. Hemp is used largely in strong twines. There seems to be little competition from flax, except in industrial fields. The peacetime uses of both the fiber and the by-products under favorable conditions might well be extended inasmuch as the fiber was on the "critical" list for national defense. Consumer uses include upholstery, drapery, toweling and some clothing.

[21] Turner, *op. cit.*

$\mathcal{C}hapter\ \mathcal{F}ive$

$\mathcal{J}ute$

JUTE (*Corchorus capsularis* L. and *Corchorus olitorius* L.) is a bast fiber and is one of the world's nine commercially important fibers.[1] *C. capsularis* is called white jute and varies in color from white to cream or dark gray. *C. olitorius* is known as red jute and varies in color from yellow to brown or dark gray. The texture in the latter variety is usually finer and softer. In both types, the color is determined in part by the water in which the stems are retted. Jute is a utilitarian fiber and has never been involved in fashion uses. Economy has been the keynote of production.

HISTORY

Early History. The history of wool, flax, hemp, silk, and cotton production in India goes back many centuries, but jute seems to have come into use relatively recently. For a major fiber, jute has a comparatively short early history. The Bengal Board of Trade was sending jute out of India by 1791.[2] Even today, most jute is grown in India. For several years, it was used only for twine, rope, and door mats. By 1820, the first jute was being spun in England. Two years later, the flax spinners

---

[1] The botanical names of plants are given in this order: genus, species, family. In the case of white jute, *Corchorus capsularis* L., the genus is *Corchorus*, the species is *capsularis*, and it belongs to the Linden family.

[2] Horace G. Porter and Maurice R. Cooper, *Statistics on Jute and Jute Manufactures with a Brief Survey of the Industry* (Washington, D. C.: Bureau of Agricultural Economics, U. S. Department of Agriculture, 1945).

in Dundee, a whaling center, tried to spin jute on flax equipment but found that to be impractical until it was observed that whale oil conditioned the jute fibers which before had seemed to be too dry to spin. After that, jute was used extensively. In 1828, Calcutta began giving jute a separate market listing, and the next year the first shipment reached the United States. The quality of the manufactures continued to improve in the Dundee mills, followed by improvement in other areas including India herself.

By 1838, the Dundee mills were making pure jute cloth. The Dutch government decided to use jute instead of flax for bags in which to ship coffee from the Dutch East Indies. This demand established the jute bag industry.

During the Crimean War, Russian hemp was shut off from the west, and jute got another boost in use. Later, when the American Civil War caused the supplies of cotton to be curtailed, the Dundee jute industry again experienced a period of expansion. The growth of the jute industry depressed flax not only in England and Scotland but in Continental Europe as well. Jute was cheaper than flax.

Jute has been valuable as a fiber of commerce for very little over a hundred years, but its annual world production has grown until today it ranks second only to that of cotton (see Fig. 1.3).

The planting, cultivation, and harvesting of jute in India was formerly one of the world's most efficient textile fiber industries.[3] Today the political and social upheaval in India has disrupted the efficient production and marketing of jute.

Present Conditions. This is a period of transition in the jute industry. Government-controlled markets, aimed at keeping the prices up, have led American users of burlap to turn to a coarse cotton fabric known as osnaburg, multiwalled paper containers, and bulk shipping.[4] In the past, jute was second only to rubber in export value to the British Empire. Jute is India's most important source of foreign exchange. The United States provides the largest single market. (See Fig. 5.2.)

Jute has for some time been increasing in price. In 1948, it sold at over four times its 1934–1938 average. Because of favorable prices and because of the need for a medium of trade, India hopes to increase the output of jute by:

a) using better seeds and fertilizer
b) utilizing waste land
c) double cropping with other plants
d) extending irrigation

[3] S. G. Barker, "Jute and Its Utilization," *Journal of the Textile Institute*, 31-2 (1940), P12.

[4] Porter and Cooper, *Statistics on Jute and Jute Manufactures with a Brief Survey of the Industry* (Washington, D. C.: Agricultural Economics, U. S. Department of Agriculture, 1945).

In the meantime, competition has been mounting for the fiber which provides a cover for much of the world's agricultural equipment and farm products on their way to the markets.

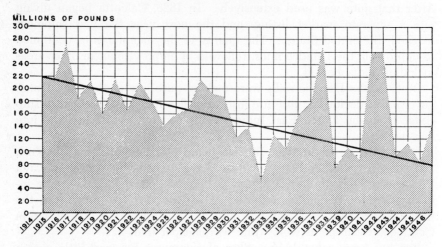

Fig. 5.1. Raw jute, United States imports from India. *Source: J. G. Schnitzer,* WORLD TRADE IN COMMODITIES, TEXTILES, AND PRODUCTS VI, *19-28 (Washington: Department of Commerce, 1948).*

The Argentine government has set up a five-year program to initiate a textile industry based on long vegetable fibers. Brazil is interested in establishing a jute industry and hopes that United States technical advice and capital will be available to mechanize the industry.[5] The Union of South Africa is establishing a bag industry of her own to provide both grain and wool bags for her own products for exports. The recovery of India's jute industry will depend, therefore, upon the success of the emerging competitors. Jute will grow in the southern part of the United States but, under present economic conditions, could not compete pricewise. Jute production, like that of cotton, has been underwritten by the governments concerned.

PRODUCTION

The areas in which the climate and soil are suitable for jute production are more numerous than the areas in which labor conditions are favorable.

Centers of Production. The world's jute crop has been centered in the eastern part of the province of Bengal, which in 1947 was divided between India and Pakistan.[6] About three million acres are planted in

[5] L. H. Dewey and B. B. Robinson, *Jute* (Washington, D. C.: Bureau of Plant Industry, U. S. Department of Agriculture, 1945).

[6] *World Fiber Review* (Washington, D. C.: Food and Agriculture Organization of the United Nations, 1948).

jute in these areas. The plantings take place from February in the lowlands to May in the highlands. In the past, all the seed were sown by hand. Weeds are usually pulled twice, always by hand.

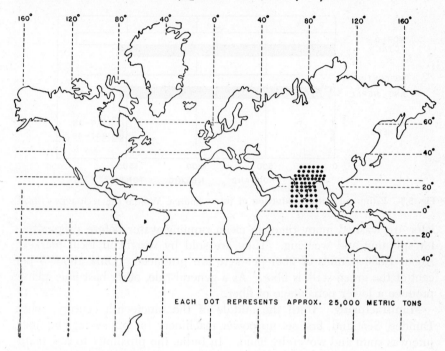

EACH DOT REPRESENTS APPROX. 25,000 METRIC TONS

Fig. 5.2. The world's jute. *Source:* WORLD FIBER SURVEY *(Washington: Food and Agriculture Organization of the United Nations, 1948).*

Jute requires a hot steaming climate with temperatures from 70 to 100 F and at least 40 inches of rainfall distributed over the four-month growing season.[7] The plants grow to a height of 8 to 10 feet.

India produces 98 per cent of the world's supply of jute and exports almost all of the crop either as raw jute or jute manufactures. (See Fig. 5.3.)

Processing. The principle of processing jute is similar to that of other bast fibers. The details vary with conditions under which it is produced. As with other bast fibers, jute is finer and more silky if the stalks are harvested early. Since the fiber is sold by weight, the relative prices of coarse and fine fibers determine in a measure the degree of maturity at which jute is harvested.

The bundles of stems are retted for 10 to 20 days in slow running streams. The water in which the retting is done affects the quality of

[7] Porter and Cooper, *Statistics on Jute and Jute Manufactures with a Brief Survey of the Industry.*

fiber. When the fibers slip easily from the woody part of the stem, laborers break the stalks with mallets, strip off the fiber, and clean it by threshing it on the surface of the water.[8] The fibers are dried and

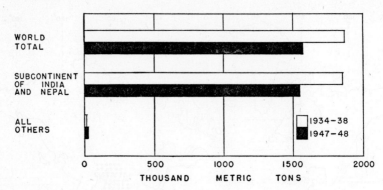

Fig. 5.3. Estimated world production of jute. *Source:* WORLD FIBER SURVEY *(1948).*

later are washed many times in clean running water before preparation for spinning and weaving. They are sold by weight at local markets. About 1,300 pounds of fiber per acre are produced. Only about 5 per cent of the green stalk is fiber. As a general rule, other bast fiber plants produce a lower percentage of fiber.

Manufacturing. Until the middle of the nineteenth century, when Dundee, Scotland, first set up power machinery for processing the fiber, jute was spun and woven by hand. In India, the proximity to raw materials and the almost unlimited supply of cheap labor gave manufacturers a tremendous advantage. As the Indian industry grew, the number of people employed practically trebled from 1900 to 1931. By 1940, Germany ranked next to India though far below her in jute manufacturing. France, Brazil, and Italy each had manufacturing industries over half the size of that in Germany (Table 5.I).

TABLE 5.I

JUTE MANUFACTURING, 1940

Country	Looms (approximate)
India	66,000
Germany	9,600
France	5,000
Brazil	5,000
Italy	5,000

Source: World Fiber Review. (Washington, D. C.: Food and Agricultural Organization of United Nations, 1948.)

[8] Lyster H. Dewey, *Fiber Production in the Western Hemisphere,* U. S. Department of Agriculture, Miscellaneous Publication No. 518 (Washington, D. C.: Government Printing Office, 1943).

The Indian Central Jute Committee. This organization is aware of the struggle for survival going on within the industry. Much time and money are being spent in an effort to mechanize and modernize the industry. Ambitious plans are under way. Social and economic changes have outmoded the industry. Food shortages, labor troubles, transportation problems, political tangles, and lack of fuel, to say nothing of the development of jute-growing interests in other lands, are problems harassing the Indian industry at present. Five research centers are being established in India to try to find a basis for maintaining world supremacy.

PROPERTIES

The properties of jute are such that the fiber has neither great beauty nor a pleasant hand.

Physical Properties. The physical properties of jute are determined in part by the large amount of lignin present. The fiber has limited uses because it is stiff and harsh and lacks elasticity. A microscopic examination of the physical structure of the jute fiber shows it to be a typical bast fiber composed of long cells which taper at each end and are staggered in their arrangement in the fiber bundle so that the tips of some cells fit next to the larger central portion of others to form a compact arrangement. (See Fig. 5.4.) This arrangement of cells is

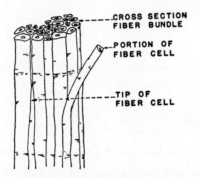

CROSS SECTION
FIBER BUNDLE

PORTION OF
FIBER CELL

TIP OF
FIBER CELL

Fig. 5.4. Jute cells in fiber bundle. *Source: Gordon G. Osborne,* "Micro-analysis of Textile Fibers," TEXTILE RESEARCH, 5-10 (1935), Part IV, "Observations on the Structure of Flax, Manila, and Jute," 431–460.

typical of bast fibers. The lumen of the cells is unusually irregular in size, but on the average it is about 1 to 7.5 per cent of the volume of the cell.

The cells vary from 1.5 to 5 mm in length and from 10 to 25 mu in diameter. The cross sections of the cells are quite angular. At any one point in a fiber, a cross section would cross cells from tip to center (see Fig. 5.5) so that a variety of sizes of cross sections will appear in any one cut. The individual cells in bast fibers are held together with pectins and associated materials. At ordinary magnifications with transmitted light, each single cell shows a number of transverse cross mark-

Fig. 5.5. Serial sections of jute fiber. *Source: Osborne, ibid., 351–369.*

ings (nodes) known to be fissures (Fig. 5.6) similar to those found in ramie, flax, and hemp. They are usually at an angle to the major axis of the fiber.

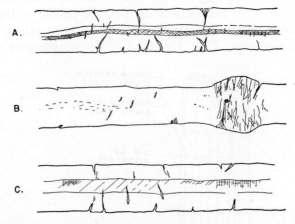

Fig. 5.6. Diagram of jute cells showing fissures in the walls. A and C show breaks or cross-markings leading into the lumen of the fiber. B shows a node on a fiber. *Source: Osborne, ibid., 431–460.*

Chemical Properties. The composition of jute differs greatly from that of the other stem fibers in that it contains a high percentage of lignin and associated substances and has a lower cellulose content (Table 5.II).

The fact that jute rotted readily, when used for sand bags during the war, stimulated further investigation of jute and its reactions.[9] It was found, however, that flax, hemp, and jute rotted at about the same rates

[9] Barker, "Jute and Its Utilization," P12–P17.

TABLE 5.II

COMPOSITION OF JUTE

Substance	COLOR OF FIBER		
	Light %	Fawn %	Brown cuttings %
Cellulose	64.24	63.05	61.74
Water	9.93	9.64	12.58
Water extract	1.03	1.63	3.94
Fat and wax	0.39	0.32	0.45
Ash	0.69	—	—
Lignin, pectin substances	24.41	25.41	21.29

Source: S. A. G. Caldwell, "Jute, Newer Uses, Newer Methods," *Dyestuffs*, 38-2 (1946), 51–55.

when tested under comparable conditions. Cotton was almost twice as resistant as jute but cotton was too expensive to use in sand bags.

It has been observed that jute fibers may be treated with cold concentrated solutions of caustic alkali to produce a curled wool-like appearance. Jute treated in this manner may be mixed with wool to produce a fabric with a tweed-like appearance. Such jute fibers would not be satisfactory in plain colored wool-jute fabrics. Even though jute dyes quite satisfactorily, it fades much more readily than wool.

For many possible uses of jute, it is desirable to bleach the fibers. This is especially true when the fibers are to compete with flax and cotton. Large amounts of the pectic materials and of the lignin are removed during the bleaching treatments. If the costs of chemical treatments can be controlled and some qualities of the fiber improved, jute may be able to expand into higher-priced markets. Jute fabrics may be laundered with the same precautions as used with linen and ramie fabrics.

CONSUMPTION AND USES

Cheapness and abundance are the chief qualities of jute which have enabled it to maintain its competitive position. Jute is the most easily spun, cheapest, weakest, and least durable of the important textile fibers, and it is used in larger quantities than all other plant fibers combined, except cotton.[10]

Consumption. The 1946–48 quotas for export from India showed that over half of all the jute was sent to the United States (Fig. 5.7) and the United Kingdom. The Indian jute mills themselves consume large quantities of jute; yet India has exported raw jute to the amount of many thousands of tons as well as quantities of jute manufactures (Fig. 5.8).

[10] Schnitzer, *World Trade in Commodities, Textiles and Products.*

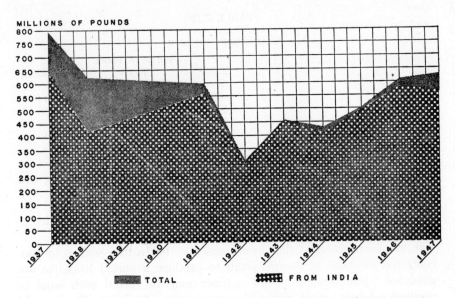

Fig. 5.7. United States import of jute manufactures. *Source: Schnitzer, op. cit.*

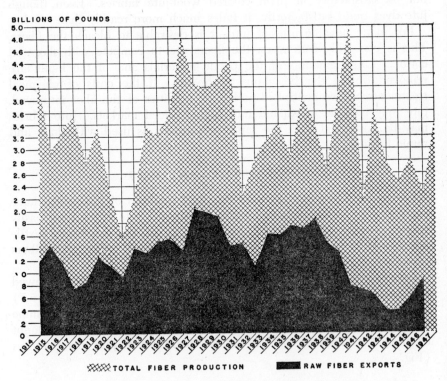

Fig. 5.8. Indian jute production and exports. *Source: Schnitzer, op. cit,*

These exports constitute about a quarter of the total value of the exports of Indian merchandise.

Uses. In the past, 70 per cent of raw materials (food materials, cotton bales) were transported in jute containers. Paper, bulk handling, box cars, and cotton are the most important competitors.[11] There are, how-

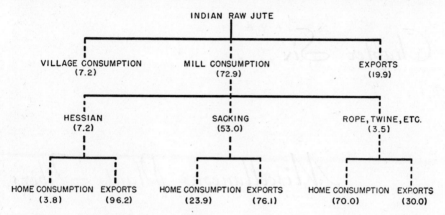

Fig. 5.9. **Utilization of jute for different purposes.** *Source: Schnitzer, op. cit.*

ever, synthetic products emerging which could prove to be more ruinous to the industry than any natural product. Even so, jute is still the most economical and satisfactory fiber for such uses as bagging and linoleum backing. Jute cloth has a number of miscellaneous uses.[12]

The United States is the only large cotton-producing country that uses jute to cover the cotton bales. That use could disappear, because of agitation to have cotton cloth used for coverings on cotton bales. Thus, both political and economic factors are involved in the survival of jute.

[11] *Ibid.*
[12] S. A. G. Caldwell, "Jute, New Uses, New Methods," *Dyestuffs*, 38-2 (1946), 51.

Chapter Six

Miscellaneous Plant Fibers

MISCELLANEOUS PLANT FIBERS consist of a number of materials of limited commercial value which nevertheless serve useful purposes. Some are used chiefly for upholstery stuffing for furniture in homes, offices, public buildings, and for automobiles, consuming most of this group of materials. By no means all of the interesting or useful plant fibers have been included; only those thought to be of most general use in the United States.

Kapok. A single-celled seed hair, kapok *(Ceiba pentandra)* is produced in the tropics. The fibers are ¾ to 1¼ inches long and are very thin-walled with a large lumen. In 1937, the United States imported 11,710 tons valued at $3,372,649. The southern part of Florida is warm enough for kapok to grow there. Many of the prewar uses of kapok are being filled by other materials, e.g., foam rubber and spun glass.

Crin vegetal. Crin vegetal *(Charmaerops humilis)* is obtained from hemp palm leaves along the Mediterranean. There were 6,079 tons valued at $244,495 imported into the United States in 1937. It is used for stuffing.

Spanish moss. Spanish moss, an epiphytic plant *(Tillandsia usneoides)* belongs to the Bromeliaceae family and is found growing on trees in the southern part of the United States. It is used as a substitute for curled horsehair which has declined in importance. Only a few thousand tons of this plant are collected annually to be used as stuffing and filling fibers. A chemical means of "debarking" is needed in order to increase its value.

Cabbage palmetto. The cabbage palmetto (Sebal palmetto) grows on the southern coast of this country and in the Bahamas. The fibers of this plant are multicelled root fibers, used in some brushes.

Grasses. Some slough grass is cut along the Mississippi River, dried, and used to make mats. Esparto and related grasses grow in southern California and are used in paper making. There are 12 to 13 million acres of wild esparto in northern Africa where cheap native labor can gather the grass at small cost.

Coir. Coir (*Cocos nucifera*) is a multicelled fiber resulting from differentiation of cells in the inner part of the outer hull of the coconut and is found in the tropics.

Pineapple fiber. The pineapple plant (*Ananas comosus*) is a close relative of the Bromeliaceae family. The preparation of fiber from the leaves is a household industry in the Philippines. Beautiful lustrous pale yellow fabric known as piña may be made from the fibers, which are sometimes erroneously called silk grass.

Wild banana fiber. Samples of wild banana fiber from the Cameroons have been submitted to the trade in India. Although inferior in strength to Manila hemp and sisal, this fiber is considered to have sales possibilities under the present hard-fiber shortage.

Congo jute. Congo jute (*Urena lobata*) is a member of the Malvaceae family. This tropical shrub produces a bast fiber of commercial value in the Congo where it has been used for centuries for cordage, sacking, mats, and nets.[1] It is grown in prepared fields from seed furnished by the consuming firms. The plant needs lots of sunlight and rain. It is used in some areas instead of jute. Since the plant grows relatively slowly, much labor is required to destroy weeds. When the plant blooms five to six months after sowing, the stems are cut. They are left in running streams to ret for two weeks, after which the bark is easily removed. The fiber bundles are sold in this condition to local collectors who sell to exporters. Growers in the Stanleyville area prefer raising *Urena lobata* to raising cotton because of the shorter work year.

Redwood bark fibers. Fibers from the bark of the redwood tree are comparatively short but have the unusual distinction of being one of the few cellulose-containing fibers which will form a felt quite satisfactorily with wool. It was found that the fiber could be bleached to a pale tan and could be dyed with a number of dyes, some of which were fast to washing.[2] The fiber is naturally a reddish brown, an attractive color in itself, and is being considered as a blend with wool in blankets,

[1] Lewis Dean Brown, "Belgian Congo Fibers," *World Trade in Commodities, Textiles and Products,* Vol. 6, Part 19, No. 10 (Washington, D. C.: Department of Commerce, Office of International Trade, 1948).

[2] H. Luttringhaus, "The Dyeing of Redwood Fibers," *Rayon Textile Monthly,* 24-2 (1943), 115.

overcoat fabrics, and hats. A cross-sectional view of the cells shows them to be quite large and rectangular in shape.

Kenaf. Sometimes called Java jute, kenaf (*Hibiscus cannabinus* L.), like many other fibers, was first known in India. The bast fibers which are about 5 to 10 feet long and composed of cells about 5 mm long and 20 mu wide are extracted by power-driven decorticating machines or by retting in water before passing through fluted rollers and on to a beating machine. Kenaf is used in the Asiatic countries and in Africa. Production is being encouraged in several Caribbean countries in an effort to avoid the use of high-priced jute. It appears to be adapted to soil conditions in the southern parts of Florida and Texas. At present, this country seems to be the center of kenaf production because of the efforts of the United States Department of Agriculture.[3] Kenaf may replace jute in many of its uses in the future.

Additional Fibers. Fibers which are of no commercial value at present, but which have certain potentialities, are: sunn hemp, Colorado hemp, swamp milkweed, Indian hemp, and fibers from nettles.

Evaluation of Stuffing Materials. Miscellaneous fibers and fibrous materials useful for stuffing pillows and upholstery are useful because of their resiliency and their filling capacity, as well as their low price.[4] In Table 6.I some fibrous materials are ranked according to total resiliency and filling capacity from greatest to least.

TABLE 6.I

RANK OF SOME FIBERS USED IN UPHOLSTERY

		RESILIENCY	
Fiber	Filling capacity	After 1 compression	After 150 compressions
Kapok	1	3	
Linter pods	2	2	3
Cotton	3	5	4
Sisal combings	4	6	5
Coir	5	8	6
Crin vegetal	6	4	2
Southern moss	7	1	1
Flax tow	8	7	

Source: Adapted from Brittain B. Robinson, "Resilience and Density of Some Upholstery Plant Fibers," *Textile Research,* 8 (1937–38), 310.

The above upholstery materials are used commercially in different types of work. Recently, other stuffing materials have come into use. Foam rubber is much favored. Feathers and some curled synthetic materials are used. Cotton linters are widely used.

[3] Will H. Shearon, "Natural Fibers," *Chemical and Engineering News,* 30-16 (1952), 1618.
[4] Brittain B. Robinson, "Resiliency and Density of Some Upholstery Plant Fibers," *Textile Research,* 8 (1937–38), 310.

Many upholsterers point out that the age and usage of fibers affect the resiliency. Southern moss which has a very long life is considered to have 78 per cent greater resiliency than coir. By weight, it requires more than three times as much flax tow as kapok to fill the same volume. Kapok and cotton do not pack down on repeated compressions as other fibers do. In dry weather and in dry climates, the resiliency as well as the filling capacity of all these materials are greater than in more humid atmospheres. Other factors to consider in making choices of stuffing materials are the serviceable life of the fiber and the particular use to be made of the article after stuffing. Kapok is brittle and therefore has a relatively short period of usefulness. For average household purposes, it lasts only five to ten years.

These materials and others (feathers, down, cotton, wool, new and secondhand) come under careful inspection in the majority of states which have adequate laws governing the manufacture and sale of bedding and upholstered furniture.[5]

Many governments through agricultural research institutes throughout the world are subsidizing study on other fiber plants of potential value.

[5] Temporary National Economic Committee, *Consumer Standards, Monograph 24,* 76th Cong., 3rd sess. (Washington, D. C.: Government Printing Office, 1941), 243–254.

J. Davis Donovan, "National Bedding Standards—To Protect against Disease and Fraud," *Industrial Standardization,* 8-11 (1937), 297.

Samuel Mermin and John M. Mayer, *Survey of State Laws and Judicial Decisions on Bedding and Upholstery,* U. S. Department of Agriculture, Division of Consumers' Council, Agricultural Adjustment Administration (Washington, D. C.: Government Printing Office, 1940).

Definitions for Filling Materials for Bedding and Upholstery (New York: American Standards Association, 1946), American Standards L12.1, L12.2, L12.4.

Chapter Seven

Wool

EVIDENCE OF WOOL used for clothing at an early date has been gained from fragments of fabrics which have survived civilizations of the past.

EARLY HISTORY

Sheep are thought to be the earliest of domesticated animals. Wool fabrics were woven by the Swiss lake dwellers thousands of years ago. The literature of the past contains many references to the raising of sheep and to the value of the sheep's fleece. In Mesopotamia, now Iraq, small figures of sheep carved from bone and from gold, which were buried with other royal treasures around 3500 B.C., have been unearthed. Even today, Iraq is known for its production of Oriental rugs from wool grown in that region.[1]

The Medici family were originally wool merchants and manufacturers of wool and silk.[2] Great flocks of sheep were raised in the country surrounding Florence. The fact that the Medici family had deep roots in the powerful Florentine wool industry enabled them to emerge as the bankers and rulers of Florence. The Cathedral of Florence was made possible and completed under the supervision and with the support of the Cloth Makers Guild.

[1] Jevet A. Michel, "The Great Centers of Production of Oriental Carpets," *Textile Colorist*, 61 (1939), 671.
[2] Anon, "The Genius of Florence," *American Fabrics*, No. 13 (1950), 45.

In medieval times (8th to 15th centuries A.D.), monasteries were the centers of the weaving crafts. In fact, one of the first trademarked Florentine fabrics was a "stout woolen" Humiliate Cloth which had been woven and processed by the Humiliate Order.

Social Values. Wool garments from time to time have been considered either as being exclusively clothes for the poor or as being apparel of distinction. Before the Industrial Revolution, cotton was a more precious fiber than wool in the eyes of men and women of fashion. The development of the spinning frame in 1769 by Arkwright, and of the cotton gin in 1793 by Eli Whitney, put cotton fabrics within the reach of the majority of people. Since then, wool has become a more expensive fiber than cotton, partly because the latter is produced in far greater quantities. Economic and technological developments do much to dictate fashion's preferences and thus the fate of industries.

Sheep as a Source of Food and Clothing. Sheep have played a very important part in man's life since we have had written history.[3] Sheep raising was a most important occupation at the time of the Norman Conquest. Sheep were kept for wool and milk. The shepherd, who was a key man in agriculture during the Middle Ages, milked the ewes and made the cheeses. He had whey through the summer and milk on Sundays for his own use. He was given a lamb at weaning time and a fleece at shearing time. He could own and keep some of his own sheep with his lord's flock on the best pastures. In addition, he could keep his master's flock on his own land for two weeks at Christmas to manure the land.

Both food and fiber for clothing are still produced by the dual-purpose sheep which are predominant today.

Wool in English Commerce and Politics. Wool was introduced into ancient Britain about 50 B.C. by the Romans. For at least 1,000 years the political and economic developments of England might be regarded as having been largely built on wool. The relations of England with other countries can be traced in the history of wool.[4] In fact, to this day, the Lord Chancellor in the House of Lords is reported to sit on a woolsack.[5] In 1193, England's entire clip of wool for one year was required as a ransom for King James I. This brought considerable recognition to the monasteries where large numbers of the sheep were raised.

In order to expand her wool industry, about 1327 to 1377, England granted special protection to Flemish weavers, dyers, and wool pullers who would settle in England to follow their trade. As a result, wool

---

[3] John Foster Beaver, "The Romance of Wool," *Journal of the Textile Institute,* 40-1 (1949), 39.
[4] Beaver, "The Romance of Wool," 39.
[5] *Ibid.*

cloth making grew and prospered under England's protection. The production became so important to England and the world that one type of wool cloth got its name from England. Worsted cloth gets its name from the town of Worsted, England, where a similar type of fabric was first manufactured.

As early as 1500, England and Spain were recognized as the greatest sheep-producing countries of the world. Spain developed the fine Merino breed of sheep. It was, however, a crime punishable by death to send Merino sheep out of Spain until 1808 when Napoleon overthrew the Spanish government. After that, many sheep were sent out of the country, and as a result other lands such as our own profited by Spain's loss.

By the time of Queen Elizabeth I (1558–1603), wool was the chief source of wealth for traders and of revenue to the crown, and it was a controlling factor in the foreign policy of England. In 1938, wool constituted the fifth great export commodity. Even today, wool fibers and fabrics are of primary interest in British commerce.

Early Wool Industry in the United States. Except for the Navajos, the Indians had no sheep but found other means of making warm clothing. In 1609, the colonists brought a few sheep to Jamestown, but it was not until 1650 that a group of carders and combers came from Yorkshire, England, to Rowley, Massachusetts, and established the first *fulling mill*. A fulling mill is a machine used in finishing wool cloth to give it more body. The fabric is "fulled" or shrunk before being made into garments. About ten years later, in 1660, the British Parliament passed an act prohibiting the exportation of sheep in order to protect the British home industries, thus cutting off the source of supply for American sheep raisers. This situation lasted about 100 years, or until the American Revolution, when the colonists established themselves as an independent people. The Revolutionary War lent encouragement to sheep raising but peace was followed by a supply of British wool manufactures and consequently a decline in sheep raising in this country. The Embargo Act of 1807 and the Nonintercourse Act of 1809 gave support again to domestic sheep production. The War of 1812 added stimulation to sheep raising and the wool textile industry, but peace in 1815, as before, brought a flood of foreign goods. Wars have almost always stimulated the production of sheep for wool.

From 1830 to 1837, improvements in machinery and transportation, and the increase in population favored the wool industry. Sheep raising was moving westward to the ranges in advance of the cities. The general industrial development after the Civil War, together with the Tariff Act of 1867, proved to be the needed encouragement for both wool growers and wool manufacturers. By 1897, over 90 per cent of our domestic requirements for wool were being met at home.

PRODUCTION

Wool is produced in most of the countries of the world. Its production is more widespread than that of any other textile fiber, and it is

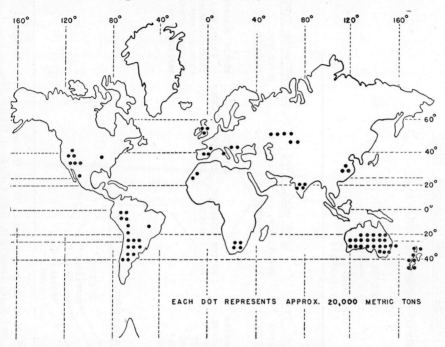

EACH DOT REPRESENTS APPROX. 20,000 METRIC TONS

Fig. 7.1. The world's wool—major producing countries. *Source:* WORLD FIBER REVIEW *(Washington: Food and Agriculture Organization of the United Nations, 1948).*

considered by many to be one of the irreplaceable fibers for use in both clothing and household fabrics. The production and use of wool in such fabrics is largely a matter of economics. When it is profitable to produce sheep for wool alone, that is done. At present, however, producers throughout the world generally consider it to be more profitable to raise sheep which produce both meat and wool. The peak year in the wool industry in the United States was 1884. From that time on, range operators realized that it was also profitable to fatten and sell the sheep for mutton. A dual-purpose animal gives the producer two chances to make a profit. Today, about two thirds of the profit of the sheep breeder is from meat, and about one third from wool. One reason for wool's being only one third of the profit is that the dual-purpose animal produces coarser, less valuable, wool than sheep bred for fine wool.[6]

[6] Marion E. Ensminger, *Animal Science* (Danville, Ill.: Interstate Printers and Publishers, Inc., 1950).

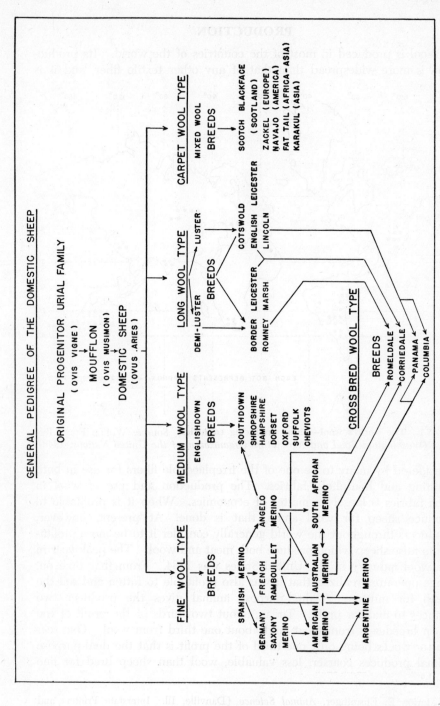

Fig. 7.2. *Source: Werner Von Bergen and Herbert R. Mauersberger,* American Wool Handbook, *2nd ed. (New York: Textile Book Publishers, Inc., 1948), 78, and M. E. Ensminger, State College of Washington.*

GENERAL PEDIGREE OF THE DOMESTIC SHEEP

ORIGINAL PROGENITOR URIAL FAMILY
(OVIS VIGNE)

MOUFFLON
(OVIS MUSIMON)

DOMESTIC SHEEP
(OVUS .ARIES)

FINE WOOL TYPE

BREEDS

SPANISH MERINO

FRENCH RAMBOUILLET

ANGELO

GERMANY SAXONY MERINO

AMERICAN MERINO

AUSTRALIAN MERINO

SOUTH AFRICAN MERINO

ARGENTINE MERINO

MEDIUM WOOL TYPE

ENGLISHDOWN

BREEDS

SOUTHDOWN
SHROPSHIRE
HAMPSHIRE
DORSET
OXFORD
SUFFOLK
CHEVIOTS

LONG WOOL TYPE

LUSTER

DEMI-LUSTER

BREEDS

COTSWOLD
ENGLISH LEICESTER
LINCOLN

BORDER LEICESTER
ROMNEY MARSH

CARPET WOOL TYPE

MIXED WOOL

BREEDS

SCOTCH BLACKFACE (SCOTLAND)
ZACKEL (EUROPE)
NAVAJO (AMERICA)
FAT TAIL (AFRICA – ASIA)
KARAKUL (ASIA)

CROSS BRED WOOL TYPE

BREEDS

ROMELDALE
CORRIEDALE
PANAMA
COLUMBIA

Centers of Wool Production. Apparel wool is produced chiefly in the southern hemisphere: Argentina, Uruguay, Union of South Africa, Australia, and New Zealand. Production by countries (see Fig. 7.3) for

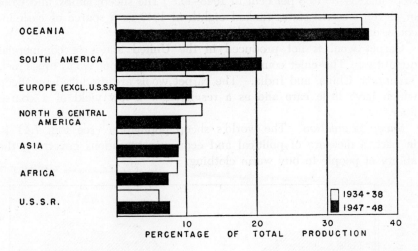

Fig. 7.3. **Wool production by continents.** *Source:* WORLD FIBER REVIEW *(1948), 30.*

the periods 1934–1938 and 1947–1948 show that Oceana (Australia and New Zealand), South America, and Russia are the only countries in which production is gaining.

An excellent estimate of the importance of areas in sheep and wool production may be gained by a comparison of the number of sheep, total pounds of wool, and the average pounds of wool per sheep in various producing areas (Table 7.I).

TABLE 7.I

NUMBER OF SHEEP, AND WOOL PRODUCTION,
IN THE CHIEF AREAS BEFORE 1939

Country	No. of sheep, millions	Wool, grease million lbs.	Average lb. per sheep
Australia (1939)	110	1010	9.18
Australia (1946–47)	95	901	8.9
North America, including U.S.A.	63	492	7.8
Union of South Africa	41	285	6.9
South America	108	601	5.6
Europe	191	730	3.8
Asia	133	355	2.7

Source: C. Luetkens, "History of Australian Wool Production," *Ciba Review,* 5-74 (1949), 2706–2740.

Australia, which ranks first in wool production, needs 10 to 30 inches of rain to produce pasture for sheep. Too much rain produces foot-rot;

too little produces a low grade of wool.   Western Australia is a dry and
dusty area which yields a coarse wool.

Wool production in this country was down from 12 per cent of all
wool in 1934–38 to 8 per cent in 1948–49.[7]   The sheep, lambs, and wool
in eleven western states ranked eighth in 1943 as a source of cash income, or 5 per cent of the total income.

Carpet wool is not produced in the United States in commercial
quantities.   The chief countries which produce carpet wools are Tibet,
Argentina, China, and India.   The carpet wools are produced by sheep
which have little care and as a result show a low yield of a coarse
fiber.[8]

Sheep population.   The world's sheep population (see Fig. 7.4) is,
in part, a measure of political and economic conditions governing the
ability of people to buy warm clothing.

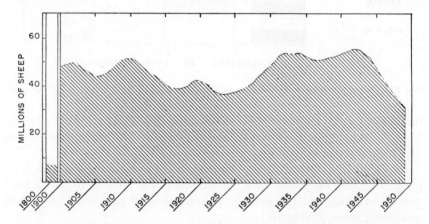

Fig. 7.4.   **Sheep population.**   *Source: Von Bergen and Mauersberger, op. cit., 77,
and* AGRICULTURAL STATISTICS *(Washington: United States Department of Agriculture, 1949), 375.*

The numbers of sheep fell sharply from 57 million in 1942 to 44 million
in 1946, a drop of over 22 per cent in four years.   Sheep, like other
items, are produced when it is economically profitable to do so.   This
country may, however, have to produce wool if it is to wear wool, because the demands for apparel wool are increasing in other parts of the
world.[9]

The growth of wool interests in the British Empire is well illustrated
by the increase in numbers of sheep in different parts of that empire
(see Fig. 7.5 and Table 7.I).

[7] *World Fiber Review* (Washington, D. C.: Food and Agriculture Organization of
the United Nations, 1949).

[8] R. H. Burns, A. Johnston and W. C. Chen, "Improvement of Chinese and Other
Carpet Wools," *Journal of the Textile Institute,* 30-4 (1940), T37–T48.

[9] *The Wool Digest,* 2-26 (New York: The International Wool Secretariat, 1948).

A comparison of the number of sheep per person will give an estimate
of the relative importance of sheep raising as an industry in some of the
chief wool-producing areas (Table 7.II).   In the United States, sheep
raising is relatively unimportant today.

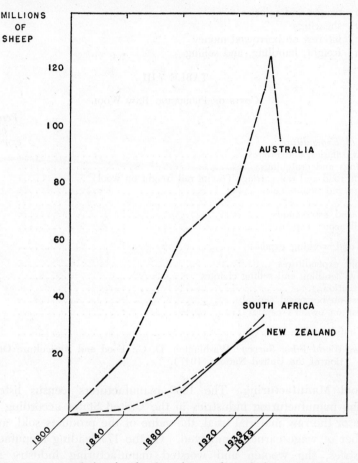

Fig. 7.5. Sheep population in the 3 major wool producing countries. Drought
and high meat prices helped to reduce numbers of sheep in Australia. *Source:*
J. F. Beaver, "The Romance of Wool," JOURNAL OF THE TEXTILE INSTITUTE, *40-1*
(1949), P42.

TABLE 7.II

RELATIVE IMPORTANCE OF SHEEP
RAISING IN SOME COUNTRIES

Country	Sheep/person
New Zealand	18
Australia	17
South Africa	5.7
United States	0.4

Source: C. Luetkens, "History of Australian Wool Production," *Ciba Review,* 5-74 (1949), 2706–2740.

Expenditures. An estimate of expenditures for producing raw wool may be gained from an examination of average 1938 costs in Queensland (Table 7.III). The examination will show that over half of the cost per pound of raw wool was accounted for by:

a) wages and salaries
b) shearings
c) interest on borrowed money
d) freight, handling, and selling

TABLE 7.III

COSTS OF PRODUCING RAW WOOL

Type of Expenditure	Percentage of total expenditure
Wages, salaries, and rations	18
Shearings and crutchings	14
General road and rail carriage (exclu. rail freight on wool)	3
Repairs and maintenance	4
Rent	6
Rates and assessments	3
Miscellaneous expenses	6
Total working expenses	54
Draught expenditures	8
Freight, handling and selling charges	10
Depreciation	9
Interest on borrowed capital	12
Interest on owner's capital	7
Grand total	100

Source: World Fiber Survey (Washington, D. C.: Food and Agriculture Organization of the United Nations, 1947).

Wool Manufacturing. The 1939 manufacturers' census listed the leading manufacturing industries in the United States according to the value of the raw material used, the value of the products sold, and the number of wage earners employed. Of the 177 leading manufacturing industries, the woolen and worsted manufacturing industry ranked twelfth in the value of raw materials, fourteenth in the dollar value of products sold, and seventh in the number of wage earners employed. The automotive industry, steel, cotton fabrics, sawmills, footwear, and bread and bakery products ranked ahead of the woolen and worsted industry in the numbers of people employed, in the order named. The present size and importance of the wool manufacturing industry means that the United States is dependent upon imports for a large part of the raw wool. Wool consumption in the United States has exceeded domestic production since 1930 (see Fig. 7.6).

Wool manufacturing is not important in Australia, South Africa or Asia but is of importance in the British Isles and the United States.

Shearing and Sorting. Shearing and sorting procedures differ from country to country. In both the United States and Australia, wool is being shorn somewhere in the country every month of the year. In the United States, the bulk of the shearing takes place between February and July. Some sheep are shorn twice each year in Texas and California.

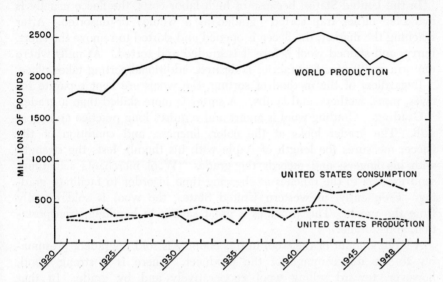

Fig. 7.6. World production and United States production and consumption of wool.
Source: WORLD FIBER REVIEW *(1948).*

Shearing is carried out in large, clean sheds where the fleece is removed by electric clippers. The shearer holds the sheep with one hand and operates the shears with the other. A helper takes care of the fleece after it is removed while the shearer goes on with the next sheep. It is hard, hot, back-breaking work, but men who make shearing a career, as men do in Australia, like the work.

Sorting is carried out by one of two systems—bench or trap sorting. In Australia, wool is skirted, bench sorted, and graded at the shearing sheds.[10] Although labor costs are high, bench sorting is by far the better system if it is desirable to have wool of great uniformity of quality. The fleece is spread on a table with the outside up. It is sorted into the different qualities of fibers. Skill is required in sorting Merino wool because a fleece varies greatly in quality and must be sorted into a number of grades. The count, a measure of grade or quality, may range from 36's to 80's (see Table 7.VII).[11] Coarser wools are usually sorted into two grades. The classified wool is then baled

[10] C. Luetkens, "Australia, the Land of Wool," *Ciba Review*, 5-74 (1949), 2706–2727.
[11] *Ibid.*

and branded with the name of the station, type of wool, and distinctions between qualities; then the bales are weighed and sent to a central market for auctioning. The types of wool are usually designated as follows: fleece (according to grade), bellies, necks, breech wool, and tags. The exact divisions differ from country to country.

In the United States, because of high labor costs, the fleece usually is marketed either trap sorted (graded as a whole) or unsorted. After reaching the market, the fleece is opened and skirted to remove the short, burry, and stained wool before it is graded and sorted. At mills where uniform quality for fine fabrics is desired, additional sorting takes place.

Regardless of the method of sorting, the wools are kept separate for ewes, rams, wethers, and lambs. A sorter is more skilled than a grader.

Grading. Grading wool is an art and requires long practice and great skill. The grader looks at the color, fineness, and condition of the fleece; measures the length of staple with his thumb; tests the strength with his fingers; and records the grades. Wool merchants sometimes send graders to the ranches at shearing time in order to facilitate grading. Frequently, in western United States, the wool is sold directly from the ranch. This provides a great saving in handling, transportation, and storage.

A large amount of the wool in this country is sold ungraded, presumably to the disadvantage of the producer. There is a strong trend, however, toward selling wool cooperatively and by grade. In that case, a portion of the grading is done at the warehouses which are usually located at such centers as Portland, San Francisco, Chicago, St. Louis, Philadelphia, and Boston. Most of the wool, however, is graded in, as well as sold from, Boston warehouses.

Pricing of raw wool. In any given market, the price of raw wool is based primarily upon the grade. Shrinkage in weight is probably the next most important point to consider. Wool grease, yolk, burrs, sand, and other materials such as dust and sticks will cause varying amounts of shrinkage. The shrinkage of raw wool in the United States is about 40 to 60 per cent. Atmospheric conditions can cause the weight to vary 10 to 15 per cent.

MARKETS

London has the chief wool market of the world and sets the prices on clothing wools. Boston is second in size and markets about three fourths of the wool used in the United States. Sydney, Australia, has the world's largest wool auctions.

Australian Wool Auctions. Only graded wool can be sold at auction. Catalogues of about 1,800 different samples of wool are made out for each buyer, who inspects representative bales and notes preferences in his catalogue before the auction begins. Each buyer has a seat with his or his company's name on it. Men from all over the world go to these auctions, for all the world buys Australian wool, over 90 per cent of which is sold at auction. Over a million bales are sold annually at Sydney.

United States Wool Markets. There have been few wool auctions in the United States, as the wool in this country is only partly graded before it reaches the factory. In the United States the grower markets his wool by one of five principal methods:

a) selling to local buyers who operate mainly in the farm flock states, buying small clips on a cash basis
b) outright sale to a manufacturer or dealer
c) contracting for the sale before the wool is shorn
d) consigning wool to dealer or cooperative in hope of higher price
e) cooperative marketing

In the last instance, the wool is then usually sold by the cooperative to the National Wool Marketing Cooperative in Boston, Massachusetts.

The usual steps from producer to consumer in this country involve producer, country (or local) buyer, country assembler, central market dealer, commission merchant, broker, manufacturer, retailer, consumer. It is important pricewise to simplify the marketing procedure. In fact, most domestic wool is produced in eleven western states where wools are often marketed in a much more direct manner.

CLASSIFICATION OF WOOL

There are a number of ways in which wools may be classified:

a) use, apparel or carpet
b) region, four in this country
c) area of fleece, quality differences
d) breed of sheep, quality differences
e) physical properties, especially fineness

Apparel Wools. According to use, wools are classified as either apparel or carpet. The finer, shorter wools are used in apparel and household fabrics; the coarser longer wools are especially valuable as carpet wools. The apparel wools are subdivided into carding wools suitable for manufacture on the woolen system, and combing wools, usually 2½ inches or longer, suitable for manufacture on the worsted system (see Table 7.VII and chapter fifteen). For the trade, the apparel wools are further divided into the following groups based on length: fine staple, strictly combing, baby combing, French combing, clothing, and stubby.[12]
Apparel wools are the only wools of significance produced in this

[12] James W. Christie, *Grading Wool*, U. S. Department of Agriculture Farmers' Bulletin No. 1805 (Washington, D. C.: Government Printing Office, 1945).

country, and for that reason, are subjected to tariff charges when imported.

In marketing practice, the grease wools are identified with the region in which they are grown. The quality is different in different regions. In the United States, sheep are raised in droves on the open range of the West or are raised as farm flocks of relatively small numbers in the Middle West, the East, and the South. Wools grown in these regions differ in shrinkage properties, color, and condition.[13] Differences in soil, grazing, breed, climatic conditions, and care are among the factors causing differences in quality of wool. The four general classifications of wool based on regions are: territory, semibright, bright, and southern wool.

1. Territory wools are from three groups of states and in general are produced by Rambouillet and Merino breeds.

   a) Washington, Montana, Idaho, Wyoming, Nevada, Utah, Colorado, the western half of North and South Dakota, and sometimes Kansas and Nebraska form one group.

   b) Texas, California, and Oregon wools are generally known by state name.

   c) Arizona and New Mexico wools are different in character from the others.

2. Semibright wool is often dark or stained by the soil but scours white. Oklahoma, eastern parts of Kansas, the Dakotas, and Nebraska, as well as parts of Missouri, Iowa, Wisconsin and Minnesota. These wools are often classed with either territory or brights, depending upon their condition.

3. Bright wools are produced in all of the remainder of the United States except the southern and southeastern states. These wools are much more uniform in quality than the territory wools.

4. Southern wool, except for Kentucky, Virginia, and Tennessee, are inclined to be of a low grade and come from sheep of no particular breed or class.

Different sections of the fleece (see Fig. 7.7) have different grades of wool; yet no one sample of wool is uniformly of a given quality even though the majority of the fibers in the sample conform to a given standard. Some wools are more uniform in quality than others. The best wool of each fleece is found on the shoulders and sides.

The length of the wool fiber varies in a given fleece, between breeds, and within breeds. Yet there are relationships between type of wool, breeds, and length of fiber (Table 7.IV). The staple length of wool fibers may vary from 1½ to 14 inches. American Merino sheep produce fine wool of 1½ to 3 inches in length. Cotswold sheep produce a coarse wool of 10 to 14 inches. The fiber from other breeds is intermediate.

[13] Christie, *Grading Wool.*

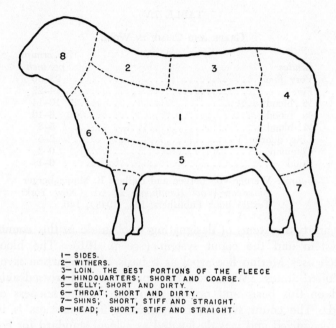

1— SIDES.
2— WITHERS.
3— LOIN. THE BEST PORTIONS OF THE FLEECE
4— HINDQUARTERS; SHORT AND COARSE.
5— BELLY; SHORT AND DIRTY.
6— THROAT; SHORT AND DIRTY.
7— SHINS; SHORT, STIFF AND STRAIGHT.
8— HEAD; SHORT, STIFF AND STRAIGHT.

Fig. 7.7. Parts of sheep producing different sorts of wool.

TABLE 7.IV

VARIATION IN AVERAGE LENGTH OF WOOL FIBERS

Wool type	Breed	Length inches
Fine	American Merino	1½– 3
	Rambouillet (U. S.)	2½– 3½
	Australian, Merino	3 – 5
Medium	English Down	2 – 4
	Corriedale	3 – 7
Coarse	Romney	5 – 6
	Leicester English	6 – 8
	Cotswold	10 –14

Source: Werner Von Bergen and Herbert R. Mauersberger, *American Wool Handbook,* 2d ed. (New York: Textile Book Publishers, Inc., 1948).

Physical characteristics such as length of staple, fineness, strength, softness, pliability, color, luster, resilience, felting properties, and number of crimp per inch are all measures of quality.[14]   The grades of wool as usually judged by the eye of the grader are based primarily on the average diameter (fineness) of the fibers.   The grade of wool is related to the number of crimps per inch which increases with the fineness of the fiber (Table 7.V).

[14] Christie, *Grading Wool.*

TABLE 7.V

GRADE AND CRIMP IN WOOL

Grades	No. crimps per inch
Very fine	22–30
Fine	14–22
½ blood	10–14
⅜ blood	8–10
¼ blood	5–8
Low quarter	2–5
Common	0–2
Braid	0–1

Source: Werner Von Bergen and Herbert R. Mauersberger,
    American Wool Handbook, 2d ed. (New York:
    Textile Book Publishers, Inc., 1948), 140.

There are two systems of designating wool grade in this country, the blood system and the count system (see p. 101). The blood system which uses Merino fine wool as a basis of comparison is peculiar to the United States. Wool from both purebred and crossed animals is classified on this basis and ranked according to the fineness of fiber produced. The count system of designating fiber fineness is internationally recognized and was designated as a legal standard for comparison in the United States by the Department of Agriculture in June, 1926. This system is based upon the limit of fineness of the yarns which may be spun from the fiber (Table 7.VI).

TABLE 7.VI

SYSTEMS OF WOOL GRADING AND PERCENTAGE OF UNITED STATES CLIP

U. S. blood	English count	Per cent U. S. clip
1. Fine	80s	
	70s	
	64s	49
2. Halfblood	62s	
	60s	
	58s	15
3. Three-eighths blood	56s	21
4. Quarter blood	50s	
	48s	13
5. Low quarter blood	46s	2
6. Common	44s	
7. Braid	40s	
	36s	

Source: Wool in the United States. (New York: National Association of Wool Manufacturers, 1947.)

The finest wools can be spun into the finest yarns. For example, 1 pound of 56s would theoretically produce 56 hanks each with 560 yards of yarn, whereas 1 pound 70s would produce 70 hanks each with 560 yards of yarn. The standard grades of raw apparel wool as established by the United States Department of Agriculture gives the relationships between grades and classes of wool (Table 7.VII).

TABLE 7.VII

COMPARATIVE WOOL CHART

	GRADES			CLASSES			
Type of wool	Count, wool quality number	Blood grade	Approxi-mate diameter (inches)	Combing wool length (inches)	French combing wool length (inches)	Clothing wool length (inches)	Maxi-mum worsted spinning counts
Very fine	80	Fine	.00077	over 2	1¼ to 2	under 1¼	80s
Very fine	70	Fine	.00083	2	1¼ to 2	1¼	70
Fine	64	Fine	.00087	2	1¼ to 2	1¼	60
Medium	60	½ Blood	.00093	2¼	1¼ to 2¼	1¼	50
Medium	58	½ Blood	.0098	2¼	1¼ to 2¼	1¼	46
Medium	56	⅜ Blood	.00106	2½	1¼ to 2½	1½	38
Medium	50	¼ Blood	.00120	2¾	1½ to 2¾	1½	34
Coarse	48	¼ Blood	.00130	2¾	1½ to 2¾	1½	30
Coarse	46	¼ Blood	.00138	3	2 to 3	2	28
Coarse	44	Common	.00144				26
Very coarse	40	Braid	.00152				22
Very coarse	36	Braid	.00157				18

Source: Courtesy of M. E. Ensminger, Chairman, Department Animal Husbandry, State College of Washington, Pullman, Washington.

Common and braid are not classified according to length because these wools are practically always of combing length. Carpet wool includes all those not suited to the three classes listed.

Carpet Wools. Carpet wools are coarse, wiry, and resilient and are produced by sheep which run under primitive conditions throughout many parts of the world.[15] Carpet wool consists of a mixture of a long hairy outer coat and a shorter, finer undercoat of true wool, together with a third type of fiber, kemp. There are all stages between. Kemp is an opaque, brittle, and slippery fiber which does not hold together in carpets, nor does it dye well. The fiber is large, medullated, and usually flat. Well-bred animals do not produce kempy fibers. In fact, kemp is not wanted in any use of either apparel or carpet wools. Efforts are being made to eliminate it from the fleece of wool-bearing animals.

[15] Burns, Johnston, and Chen, "Improvement of Chinese and Other Carpet Wools," T37–T48.

The carpet wools come into this country duty free chiefly from Asia where fat-tailed and broad-tailed, instead of thin-tailed, varieties of sheep predominate. The only carpet wools produced in the United States are from the Navajo sheep in the Southwest and a small population of Karakul sheep.

Carpet manufacturers consider a low percentage of true wool as being especially desirable. They prefer a fiber between true wool and kemp in type. The Chinese carpet wools, Vicanere [16] and Aleppo, are regarded as being among the world's best carpet wools. Hair fibers are important in adding quality.

About four fifths of the world's supply of wool is apparel wool; one fifth is carpet wool. Some of the finer carpet wools are used for apparel, blankets and tapestries. Studies are under way at present to find ways of making the harsher wools more acceptable in clothing, particularly for outer garments and sports clothes.

Off Wools. The off wools are wools which for one reason or another do not qualify under a standard grade. This group of wools includes burry, chaffy, seedy, cotted, black, and gray wools, as well as tags, dead wool, and wool from decomposed animals. In addition, pulled wool from slaughtered animals accounts for over 60 million pounds annually. These wools are used in linings and the less expensive wool fabrics.

Wool Products Labeling Act. The U. S. Government classifies wool on the basis of previous history and defines the manner of labeling wool products. There are three kinds of wool recognized by the Wool Products Labeling Act of 1939, virgin wool, reprocessed wool, and reused wool.[17] Virgin wool is that which has not been previously used or manufactured. Reused wool, also called shoddy, is made from wool from rags, old clothes, and miscellaneous items which have been worn or used. Reprocessed wool comes from mill waste, cuttings, and scraps of cloth or felt which have been made into fabric but have had no wear.

ORIGIN OF WOOL FIBERS

Wool is an outgrowth of the dermis or middle layer of the skin of certain animals and is similar in origin and composition to other outgrowths of the skin such as finger nails, horns, and hoofs. The hair follicle, which holds the root of the wool fiber, is a gland from which the cells forming the fiber develop. Both suint glands and sebaceous glands surround each hair follicle.

[16] *Vicanere* is the trade name of a mixture of Bikaner wool, a superior quality carpet wool, and of inferior carpet wools; see *Textile Research Journal*, 21-2 (1951), 94–101.

[17] Federal Trade Commission, *Rules and Regulations under Wool Products Labeling Act of 1939* (Washington, D. C.: Government Printing Office, 1939).

The growing fiber consists of a shaft and a root. The root is the living part located below the surface of the skin; the shaft is the nonliving part located above the surface of the skin. The fiber increases in length by a process in which the new cells push upward from the root. Fleece densities and the rate of growth have been shown to vary with the breed, season, and nutritional status of the sheep.[18] Fleece densities may vary from 8,000 to 60,000 fibers per square inch in different breeds.[19] Age, sex, lactation, climate, disease, and other factors may affect the growth rate and dimensional measurements of wool fibers.

PROPERTIES

In order to understand the use and care of wool and hair fiber fabrics, it is necessary to know something of the properties of the fibers.

Physical Properties. The physical properties of wool are especially prized.

The structure of wool fibers (see Fig. 7.8) is extremely complex. The fibers are composed of two and sometimes three types of cells: scale or epidermal cells, cortex or inner cells, and pigmented medullary cells.

The epidermal or scale cells overlap each other like shingles on a roof and appear to have little internal molecular organization, i.e., they

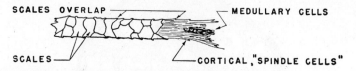

Fig. 7.8. Structure of wool fiber. *Source: Bryce Prindle,* "The Microbiology of Textile Fibers," Textile Research, 5-12 (1935), 542–568.

are not fibrous in nature. The number and shape of scale cells are a clue to the identity of the animal from which the fiber was obtained. The fibrous cortical cells constitute the largest part of the wool fiber. Some fibers have irregular medullary cells which form a more or less disconnected area or medulla along the center of the fiber. The medulla contains air pockets which help to change dyeing properties of fibers. The exposed, serrated ends of the scale cells point toward the tip of the fiber. The finer the fiber, the greater the number of serrations or scales per unit of length. Coarse fibers often have faint or indistinct serrations. The amount and ease of felting of wool fibers is related to the fineness of the fiber and thus to the scale cell structure (see Fig. 7.9). The fine fibers felt more readily than coarser fibers. Recently,

[18] J. F. Wilson, "Relation of Sheep's Health to Growth Rate of Wool," *Textile Research*, 4-9 (1933–34), 437–439.

[19] R. H. Burns, "Fleece Density of Sheep," *Journal of the Textile Institute,* 28 (1937), T113–T128.

by the use of the electron microscope, it has been shown that the scale cells are in reality a complex structure of three layers.[20]

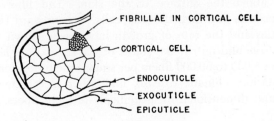

Fig. 7.9. **Diagram of scale cell of wool showing three layers.** *Source: Mercer, Lindberg, Philip, and Gralen,* "The Fine Histology of the Keratin Fibers," TEXTILE RESEARCH JOURNAL, *19-11 (1949), 674.*

The cortical cells, which constitute the main body of the fiber, give it strength and elasticity. The cells are globular in shape as they are formed but elongate as they are pushed upward from the root. They develop into long, flattened, cornified cells with a granular nucleus (see Fig. 7.10) near the center. The ends of the cells may be feathered

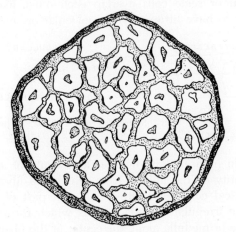

Fig. 7.10. **Diagram of cross-section of fiber, showing granular center of cortical cells.** *Source: Charles W. Hock, Robert C. Ramsay, and Milton Harris,* "Microscopic Structure of the Wool Fiber," RESEARCH PAPER RP 1412 *(Washington: National Bureau of Standards, 1941).*

out in a manner resembling a yarn which has been pulled apart. The cellular structure of wool fibers has been clarified by extensive studies of Hock, Ramsey, and Harris.[21] Mercer and others demonstrated that

[20] E. H. Mercer, Joel Lindberg, B. O. Philip, and Nels Gralen, "The Fine Histology of the Keratin Fibers," *Textile Research Journal,* 19-11 (1949), 673–677.

[21] Charles W. Hock, Robert C. Ramsey, and Milton Harris, "Microscopic Structure of the Wool Fiber," *American Dyestuff Reporter,* 30-18 (1941), 449–456, 469–470.

fibrils of the cortical cells were further divisible into microfibrils (see Fig. 7.11) when magnified 36,000 times with an electron microscope. Cortical cells are more readily attacked by chemical reagents than are

Fig. 7.11. Diagram of fibrils of wool, showing microfibrils. *Source: Mercer, Lindberg, Philip, and Gralen, op. cit.*

the scale cells. After the scales have been damaged, the fiber is much more susceptible to further damage.

Other physical properties of wool fibers which help to determine their value and use are length, crimp, fineness (diameter), and strength. The length varies from 1½ to 14 inches. The fineness is related to length and market grade. Short, fine fibers have more elasticity but are less sturdy and durable than long, coarse fibers when used in fabrics designed for hard usage. Fabrics from the finer wools require more care in cleaning than do those from coarser fibers.

A comparison of tensile strengths of various animal fibers shows that the finer fibers have less strength than coarser fibers (Table 7.VIII).

TABLE 7.VIII

STRENGTH RELATIONSHIPS OF ANIMAL FIBERS

Type of fiber	Tensile strength, %
Human hair	100
Mohair	90
Long wools	80
Horsehair	75
Camel's hair	75
Alpaca	72
Medium wools	70
Merino wools	62

Source: Werner Von Bergen and Herbert R. Mauersberger, *American Wool Handbook,* 2d ed. (New York: Textile Book Publishers, Inc., 1948), 146.

Other properties of importance in utilization of wool are luster, elasticity, resiliency, color, and moisture regain. Resilience is an outstanding property of wool and the one which enables it to recover from distortion. Wool fabrics and garments resist wrinkling and hold their shape well.

Lamb's wool is always characterized by a tapering end. After the first fleece is removed from the sheep, only new fibers, and not the major part of the fleece, will have tapering ends.

Chemical Properties. Raw wool consists of various substances (Table 7.IX), chiefly wool fiber and yolk. The yolk is a combination of suint

TABLE 7.IX

COMPOSITION OF RAW WOOL

		RANGE IN PERCENTAGE			
Type of wool	Yolk	Sand, dirt	Vegetable matter	Moisture	Wool fiber
Fine	20–50	5–40	0.5–2	8–12	20–50
Medium cross breed	15–30	5–20	1–5	8–12	40–60
Long wool	5–15	5–10	0–2	8–12	60–80
Carpet wool	5–15	5–20	0.5–2	8–12	60–80
Hairs	2–10	5–20	0–1	8–12	60–80

Source: Werner Von Bergen and Herbert R. Mauersberger, *American Wool Hand-book,* 2d ed. (New York: Textile Book Publishers, Inc., 1948), 170.

and wool grease. The suint, which is secreted by the suint glands at the base of the fiber, is composed of potassium salts of fatty acids. Wool grease, which is secreted by the sebaceous glands, is a complex mixture. According to Werner Von Bergen, it consists principally of lanolin, also a complex mixture. It is valuable commercially, especially in cosmetics and ointments. The amount of grease on a given fleece of wool is in direct proportion to the fineness of the fiber. Fine wool, 70s, may have 17 to 18 per cent wool grease, while one-fourth blood, 48s, will have as low as 8 to 9 per cent. Suint in different breeds varies from 2 to 15 per cent.

The ash content of the fiber will vary for different wools. Analysis of the ash has shown the following elements to be present: potassium, sodium, calcium, aluminum, iron, silicon, sulfur, and chlorine. These elements are valuable by-products of wool manufacturing.

Chemical reactions. Some chemical reactions of wool are of importance in the use and care of wool fabrics. Unless especially treated in the finishing process, wool is readily attacked by alkalis, oxidizing agents, and heat. In other words, wool garments and household fabrics such as blankets are sensitive to strongly alkaline laundry soaps, to bleaches encountered in stain removal, and to heat used in pressing.

Alkalis affect wool much more readily than do acids.[22] This is contrary to the behavior of cotton and rayon, which are much more sensitive to acids than to alkalis. Mild alkalis are used extensively under controlled conditions in scouring wools during the manufacturing processes. Soap which is slightly alkaline is frequently used in laundering clothing and household fabrics made of wool. Soapless detergents are safer to use.

During manufacturing and wear of wool fabrics, some mechanical and chemical damage may occur to the fibers. The wool becomes more soluble in dilute alkali as strength is lost from damage. A controlled

[22] Milton Harris, *Effect of Alkalis on Wool,* National Bureau of Standards Research Paper 810 (Washington, D. C.: Government Printing Office, 1935).

alkali solubility test has been used by Harris and others as a measure of the total amount of degradation in the wool fibers, regardless of the cause of the damage.

Oxidizing agents may be encountered in bleaching (e.g., stain removal), in finishing (e.g., chlorination during finishing), or by exposure to sunlight (e.g., in draperies and/or some clothing).[23] Sunlight produces part of the "weathering" action on wool and has been studied by Smith and Harris. The tips of the wool from the back of the sheep show the weathering effect of sunlight during growth. Stripping is a bleaching process for removing color from a fabric to correct faulty dyeing or to reclaim wool to be sold as reprocessed or reused wool. It has been shown that oxidizing agents cause a loss of strength, loss of weight, an increase in alkali solubility, and a reduction in the sulfur content of wool.[24]

Heat up to 212 F (100 C) or above, applied for any appreciable length of time to apparel wool in dry air, makes the wool lose moisture, become harsh, and lose strength. If the heat is continued for a period of time, the fiber is permanently yellowed and damaged. If the heat is allowed to act for only a limited time and the fibers again allowed to absorb moisture, they regain their softness and strength.

If the heat is combined with moisture, as in steam pressing, wool fibers become plastic and will take a "set." This is a very important consideration in shaping garments after cleaning or laundering since moisture and heat are the basis of many finishing processes. Steam (212 F) applied for a short time has little effect. If the application is continued for any length of time, however, the wool loses all its strength. Rachel Edgar and others showed that the degradation of wool by steam increased with increasing time and pressure. The laundry, dry cleaning, and pressing processes should be carefully controlled in order not to damage the wool during routine care of garments. Carpet wools are more sensitive to a high humidity than are the apparel wools. Low temperatures –40 to –60 F have no chemical effect on wool.

Shrinkage. Shrinkage of wool fabrics is of two kinds: relaxation and felting. Relaxation shrinkage is in part a result of the fabric's having been finished under too much tension. Fabric made from any fiber may suffer from relaxation shrinkage. Felting shrinkage occurs only in wool fabrics. The fiber scales are involved when marked shrinkage occurs and the fabric becomes more compact. The phenomena of fulling, felting, and shrinkage in wool are all one and the same, except for

[23] Milton Harris and Arthur L. Smith, *Oxidation of Wool: Alkali Test for Determining the Extent of Oxidation,* National Bureau of Standards Research Paper 928 (Washington, D. C.: Government Printing Office, 1936).

[24] Milton Harris and Arthur L. Smith, *State of Sulfur in Oxidized Wool,* National Bureau of Standards Research Paper 998 (Washington, D. C.: Government Printing Office, 1937).

degree. Fulling is a limited controlled felting procedure which entails a small amount of shrinkage and is a wool-finishing process. Felting is taken advantage of in the manufacture of hats, blankets, some clothing, and industrial felts. In general, however, felting and shrinkage during cleaning processes (wet or dry) cause great losses in the usefulness of clothing and household fabrics. The amount of felting and shrinkage in a wool fabric depends upon such factors as pH [25] of the cleaning solution, mechanical action of the washer, temperature of wash, type of wool, and type of construction of fabric.

The stabilized, modified, or shrink-resistant wools seem to be fairly resistant to alkali, shrinkage, moth, and bacteria. Washable wool fabrics on the market today should provide a savings to the consumer by extending the life and usefulness of wool fabrics in the home.

The felting and shrinkage of wool fabrics may be reduced by such means as:

a) use of coarser wools, some of which have little or no felting capacity, in fabrics to be washed
b) avoidance of excessive friction during cleaning and drying operations, especially during washing in water
c) use of low-temperature wash
d) control of alkalinity of wash solution
e) use of nonfelting fibers with wool
f) use of special finishes, for example resins

Mechanical Damage. In order to detect mechanical damage which affects the chemical behavior of the fiber, wool may best be examined by means of a combination of physical and chemical methods called microchemical procedures. Broken, torn, split, and abraded fibers may easily be observed optically (see Fig. 7.12). Bites in the sides of fibers caused by moths or carpet beetles may be seen.

Mechanical or chemical damage to fibers may be identified by staining with a dye and observing microscopically the rate of staining. The fiber which has been damaged either physically or chemically will stain more rapidly and more deeply than will the undamaged fiber.

The microscope is used for (a) fiber identification, (b) measuring the fineness of fibers, and (c) detecting some kinds of fiber damage. To do successful microscopic work with fibers requires the acquisition of a certain amount of delicate technique and skill.[26] Standard methods for identifying fibers, A.S.T.M. Designation: D 276–49, uses a combination of chemical and microscopic observations.

The action of microorganisms and insects on wool is discussed in chapter twenty-one.

[25] Degree of acidity or alkalinity.
[26] Edward Robinson Schwarz, *Textiles and the Microscope,* 1st ed. (New York: McGraw-Hill Book Co., Inc., 1934).

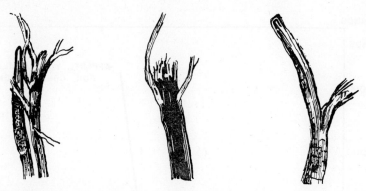

Fig. 7.12. **Diagrams of microscopic appearance of damaged wool fiber.** *Source: Von Bergen and Mauersberger,* AMERICAN WOOL HANDBOOK, *1st ed., p. 195.*

CONSUMPTION AND USES

The consumption of wool is increasing, but production is declining. As a result, world stockpiles of wool are being used up. Other fibers are replacing wool in many of its traditional uses. The world consumption of all wool is up 19 per cent from the 1934–1938 base period.[27]

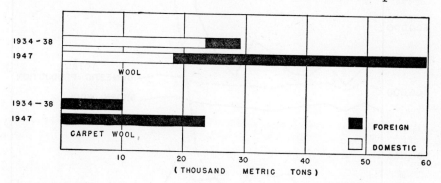

Fig. 7.13. **United States mill consumption of wool.** *Source:* WORLD FIBER REVIEW, *p. 34.*

Apparel-type wool is up 24 per cent for the same period. Each year from 1940 to 1948, United States mills (see Fig. 7.13) used about 1,000,000,000 pounds of grease wool.[28] A picture of the changes in world production and United States consumption may be gained from Fig. 7.14.

During World War II, there was a shift in demand from fine Merino

[27] *World Fiber Review* (Washington, D. C.: Food and Agriculture Organization of the United Nations, 1949).

[28] Karl Hobson, *Keeping up with the Farm Outlook,* Institute of Agricultural Sciences Circular 127 (Pullman, Washington: Washington State College, Nov. 19, 1948).

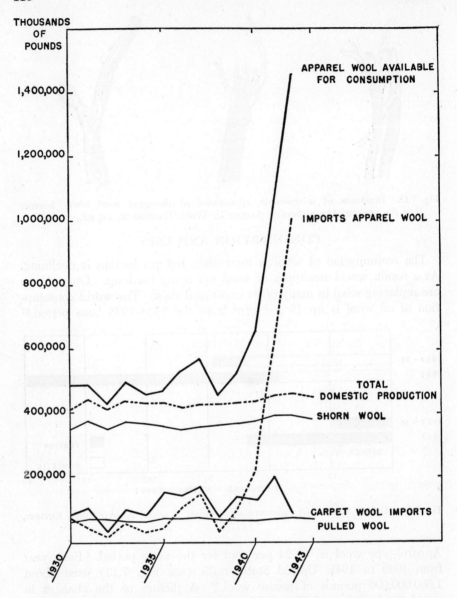

THOUSANDS
OF
POUNDS

1,400,000

1,200,000

1,000,000

800,000

600,000

400,000

200,000

1930   1935   1940   1943

APPAREL WOOL AVAILABLE
FOR CONSUMPTION

IMPORTS APPAREL WOOL

TOTAL
DOMESTIC PRODUCTION

SHORN WOOL

CARPET WOOL IMPORTS
PULLED WOOL

Fig. 7.14. Wool production and imports. Consumption of apparel and carpet wools, United States, 1930–43. *Source: U. S. Dept. Agriculture, Separate from* AGRICULTURAL STATISTICS, *No. 89 (1944), 319.*

wool to coarse crossbred wool, promoted in part by a desire for a sturdy fiber for long, rough wear. The production of fine wool requires more work, and the fabrics from fine fibers require more care, than fabrics from coarser wools. The coarse wools in general give longer service than fine wools for a given expenditure of time and money. In addition, crossbred sheep produce a more valuable type of market lambs than do ewes of fine wool breeding. Only small amounts of fine fiber wools are produced here, but a large percentage of the world's supply of fine wools are consumed here (see Fig. 7.15). In 1947, about two thirds of the mill consumption of French combing and clothing wools used by the United States were imported.

In 1948, wool ranked third in per capita consumption of apparel fibers in this country (Table 7.X).

TABLE 7.X

CONSUMPTION OF FOUR APPAREL FIBERS IN THE UNITED STATES

Fiber	Million lbs.	Per capita lbs.
Cotton	4,469.6	30.3
Rayon	1,149.4	7.8
Wool	693.1	4.7
Silk	7.4	0.05

Source: *Agricultural Statistics*, United States Department of Agriculture (Washington, D. C., 1948).

The woolen industry, believed to be the oldest of the textile industries, uses virgin wool, pulled wool, reprocessed wool, reused wool, and some other forms of wool. About the time the Wool Products Labeling Act of 1939 was passed, it was reported that in an average year the United States used 275 to 300 million pounds of new clean wool. At the same time, about 110 to 125 million pounds of wool rags were being reprocessed into fibers for lower-priced wool fabrics and garments. It should be pointed out that there is a wide range of qualities in reused and reprocessed wools, as well as in virgin wools. Whatever the origin or class of the wool fiber, it may be chemically or physically damaged. Territory wools are especially likely to have undergone deteriorating changes while on the sheep's back.

Wool fibers, whatever their history and quality, have many useful properties in common. The heavier fabrics of the melton and tweed types are usually made with a substantial amount of reprocessed and reused wool. Garments from these fabrics are thus brought within the price range of many people. Reused and reprocessed wools give valuable service in homes where warm clothing is needed. The costs of wool fabrics and wool garments are such that many people in the world who need warm clothing cannot buy wool.

The United States consumes a large proportion of the total supply of wool.[29] One tenth of all the fibers consumed in the United States is wool, one third of which goes into woolens and two thirds into worsteds.

[29] J. Williams, "The General Serviceability of Textiles," *Journal of the Textile Institute*, 21-8 (1940), 81.

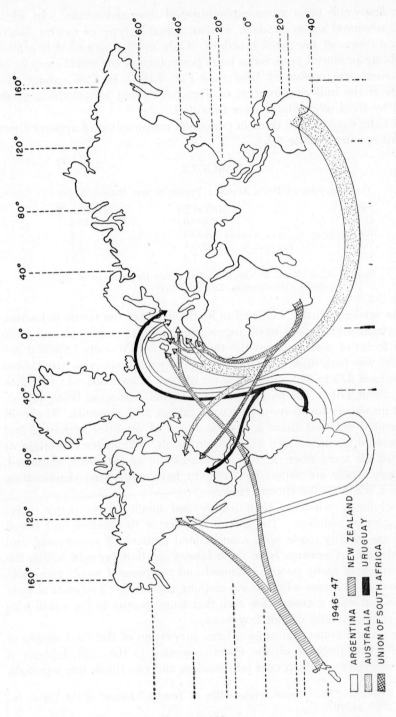

1946-47

ARGENTINA ☐ NEW ZEALAND ▨

AUSTRALIA ▨ URUGUAY ▨

UNION OF SOUTH AFRICA ▨

Fig. 7.15. World exports from the five principal exporting countries. *Source:* WORLD FIBER REVIEW (1948), 38.

This country is also the biggest consumer of carpet wools and produces none, except that from the Navajo sheep in the Southwest. From time to time, the amounts of consumed and imported wool show wide fluctuations. During the depression years, less wool was produced or used than today. Relative prices, as well as relative values, of wool and other fibers are carefully weighed when money becomes scarce. At present the demand for wool is high. Textiles and textile products, however, consume annually approximately one sixth of the average income in the United States. Of the big four, food, automobile, shelter, and clothing, the expenditures for clothing are by far the most sensitive to changes in income.[30]

Wool is used for clothing, household, and industrial purposes. A general increase in use has brought higher wool prices and a more rapid shift from the use of wool to synthetic fibers, in addition to a reduction in wool stockpiles. Woven goods, knit goods, and felts consume about 86 per cent of all wool which is used in apparel. Such items as men's, women's, and children's outer wear consume the largest proportion of apparel wools. These uses include meltons, mackinaws, and snowsuit cloths, as well as linings and interlinings. The nonapparel uses of wool include blankets and upholstery fabrics. Industrial uses include blankets for paper making.

Some other uses are in a measure dependent upon fashion. At present, lamb skins are being cured, sheared, dyed, and made into women's and girls' coats. The demand for Persian Lamb coats has caused a decline in numbers of Merino sheep and an increase in Karakul sheep in areas where these sheep are grown, for example, Union of South Africa.[31]

Carpet wools are becoming scarce as the quality of sheep is improved in those areas which formerly produced them. Other fibers are rapidly replacing the expensive wools in both carpets and rugs, as well as in clothing.

[30] J. Frederick Dewhurst and associates, *America's Needs and Resources* (New York: The Twentieth Century Fund, 1947), chap. 7.

[31] *World Fiber Review.* (Washington, D. C.: Food and Agriculture Organization of United Nations, 1948).

Chapter Eight

The Specialty Fibers,

Animal

MOST OF THE SPECIALTY FIBERS are obtained from two animal families, the goat and the camel. In addition, there are other animal fibers of limited use but of considerable value. The high-grade specialty fibers are an important group of fibers classed with wool for purposes of commerce by the Federal Trade Commission. The following tabulation shows the production of specialty fibers to be widespread:

ANIMALS	FIBERS	CHIEF COUNTRIES PRODUCING
	High grade	
1. Goats		
a) Angora	Mohair	Texas, United States
b) Cashmere	Cashmere	Tibet and northern India
c) Iran goat	Persian cashmere	Persia, India
d) Common goat	Beard hairs	Widely distributed
2. Camelidae		
a) Bactrian camel	Camel's hair	Asia
b) Llama family		
(1) Llama	Llama	Pacific Coast of South America,
Huarizo	Huarizo	Andes Mountains
Misti	Misti	
(2) Alpaca	Alpaca	Andes Mountains
Suri	Very fine alpaca	
(3) Guanaco	Guanaco	Southern Argentina and Patagonia

ANIMALS	FIBERS	CHIEF COUNTRIES PRODUCING

High Grade

3. Vicuña	Vicuña	Andes Mountains
4. Musk ox	Hair fiber	Alaska

Low grade

5. Cow	Cow hair	Siberia
6. Horse	Horse hair	China, Argentina, Russia, Canada

Fur

7. Angora rabbit	Angora	United States, Europe
8. Common rabbit	Coney hair	France, Russia, Japan, China

Feathers

9. Ostrich	Down	South Africa, Near East, Australia
10. Goose	Down	Canada, United States
11. Duck		
a) Ordinary	Down	United States, Europe
b) Eiderdown	Eiderdown	Northern parts of Canada, Asia, and Europe

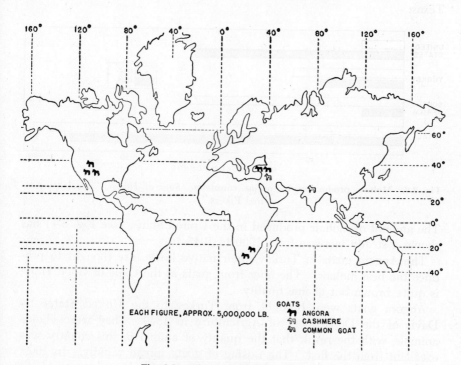

Fig. 8.1. The world's goat fibers.

GOATS: ANGORA GOAT

History and Production. Mohair is a product of the Angora goat which gets its name from the province of Angora in Turkey and is bred on a commercial basis for fiber in Turkey, Union of South Africa, and

Fig. 8.2. Angora goat.

the United States. Mohair from the Angora goat is a tough, lustrous fiber. Nearly half the world's supply is produced in the United States (see Fig. 8.3), and most of that on the Edward's Plateau in western Texas.

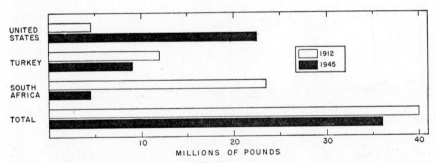

Fig. 8.3. Mohair production by major countries. *Source: Haigh,* "Specialty Animal Fibers."

The amount of mohair produced in the United States (see Fig. 8.4) has shown a steady increase from 1900 to 1945.

The Angora goats in Turkey, their native home, are thought to produce the best mohair. The fiber from goats at the Cape of Good Hope is quite brown but of fine quality.

Angora goats were brought from Turkey to the United States by Davis of the Department of Agriculture in 1849. They were choice animals, with the result that the quality of animal in this country was excellent from the first. The raising of goats spread rapidly. In 1900, a system of registry was established by the American Angora Goat

Breeders Association, Rock Springs, Arkansas. Most Angora goats are kept on range land in large herds of a few hundred to over 2,000. They seem to require little feed other than forage.

South Africa lost her goat country, the "best goat country in the world," [1] when the bush country was opened up. In the United States, great numbers of goats graze together, but in the Cape country more than half the production is from small flocks owned by farmers. The

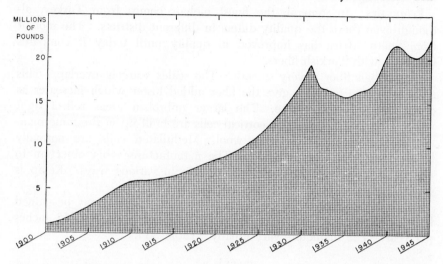

Fig. 8.4. Mohair production in the United States. *Source: Werner Von Bergen and Herbert R. Mauersberger,* AMERICAN WOOL HANDBOOK, *2nd ed. (New York: Textile Book Publishers, Inc.), 214.*

government of South Africa, investigating the reasons for the decline in the numbers of Angora goats, found that rayon consumption had increased. Also, flocks of Merino sheep, which fare better in cold, damp climates, had also increased; yet the sheep eat more than goats. A thousand goats live on the feed required for 700 sheep.

Goats are sheared at different times in different parts of this country. In Texas, for example, where the climate is warm, the goats are sheared twice each year. The average fleece weighs 4 to 5 pounds. In shearing goats, the practice is to remove all tags and stained fibers before shearing. (This is done for sheep wool after it is sheared and is called skirting the fleece.) The fleeces from animals of different ages are kept separate. There are three types of fleece: tight lock, flat lock, and fluffy lock. Fibers from the tight-lock fleece, obtained from young goats, are fine, silky, and curly. Fibers from the fluffy fleece, obtained from older goats, are coarser and have less curl than those from the fleece of

[1] H. Stanfield Haigh, "Specialty Animal Fibers," *Journal of the Textile Institute,* 40–8 (1949), P794–P813.

younger animals. The flat lock is intermediate in quality. The types of fleece are in general desirable in the order named.

The marketing of mohair is similar to that of wool, although the trip from producer to consumer has a number of variations. A possible sequence of marketing steps is producer, to country buyer, to country assembler, to central market dealer, to commission merchant, to broker, to manufacturer.

Properties. In general, the finest mohair comes from Turkey, although even there the quality differs in different districts. The mohair from South Africa has improved in quality until today it compares favorably with Turkish fibers.

The mohair fiber is very smooth. The scales scarcely overlap. This smooth surface tends to give the fiber added luster which increases as crimp and scales decrease. The larger unbroken areas reflect light which produces luster. The cortical cells are built up in the same manner as in the fibers of sheep wool. Medullated cells are normally below 1 per cent in good fiber. The manufacturer's big objection to mohair is the kemp, which causes trouble in various ways. Kemp is coarse, stiff, and brittle and does not dye well.

A fair estimate of the appearance and quality of fiber may be gained from descriptions of grades. The length ranges from 6 to 12 inches per year. The diameters vary greatly (Table 8.I).

TABLE 8.I

TENTATIVE U. S. MOHAIR GRADES, FINENESS, DISTRIBUTION

Diameter microns	Kid Fine	Kid Coarse	First Fine	First Coarse	Seconds Fine	Seconds Coarse	Thirds Fine	Thirds Coarse
10–20	20	2	5	1	1	1	..	..
20–30	11	39	37	26	20	9	2	..
30–40	9	59	56	61	35	21	31	5
40–50	..	..	2	12	25	22	41	21
50–60	..	..	..	..	15	27	18	18
60–70	..	..	..	..	4	20	6	30
70–80	..	..	..	..	..	..	2	20
80–90	..	..	..	..	..	..	..	6

Source: Werner Von Bergen and Herbert R. Mauersberger, *American Wool Handbook,* 2d ed. (New York: Textile Book Publishers, Inc., 1948), 221.

The moisture regain and chemical properties are similar to those of wool. It is apparently the physical structure which gives mohair its distinctive properties.

Uses. Mohair is a very serviceable fiber when used for summer suiting, window drapery, upholstery fabric, wigs and switches for the theater, and rugs. Kid fibers, which are remarkable for their silkiness and luster, are usable in both woolen and worsted clothing fabrics.

Most of the other high-grade specialty fibers have physical properties of softness and lightness which make them especially desirable for fine clothing fabrics.

CASHMERE GOAT

History and Production. The cashmere or shawl goat is named for the Province of Kashmir in northern India.[1] Cashmere first became famous because of the beautiful shawls made from the fiber in the Province of Kashmir. The cashmere goat is smaller than the angora.

Fig. 8.5. Cashmere goat.

There are many differences in fiber production of the two animals. The cashmere goat has a long, straight, coarse top coat and a fine, downy undercoat. It is the latter that is valuable in commerce. The coarse fibers are used by the natives for handweaving or are sold as goat hair. Cashmere fibers are not sheared like wool and mohair but are shed in the spring or combed by hand from the animal.

The individual farmer partially sorts the fibers before packing them into small bags placed across a camel's back, one on each side. Camel trains take the bags of cashmere fiber to collecting centers; Lanchow is the main one. From there, the fiber is sent to Tientsin or Shanghai for shipment to the world markets. Before the war, London was the main marketing center, but now most of the fiber goes through a Russian government agency.

In 1946, the best estimate of cashmere fiber production was about 730,000 pounds. The average annual estimate for 1934–1937 was 850,-000 pounds, of which the United States imported 350,000 pounds or over 40 per cent. Most of the fiber comes from the western provinces of China in the Tibetan regions of the Himalaya. The goats live in small

[1] H. Stanfield Haigh, "Specialty Animal Fibers," *Journal of the Textile Institute,* 40–8 (1949), P794–P813.

domesticated groups at an altitude of 10,000 to 15,000 feet. The fibers from Tibet, Mongolia, and China are the most valuable because of their fineness. Fibers from India, Iran, and Iraq are coarser and less valuable.

The raw material is sorted, in the country where it is produced, into firsts, seconds, and thirds mainly on the basis of color: white, pale fawn, and gray. It requires considerable work to clean and remove the long, stiff, black and white hairs from the white down before it is usable in fabrics for fine clothing. The fawn and gray fibers are used primarily in outer clothing. It takes a year's crop of about 30 goats to make cloth for one overcoat. Cashmere is considered to be one of the world's finest fibers.

An age-old custom of adding sand and water to the fiber has caused much difficulty in marketing this fine fiber. About 20 to 30 per cent of the raw material is noil, the fine fiber; the remainder is sand, water, and the coarse hair fiber.

Properties. Cashmere fibers are 1¼ to 3½ inches long. They have 6 to 7 scales per 100 microns of length and are 14 to 16 microns in diameter. The fibers may be identified by these facts plus the fact that cashmere, like other wool and hair fibers, has a characteristically shaped scale cell. In addition, this fiber, like camel's hair and other fibers harvested similarly, has roots attached.[2] The cashmere fiber is practically round.

The chemical properties of cashmere are similar to those of wool, with a few exceptions. Cashmere wets more readily and is much more sensitive to the action of alkali, possibly because of its great fineness. The natural colors are white or gray.

Uses. The fiber is distinctly a luxury item. Coats, suits, sweaters, and some top coats for both men and women are made from the very light, soft, fluffy fiber.

IRAN GOAT

Hairs from the Iran goats of Persia and India are sometimes called Persian cashmere. The fibers are coarser and more lustrous than cashmere and occur in cream, brown, and fawn colors. They are frequently used in rugs as well as in heavy clothing fabrics.

COMMON GOAT

Fiber from the common goat is seldom used in the manufacture of woolens or worsteds but is used in rugs.[3] The fiber ranges in diameter from 7 to 20 microns for the hair. The down resembles that from the cashmere goat.

---

[2] Werner Von Bergen and Herbert R. Mauersberger, *American Wool Handbook*, 2d ed. (New York: Textile Book Publishers, Inc., 1948).
[3] *Ibid.*

CAMELIDAE: BACTRIAN CAMEL

History and Production. There are two kinds of camels: the eastern Asiatic animal called the Bactrian, which has two humps; and the European or Syrian animal which has one hump.[4] The two-humped

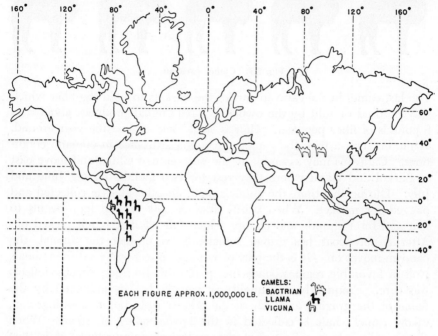

Fig. 8.6.   Camelidae.

Bactrian camel is the one which produces the fine fiber prized in clothing fabrics. The Syrian camel produces a shorter, coarser fiber which is darker than that obtained from the Asiatic animal. The fibers are used in cordage and rugs.

The present Bactrian camel is thought to be a crossbreed, lives on bitter plants of the steppes of central Asia, and serves as a beast of burden for the nomadic peoples of that area.[5] The Bactrian camel is also found in nearly all the desert regions of central Asia between Afghanistan, Turkestan, China, and southern Siberia. The pack camel can travel 20 to 25 miles per day with 125 pounds on each side of his back. The Arabian camel can cover 50 miles per day across the desert with a man and his rations. When it is necessary, the camel can travel for about seven days without water. It can eat shrubs which few other animals can digest.

[4] Haigh, "Specialty Animal Fibers," P794–P813.
[5] Von Bergen and Mauersberger, *American Wool Handbook*.

A camel caravan (see Fig. 8.7) may travel 3,500 miles in one journey of five to six months.[6] The caravans are always followed by a man called a trailer who collects the clumps of fibers lost by the animals.

Fig. 8.7.   Camel caravan.

The last camel in the caravan carries the baskets to hold the fiber which may be used or sold by the owner.[7] Each animal produces about 5 to 8 pounds of fiber per year. Hair is shed more or less the year around. While on such a trip, the camels encounter extremes in climatic conditions. Caravans may assemble in the northeast of China and move east to Barkul and Hami where they rest for two months during June and July. During this time, the animals molt, and the fiber is collected and bagged for market. When warm weather sets in, the hair begins to mat and form strands and clumps which fall off if it is not picked off. After a new coat has grown sufficiently to protect the animal, the caravan moves on. It is the part of wisdom to rest and feed the animals well in favorable regions, since the quality of the fiber directly reflects this care. Frequently, the quality of camel's hair is indicated by the name of the grazing area where the animal rests before molting; e.g., Sikow camel's hair is collected in the fertile valley of Sikow. When the camel's hair is collected at the central shipping points, it is then sent to London and from there to the important world markets, especially in England and in the United States.

To date, attempts to introduce camels into the United States have failed. An estimate of the camel hair market may be gained from some data for 1934 to 1937 (Table 8.II).

TABLE 8.II

EXPORT AND IMPORT OF CAMEL'S HAIR

	1934	1935	1936	1937
		(thousand pounds)		
China's Export	2940	3641	2338	1404
U. S. Import	206	585	526	307

Source: Werner Von Bergen and Herbert T. Mauersberger, American Wool Handbook, 2d ed. (New York: Textile Book Publishers, 1948), 237.

Properties. The properties of camel's hair are similar to the properties of other fine hair fibers. The fibers may be sold in the raw state,

[6] Haigh, "Specialty Animal Fibers," P794–P813.
[7] S. I. Stroock, The Story of Camel Hair (New York: S. Stroock, Inc., 1936).

in which case all qualities are mixed together, or they may be scoured and combed. Combing separates the fibers into the long coarse fibers called *tops* and the short fine fibers called *noils*. The noils vary in color from light tan to a warm, rich, brown. Tops in sheep's wool indicates fine quality, but it is the noils in goat and camel fibers which are most desirable (Table 8.III).

TABLE 8.III

FINENESS OF CAMEL'S HAIR

| Type | TOP | | | NOILS | |
	Fine	Coarse	No. 1	No. 2	No. 3
Average microns diameter	18.2	23.1	18.1	20.9	22.8

Source: Werner Von Bergen and Herbert R. Mauersberger, *American Wool Handbook,* 2d ed. (New York: Textile Book Publishers, Inc., 1948), 240.

Uses. In the manufacturing process, the best fibers are usually left in their natural color. Other grades are often dyed dark colors. Frequently, camel's hair is blended with other fibers. Often special effects are obtained by using other specialty fibers. At other times, the camel's hair is blended with cheaper fibers to secure less expensive grades of fabric. Camel's hair is especially sought after in both men's and women's top coats because of the high insulating properties and long-wearing qualities.

Camel's hair is also used in oriental rugs, sweaters, and blankets. The stiff outer hairs are used in ropes, tents, rugs, and blankets of the desert tribes. The Bactrian or two-humped camel of Asia is the only one that furnishes hair of commercial importance. Other fibers are coarse and are used where they are produced.

LLAMA FAMILY

The Llama. The llama family of the Andes includes the llama, alpaca, and guanaco. The llama family is one branch of the family of animals

Fig. 8.8. The llama.

known as camelidae. The camels belong to the other branch.[8] The llama and alpaca are thought to be descendants of the guanaco. The llama lives about two and a half miles above sea level on the great plateaus in the Andes Mountains of Bolivia. Today, they are owned chiefly by the Indians. Smaller numbers are found in Peru, Ecuador, Chile, and Argentina. The llama appears to be the only beast of burden which can live at such altitudes. Hair is left on the male to provide padding for the heavy loads he must carry. Only the female is shorn. The wool is of less value than that of other species. The llama, like the camel, travel in caravans. They are found only on the western coast of South America. There are about three million of them today.

The llama and alpaca mix freely. The hybrid huarizo has a llama father and an alpaca mother. The misti has an alpaca father and a llama mother. The hybrids have coarse fiber but soon revert to type. The llama is 4–5 feet tall and is usually brown or black.

The llama was known during the Inca era, 1400–1500 A.D.[9] The Peruvian llama was considered to be the joint property of the Sun, symbol of the spiritual king, and of the Inca, the earthly king. The animals were cared for by shepherds who had strict regulations for their care. Each year, large numbers of llamas were sent to the capital, probably for the purpose of feeding and clothing the public and the Court. The llama were used as food at religious ceremonies.

When the animals were shorn, the fleeces were sent to public collection centers. From there, the fibers were distributed to all the households. Every family had to share fabrics they made with the Inca and his family. Officers inspected homes at will to see that all went as expected. The quality and color of fabrics made during the period of the Incas were of the best.

The Alpaca. The alpaca is the important fiber-producing member of the llama family and yields 4 to 8 pounds of fiber every second year. The suri is a breed of alpaca which produces the finest and most abundant fiber. The alpaca lives at an altitude of about 12,000 to 17,000 feet. It also must live south of the equator, because ichu, a type of grass on the upper Andes Mountains which is its principal source of food, does not grow north of the equator. The alpaca does not live in captivity.

From 1938 to 1942, Peru exported annually 7,100,000 pounds of fiber, 88 per cent of which was alpaca. The color of the fiber ranges from white to black. The alpaca is grown for its fleece which is used chiefly for pile fabric coatings. The fiber is silky, of fine texture, and has good luster and strength. The fibers grow to a length of 8 to 12 or 16 inches and will become 30 inches if allowed to grow. The animals are shorn

[8] Von Bergen and Mauersberger, *American Wool Handbook.*
[9] Haigh, "Specialty Animal Fibers," P794–P813.

every two years. The bacaya, the larger breed of alpaca, yields about 5½ pounds; the suri, the smaller breed, yields about 6½ pounds. There are well over two million of these animals. The Peruvian gov-

Fig. 8.9. The alpaca.

ernment prohibits by law any exportation of animals in order to protect natural resources of the country (Table 8.IV). It has not been possible to raise the animals on a large scale.

Fig. 8.10. The suri.

Most of the year, woolen clothing, chiefly home woven and hand made, are worn by the entire population at the higher altitudes in the Andes Mountains.

TABLE 8.IV

FIBER EXPORTS FROM PERU

Fiber	1938–1942 yearly average (thousand pounds)
Alpaca	6,230
Llama	320
Huarizo short	91
Huarizo fine	470

The Guanaco. The guanaco is the parent stock of the llama family and is found in largest numbers in Patagonia. The animal resembles the vicuña to some extent but is larger. The fibers are reddish brown

Fig. 8.11. The guanaco.

to white and are slightly finer than the vicuña, about 80s instead of the 64s to 70s of vicuña.

Fineness is a measure of diameter in microns. Table 8.V shows various fibers in the order of fineness.

TABLE 8.V

FINENESS OF SOME WOOL AND HAIR FIBERS

Animal	Diameter, microns
Vicuña	13–14
Cashmere	15–16
Fine camel hair	17–20
Fine wools	17–23
Medium to coarse wools	23–41
Alpaca	25–29
Mohair	24–60

The guanaco runs wild but is a source of both food and clothing for people in Patagonia in the same way as sheep are for the people of the United States.

OTHER SPECIALTY FIBERS

Vicuña. The vicuña is thought to be a distinct species and not a member of the llama family.[10] It has been possible only recently to raise the vicuña in captivity. Formerly, it was necessary to kill the animal in order to obtain the fibers. The vicuña lives in the Puna between the Cordilleras and the Andes in South America and is found at altitudes above which no other living thing except the condor can live. The

[10] Von Bergen and Mauersberger, *American Wool Handbook.*

animals live upon the ichu grass which grows only in this area. They are found in Bolivia, Chile, and Peru where, in 1946, there was an estimated 50,000. The Ministry of Agriculture in Peru is charged by the government with the responsibility of breeding and domesticating this

Fig. 8.12. The vicuña.

animal, which produces the most valuable wool fiber known, with the possible exception of fiber from the musk ox in Alaska, a fiber which is not yet available in commercial quantities.

Even during the Inca period, the vicuña were protected by law.[11] Once each four years, a great hunt was held, led by the Inca himself. Many thousands of animals—llama, alpaca, vicuña, and guanaco—were killed. The wool was collected and later distributed to the households for manufacture. The Inca Court wore vicuña and were the only people who had clothing and household fabrics made from this rarest of fibers. The cloth is very light and soft.

The finest of vicuña fibers are about 63s to 70s.[12] Production has been limited (Tables 8.VI and 8.VII). Each animal produces 8 to 9 ounces annually; a total of 2,000 to 3,000 pounds is produced. When the fiber is converted into cloth, it sells at fabulous prices.

TABLE 8.VI

EXPORTS OF PERUVIAN WOOL TO THE UNITED STATES

Year	ALPACA Lbs.	%	VICUÑA Lbs.	%	LLAMA Lbs.	%	HUARIZO Lbs.	%	TOTAL Lbs.	%
			(thousand pounds in the grease)							
1938	1237	19	1	33	..	..	11	24	1249	17
1942	4084	80	..	..	177	72	195	39	4456	76
1943	5235	89	..	..	190	79	429	80	5854	88
1944	6295	94	..	..	142	92	455	95	6892	94

Note: The per cent is that quantity of the total export taken by the United States.

Source: Werner Von Bergen and Herbert R. Mauersberger, American Wool Handbook, 2d ed. (New York: Textile Book Publishers, Inc., 1948), 251.

[11] Haigh, "Specialty Animal Fibers," P794–P813.
[12] Ibid.

TABLE 8.VII

Vicuña Wool Exports

COUNTRIES OF DESTINATION

Year	Great Britain	United States	Italy	Total pounds
1933	1107	..	..	1107
1936	3881	1173	..	5054
1938	1916	1379	132	3427
1939	246	1173	..	1419
1940	..	7995	..	7995
1941	..	906	..	906

Source: Werner Von Bergen and Herbert R. Mauersberger, *American Wool Handbook,* 2d ed. (New York: Textile Book Publishers, Inc., 1948), 250.

The possible uses of vicuña fibers are those of any fine hair fiber. The actual uses are few because of the limited quantity available. Top coats, especially for men, have been a choice article in the United States. Scarves, blankets, rugs, and knit wear are possible uses. About 40 fleeces are required for fabric for one coat. Since the fiber is very resistant to dye, it is usually used in its natural color, a rich cinnamon brown.

Musk Ox. The musk ox resembles a small bison. It has a beard, long droopy horns, and a shaggy appearance. There are four known species. The white-faced musk ox is being domesticated at present. It produces a very fine, downy, gray wool much like cashmere. Probably 50 pounds of fiber are produced annually in Alaska by the present herd which is carefully protected by the United States Government.

Cow. Siberia is the principal producer of commercial cow hair—a low-grade fiber for use in coarse carpets, blankets, rug pads and felts. The United States obtains some cow hair from slaughtered animals but imports large quantities from Canada, Japan, England, and Spain. It has been estimated that annual imports are well over six million pounds.

Horse. China, Argentina, Russia, and Canada are the chief producers of horse hair. The United States imports approximately three million pounds annually. Horse hair is used in making fabrics for interlinings in men's suits and coats and for stuffing in upholstery.

Rabbits. *The Angora rabbit* has long been the source of a luxury fiber used chiefly in knitting, but it is also used in filling yarns to give a soft hand to the fabric. About 70 per cent of angora hair may be mixed with wool to make the filling yarns. The French first used the fiber. Today England, the Netherlands, Belgium, and the United States raise the animal for its long silky hair which is usually cut four times each year. Ten to 16 ounces of hair annually is the usual yield per animal. The hair grows 5 or 6 inches in a year. Figures are not available on quantities produced.

About 1930, the English mills adopted a "buy-at-home-exclusively" policy which caused a surplus of angora rabbit wool to develop in the United States. Since the Northwest produced a large amount of this fiber, the Bishop brothers of the Pendleton and Oregon wool mills undertook to handle the domestic crop. Careful experimentation on lightness, fineness, softness, dyeing properties, tensile strength, and smoothness enabled the manufacturers to produce both yarns and fabric. In general, the fiber is used in knitting yarns, but some fiber is used for novelty effects in other yarns.

Common rabbit hair. Most of this type of fiber is used in making felt hats. Small amounts are used for effect in some woolen fabrics. The most desirable hair is obtained from a white French-type rabbit found in Europe, North America, and parts of China and Japan. The pelt is sold for coats and capes. Russia produces another variety of rabbit fur. The cheapest grades of rabbit hair come from the gray, wild rabbit from Australia, New Zealand, and Great Britain. It has been estimated that in 1946 about seven million pounds of rabbit hair were cut in the United States.

Fowl. Down from the ostrich, goose, and duck is used to produce luxurious effects in fabrics. The down is incorporated in the yarn during the spinning process. The barbs of feathers are sometimes stripped from the quills and mixed with other fibers and spun into yarns. Differences in dyeing properties of the down and wool fibers produce attractive two-tone effects. The fabric is not recommended for durability but is quite soft and warm, as well as expensive. At present, the fabrics should be considered luxury fabrics, although not lacking in utilitarian qualities.

The sale of feathers and down in comforts, pillows, and upholstery are covered in most of the states by bedding laws.[13] Federal purchase specifications define kinds of feather, length, condition and percentages of each used.

[13] Samuel Mermin and John M. Mayer, *Survey of State Laws and Judicial Decisions on Bedding and Upholstery,* U. S. Department of Agriculture, Division of Consumers' Council, Agricultural Adjustment Administration (Washington, D. C.: Government Printing Office, 1940).

Chapter Nine

Silk

SILK is one of the oldest known fibers, but it is still produced by painstakingly slow processes.

HISTORY

Silk, unless otherwise specified, is understood to mean the product of the *Bombyx mori* or mulberry silkworm.[1] Silk is produced, however, by other moths as well as by spiders. The life cycle of the silkworm is the same as that of all moths: egg, larva (the silk-producing stage), pupa or chrysalis, and moth.

Discovery. Although the date of discovery of silk is unknown, a Chinese princess is credited with originating the idea, in 2700 B.C., that the silk of the cocoon could be unwound and made into fabric. It is also reported that silk weavers and dyers many centuries ago produced beautiful fabrics and colors for the emperors to wear.[2] Shantung, China, is thought to have been the cradle of silk weaving. One type of silk fabric is called shantung.

The use of silk exclusively by the imperial court continued until China was divided into principalities. Then the demand for silk increased greatly because the privilege of wearing it was extended to all the nobility. Serf labor did all of the work of producing the silk. This practice continued until the principalities became impoverished by cor-

[1] E. Handschin, "The Silkworm or Bombyx mori Linné," *Ciba Review*, 5-53 (1946), 1902.
[2] A. Varron, "The Origins and Rise of Silk," *Ciba Review*, 1-11 (1938), 350–354.

rupt and indifferent governments.[3] This led to extensive reforms about the sixth century, B.C. At this time, silk became popular among all classes of Chinese.

The Old Silk Road. The story of silk as a commodity of trade must begin with the story of the Old Silk Road from China to the Western world, one of the famous roads in history. It originated through the early efforts of China to trade with the Western world when silk was her main product for trade. The story has been very well told by Goldthwait.[4] The road led from China 9,000 miles from the Pacific to the Atlantic. It has been said that it was "silk which paved the road from China to Europe." [5]

In 138 B.C., the Chinese emperor sent an emissary westward to get support for a war against the Huns in the Gobi Desert. The diplomat failed to get the necessary support, but he did bring back news of a road from Kashgar to India and Persia. The emperor was able to organize a couple of military campaigns to clear the route and open the way to the Western world. New roads had to be built. The most important one of all was the Imperial or Old Silk Road. The Great Wall of China had been started much earlier to shut out the nomad Huns from the North and West. Later, it was extended to protect parts of the Old Silk Road.

Over 2,000 years ago, it was trade in silk that formed the bond between the East and the West. For several centuries, camel caravans were so numerous on the Silk Road that one was scarcely out of sight of another. On the way they had plenty of discouragement from raiders. The Old Silk Road led 2,000 to 3,000 miles north and west from Shanghai to Tun-huang in the Tarim basin, then 2,000 to 3,000 miles through Kashgar to Bagdad (the city of Arabian Nights), then on to Damascus (one of the oldest inhabited cities in the world), and north and west 3,000 or more miles through Rome and finally to France and England. The caravans crossed the Gobi Desert and went over mountain passes at 13,000 feet.

After hundreds of years, Lou-lan, the gateway from China to Persia, India, Syria, and Rome, fell to the barbarians. This was the first of the cities on the Silk Road to fall. But it was followed by others, until the road was abandoned for a sea route which was both less expensive and less hazardous. Lou-lan had been prosperous in 310 A.D. Records were found written in wood and stone telling of 4,320 bolts of silk shipped to Lou-lan where some of the oldest known silk of geometrical design was found in a cemetery. Lou-lan was discovered by Sven A. Hedin, a noted

[3] *Ibid.*

[4] Charles F. Goldthwait, "The Old Silk Road," *American Dyestuff Reporter,* 30-8 (1941), 218–219.

[5] A. Varron, "Silk and the Development of Trade," *Ciba Review,* 1-11 (1938), 376–380.

Swedish explorer in 1900. Hedin said that "the old Imperial Road of Chinese Silk, the longest, oldest, best known, as well as the most picturesque of all roads on earth" should be revived. The Burma Road of World War II covered, in part, the same route.

Growth of Trade. The spread of civilization and trade continued westward. Difficulties, however, were growing for the silk merchants. Although silk continued to be shipped west, from time to time, the Huns destroyed parts of the road. The fall of cities on the Silk Road, coupled with the need to deal directly with the silk merchants, led the European merchants to search for a sea route. It was not easy, in those days, because there were no accurate maps. Language difficulties and lack of knowledge of geography helped to delay direct trade between East and West until 11 A.D. About the end of year 1 A.D., a great silk industry had been developed on the eastern Mediterranean. Alexandria, Jerusalem, and Antioch were weaving centers, and Sidon and Tyre were dyeing centers.

Under the rule of King Sapor III in 360 A.D., Persia became the center of silk culture for Europe and Asia. The Persians, determined to maintain their trade position, acted as exchange merchants for the trade from both the East and the West, and profited greatly thereby. The Arabs were the master weavers, dyers, merchants, and buyers of the Middle Ages. They developed great wealth and power and were not challenged seriously until the Crusades when Sicily was able to establish a silk industry which later spread to Italy. By the thirteenth century, the silk industry had helped lay the foundation for the Renaissance during which the silk fabrics produced in the Far East, the East, and in Europe were classic in their beauty.

From time to time in history, there have been great extravagances in clothing. Silk was of economic importance during the period of the Roman empire, but it was felt that the great sums of money sent out of the country for the coveted silk in part helped bring economic ruin to the Roman Empire.[6]

Silk was sold for its weight in gold. The word *denier* has its origin in that fact. Christianity grew up beside "a riot of fantastic luxury," as described by Varron. A striking similarity is observed between the extravagances of that period and those of the American people during the "silk shirt" period from 1920 to 1929.

Often laws or custom have forbidden certain groups of people to wear one fiber or another, and one color or another. During the Byzantine era (5th and 6th centuries), laws forbade the masses of people to wear silk. People were criticized for "going about like painted walls." Fabrics painted with landscapes and animals in vivid colors were very

[6] A. Varron, "The Lavish Use of Silk among the Ancient Peoples," *Ciba Review*, 1-11 (1938), 354–359.

popular but were frowned upon by those who felt responsible for the moral and spiritual welfare of the people. Fifteen centuries later, designers are again using landscapes and animals in vivid colors in contemporary fabrics for men's, women's and children's clothing, as well as for household fabrics.

Silk continued to be a symbol of culture and refinement. The Germanic tribes took childish delight in adorning themselves in elaborate silk robes and precious stones in an effort to simulate the greater culture of their neighbors. It was probably in Persia that the greatest extravagances in the use of silk existed. The king and all of his servants wore only silk. Bed coverings, carpets, wall hangings, and even awnings were made of silk. In Europe, the Norman princes had many silk tapestries and wall hangings. Silk has always been used as clothing for the dead because of the ancient belief that man's life after death should continue; therefore, man must be buried in his best clothes. During a long period, people were not only buried in silk but had great quantities of the cloth placed in the graves with them. Silk was used extensively in the churches, and thus many fine pieces have come down to this day.

Of great significance in the use of silk was the rise of the middle class in the fourteenth century. The wealthy merchant classes all wore silk. By the fifteenth century, artisans and tradesmen wore silk. By the twentieth century, everyone wore silk so far as law or custom was concerned.

Silk was not introduced into America until 1522, when Cortez brought both mulberry trees and silkworm eggs to Mexico. The venture evidently did not succeed. King James I started a shipload of mulberry trees and silkworm eggs to America in 1609, but the ship was lost at sea. About 10 years later, silkworms were introduced into Virginia by King James I who wanted the colonists to raise silk instead of tobacco for the English trade. Tobacco raising was more profitable, and sericulture died out. In the early part of the nineteenth century, Pennsylvania tried to develop silk raising, but the weather was too severe. Today the United States is the world's biggest consumer of silk and does not produce a pound, partly because of the high cost of labor.

In the nineteenth century, when European sericulture was almost destroyed by disease, the Japanese abandoned cotton cultivation and developed silk culture. The rise of the Japanese silk industry occurred during a period of rising incomes, of expanding markets, and an increasing demand for luxury goods. The industry could develop in Japan because of the dense rural population and the availability of poorly paid women to do the large amount of hand labor. The production was under rigid governmental control, but even so political and technological developments in other fields, added to World War II, have almost wiped

out the industry.   By 1946, production (see Figs. 9.2, 9.3) was exceed-
ingly low.[7]

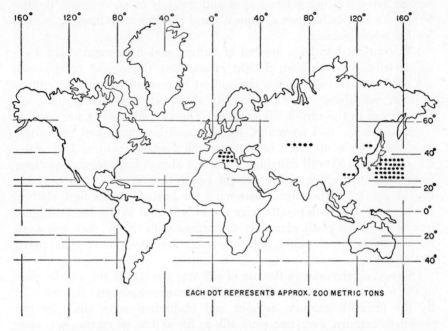

Fig. 9.1.   The world's silk.   *Source:* WORLD FIBER REVIEW *(Washington: Food and Agriculture Organization of the United Nations, 1948).*

Silk, however, remains a valuable fiber but not so valuable as food.
Many mulberry trees gave way to food crops in Japan.   In addition, new
fibers have reached the market in the United States where the bulk of

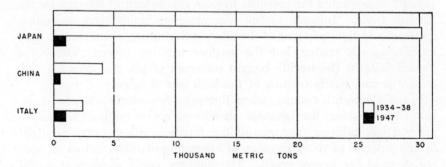

Fig. 9.2.   Raw silk exports from Japan, China, and Italy. *Source:* WORLD FIBER REVIEW, p. 110.

[7] Gerda Blau, *World Fiber Survey* (Washington, D. C.: Food and Agriculture Organization of United Nations, 1947), 110.

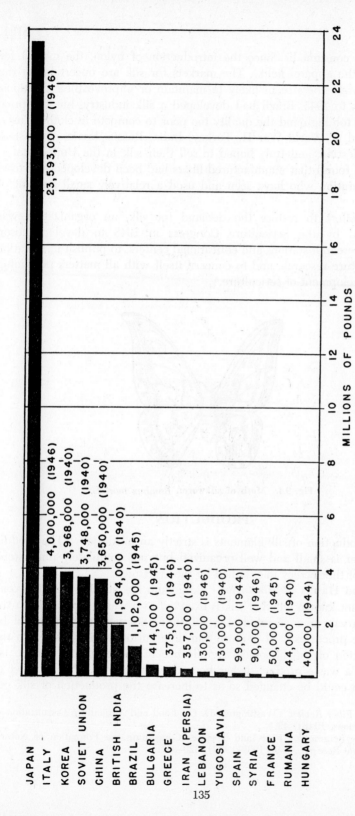

Fig. 9.3. Raw silk production in principal countries. *Source: Textile Division, U. S. Tariff Commission, July 1946.*

the silk is consumed. Since the introduction of nylon, the market for silk is in the apparel field. The markets for silk are uncertain, as the manufactured fibers seem likely to maintain or improve their positions.

Previous to 1945, Brazil had developed a silk industry, but the price was much too high and the quality too poor to compete in clothing uses. At the end of World War II, Turkey, India, Russia, Spain, Damascus, Japan, Palestine, and Italy hoped to sell their silk in the United States, but it was found that manufactured fibers had been developed and used by a generation who have seen and used a relatively small amount of silk.

In an effort to restore the demand for silk, an organization was established by the Sericulture Congress in 1948 to develop liaison between research stations and educational centers, to publish information on sericulture research, and to concern itself with all matters pertaining to the development of sericulture.[8]

Fig. 9.4. Moth of silkworm, *Bombyx mori L.*

PRODUCTION

The production of silk filaments is strictly an inside job. The production center is small and well organized but not completely understood because of the secrecy maintained by the craftsmen.

Life and Habits of Silkworms. Bergmann has studied the silkworm, but it is not known whether silk is excreted as a waste product from the worm (larva) or is secreted as a substance not normally produced by metabolic processes.[9] It is more than idle curiosity that has led to the investigation of the biological significance of the origin of fibroin. If fibroin is a waste product, it has been thought possible that the diet of the worm could be changed so as to increase the production of silk per

[8] *World Fiber Review* (Washington, D. C.: Food and Agriculture Organization of United Nations, 1948), 42.
[9] Werner Bergmann, "Facts and Theories Concerning the Formation of Natural Silk," *Textile Research,* 9-9 (1938–1939), 329–347.

worm. If, however, the fibroin is a secretion the sole purpose of which is to protect the insect during its pupal state, then the worm would secrete only as much silk as is required for that purpose, regardless of

Fig. 9.5. Eggs of silkworm, *Bombyx mori* L. Source: Handschin, *"Breeding of Silkworms and Their Diseases," 1904.*

diet.[10] Investigations to clarify that point have not been conclusive. The requirements of the larva are very exacting as far as food, warmth, and cleanliness are concerned. The larva develop in definite stages (Table 9.I).

TABLE 9.I

DEVELOPMENT OF THE LARVA OF THE SILKWORM

Development of larva	Length mm	Weight gms	No. days	Temp. C	Food needed gms
Day of hatching	3	0.00045	..	..	...
1st moult	8	0.00657	5	19	0.104
2nd moult	18	0.0423	5	20	0.312
3rd moult	28	0.18	6	22	1.036
4th moult	45	0.733	8	23	3.11
Before pupation	87	4.0	7	21	18.72

Source: E. Handschin, "Breeding of Silkworms and Their Diseases," *Ciba Review,* 5-53 (1946), 1909–1914.

It takes about 10 days for the eggs (see Fig. 9.5) to hatch after they are taken from their storage rooms at 17 C and placed in incubators at 25 C. In 31 days, the worm (see Fig. 9.6) is fully grown and ready to stop eating, find a quiet place, and rest up for cocooning. With a figure-eight movement, the worm spins a net of silk threads in which it gradually encloses itself. The worm then rests before beginning the

[10] E. Handschin, "Breeding of Silkworms and Their Diseases," *Ciba Review,* 5-53 (1946), 1909–1914.

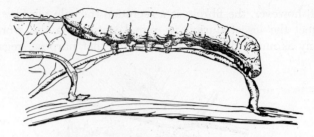

Fig. 9.6. Adult caterpillar of mulberry silkworm, *Bombyx mori Linné*. Source: Handschin, ibid., 1945.

COCOON OF   COCOON OF
A   FEMALE   A   MALE
PUPA   PUPA

Fig. 9.7. Cocoons of Bombyx mori L. *Source: Handschin, ibid., 1911.*

cocoon proper. The cocoon takes shape in about 15 hours. In 36 hours, the body of the worm is no longer visible, and in 60 hours the structure of the cocoon (see Figs. 9.7, 9.8) is complete. The spinning

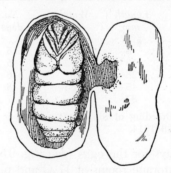

Fig. 9.8. View of interior of *Bombyx mori* L. cocoon. *Source: Handschin, ibid., 1905.*

glands are exhausted. The worm becomes slack and spent and, after a final moulting (the fourth), changes into the pupa or chrysalis. To obtain filament silk, it is necessary to kill the insect at this stage by steaming, heating, or by other means before it cuts its way out of the

cocoon. Only the chrysalises used for reproduction are allowed to
mature—that is, to become moths. Four hundred to 700 yards of usable
silk filament per uncut cocoon are realized. The cocoons from which
the moths emerge are used for spun silk. Silk obtained from wild worms
is also used for spun silk.

The cocoons are thrown into pails of warm water to soften the gum
so that the filaments may be reeled. In reeling, four (two pairs) or
more filaments are doubled together to form the number of the raw silk
yarn desired. The raw silk, as received from the primary market, is
converted at later stages of manufacture into the various silk yarns.

Anatomy of silk glands. The silk glands have been studied and described in so far as they are understood.[11] In the mature worm, the
silk glands occupy a considerable portion of the body (see Fig. 9.9).

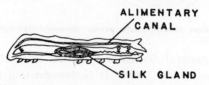

Fig. 9.9. **Silkworm, showing location of silk glands.** *Source: Bergmann, "Facts and
Theories Concerning the Formation of Natural Silk."*

The A-B posterior portion of the gland (see Fig. 9.10) is the region
of greatest activity. It is about 0.3 mm long and 0.1 mm wide. The
B-C section is the reservoir for storage and is about 3.7 mm long and

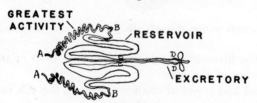

Fig. 9.10. **Diagram of silk gland of** *Bombyx mori* L. *Source: Bergmann, ibid.*

0.5 mm wide. The C-D section of the gland forms the excretory tubes.
The walls of the silk gland have three layers. The cells are all large.

There is general agreement that silk is produced in the posterior part of
the gland. Small droplets of liquid fibroin have been found in cells in
this region and in no other cells. The droplets coalesce, and when the
worm begins to spin, the liquid mass of fibroin is transported by way of
two excretory tubes into the common duct which is a thick-walled tube.
When the fibroin enters this common duct from the two excretory tubes,
it does not coalesce but is glued together with sericin.

[11] Bergmann, "Facts and Theories Concerning the Formation of Natural Silk,"
329–347.

There is no agreement as to the origin of the silk gum or sericin. The best information at present indicates that sericin is produced through the entire length of the middle portion of the reservoir section.

Strong muscles of the silk press (see Figs. 9.11, 9.12) control the shape and thickness of the fibers and can cut off production. The diameter of

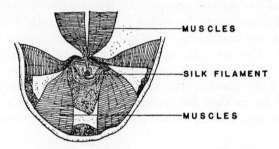

Fig. 9.11. **Cross-section through silk press.** *Source: Handschin, op. cit., 1907.*

a silk filament in general decreases from the beginning of cocoon construction to the end of the fiber. It is thought that the muscles of the silk press relax, causing a flattening of the fiber. The silk press there-

Fig. 9.12. **Length section through silk press.** *Source: Bergmann, loc. cit.*

fore regulates the filament's shape and diameter, both of which influence physical properties of the fiber.

Both chemical and physical changes occur in the silk on its way from the reservoir to the cocoon. Aside from changing from a liquid to a solid, certain changes take place in the solubility of the silk fibroin. The sericin changes, also, on its way from the reservoir to the outside, from an insoluble to a soluble substance (in dilute alkalies). It takes some hours after spinning for the sericin to harden. It is not known when or how silk gum is added to the silk. It has been shown, however, that the sericin is a single compound and not two, as was formerly thought.[12]

Food of the silkworm. The silkworm's diet consists chiefly of mulberry leaves.[13] An extended study was made by Bergmann of the silk-

[12] Henry A. Rutherford and Milton Harris, "Concerning the Existence of Fractions of Sericin in Raw Silk," *Textile Research*, 10-6 (1939–1940), 221–228.

[13] Werner Bergmann, "Facts and Theories Concerning the Formation of Natural Silk," 329–347.

worm's diet to see if improved feeding would result in better or more silk fibroin.[14] The worms were fed on a variety of diets (Table 9.II).

TABLE 9.II

EXPERIMENTAL DIETS OF SILKWORMS

Food	Results
1. *Maculara aurantiaca* (osage orange)	Poor silk, 80% of worms died
2. *Scorzonera hispanica* (black salsify)	Too acid, worms died
3. Lettuce	Big worms, thin skins, less silk, and is very fine
4. White mulberry leaves	Best food for worm, best quality silk
5. Black mulberry leaves	Inferior silk

Source: Werner Bergmann, "Relations between the Food and Silk of Silkworms," *Textile Research,* 10-11 (1940), 462–475.

The maturity of the leaves greatly affects the quality of silk obtained. Younger leaves produce better silk. However, if leaves are too young, they lack proteins, and the worm has to use reserve protein.

It was decided to see what effect a food supplement would have on the worms and the silk (Table 9.III). Soya milk (con.) increased the weight of silk and reduced mortality of the worms.

TABLE 9.III

EFFECT OF SUPPLEMENTARY DIETS ON THE MORTALITY OF *Bombyx Mori* AND THE PRODUCTION OF SILK

Type of supplementary diet	MORTALITY		Weight of silk
	Larvae	Pupae	
Controls	100	100	100
Beef extract	161	112	109
Pea leaves	92	240	106
Soya bean milk (dilu.)	77	112	101
Soya bean milk (con.)	70	77	110
Peptone	70	111	107

Source: Werner Bergmann, "Relations between the Food and Silk of Silkworms, *Textile Research,* 10-11 (1940), 462–475.

Numerous salts and other food elements were also tried with varying results.

PROPERTIES

The properties of silk fibroin are such that silk fabrics may be, at one and the same time, the most serviceable and most beautiful of fabrics.

Physical Properties. Silk fibroin is the only commercially important extruded filament among the natural fibers. It is prized for its softness, resilience, high tensile strength, smoothness, and beauty.

The variations of shape and size of silk filament cross sections have a

---

[14] Werner Bergmann, "Relations between the Food and Silk of Silkworms," *Textile Research,* 10-11 (1940), 462–475.

definite effect upon their extensibility.[15] Even though the shape of the filament varies greatly over the length, the cross-section area rarely varies as much as 20 per cent from the mean. It has been found that with

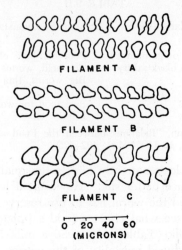

FILAMENT A

FILAMENT B

FILAMENT C

```
0   20  40  60
   (MICRONS)
```

Fig. 9.13. Series of cross-sections at 20 μ intervals. *Source: Goodings and Turl, op. cit.*

all the variations in cross-section shapes (see Fig. 9.13), the variations in cross-section area approximate a normal distribution curve (see Fig. 9.14). The diameters of individual filaments vary for the different kinds of silk from 10.8 to 28.48 microns.

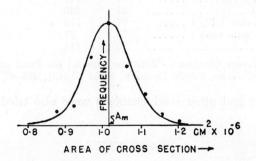

AREA OF CROSS SECTION →

Fig. 9.14. Frequency distribution curve for area of cross-sections of silk. *Source: Goodings and Turl, op. cit.*

The natural color of silk fibroin varies with the race of the worm. The various races of domesticated *Bombyx mori* may be divided into three general classes, depending upon the color of fiber produced: white,

[15] A. C. Goodings and L. H. Turl, "Variations of Shape and Size of Cross-Section of Silk Filaments," *Journal of the Textile Institute*, 31-9 (1940), T207.

yellow, and yellow-green.[16] The wild silkworms may also be classified according to color of fiber produced: white (very few), light and dark brown (most Tussah silks), green, and golden yellow. Tussah silk is the most important of the wild silks and is coarser and stronger than cultivated silk.

Fibroin degummed in a soap solution has its insulating properties greatly reduced by the film of fatty acid left by the soap. The film can be removed by boiling in a fat solvent such as alcohol.

Chemical Properties. Silk is a comparatively simple protein fiber.[17]

The pigment, which gives the natural color to some silk, appears in the posterior part of the silk gland and moves forward a few days before the silk is spun. Worms which spin yellow silk also have yellow blood except one pure race which has yellow blood and yields white silk. With one exception, white silkworms produce white silk. Others have white blood and yield yellow silk.[18]

Blanc suspected a relationship and found the color of each showed absorption in the same region of visible light. The work of a French physiologist, Dubois, led him to conclude that the yellow color was closely related to the vegetable carotene. Then followed long discussions of Dubois's findings and much work by researchers to show whether the worms could or could not ingest coloring matter and transfer it to the silk. Silk of the brown cocoon is white until 24–48 hours after the cocoon is finished when the worm thoroughly wets the cocoon with its last excretory liquid before pupation takes place. The fresh white cocoons of some species will turn brown if placed in water to which oxygen of air or an oxidizing agent is added. Color change is impeded by hydrogen. Boiling water poured over the cocoons leaves them white, but the aqueous extract is brown. All this indicates that the brown color was caused by a soluble pigment such as that which is widely distributed in the insect world.

The silk wax plays an important role in the production of silk fibroin.[19] The waxes (gums) are water repellent and are resistant to chemical action. The waxes are found not only on the silk but also on the skin of the worm, in droppings, on the chrysalis, on the egg shell, and on the cuticle of the moth. Wax protects the silk from wide changes in humidity.

Von Bergen studied the distribution of wax in the silk cocoon.[20] The

[16] Werner Bergmann, "Natural Pigments of Silk," *Textile Research,* 9-11 (1939), 397–408.

[17] Walter M. Scott, "Silk Chemistry and Silk Processing," *American Dyestuff Reporter,* 29-21 (1940), 534–538.

[18] Werner Bergmann, "Silk Wax and Certain Physical Properties of Raw Silk," *Textile Research,* 9-5 (1939), 175–182.

[19] Bergmann, "Silk Wax and Certain Physical Properties of Raw Silk," 175–182.

[20] Werner Von Bergen, "Distribution of Wax in Cocoon of Silk," *Textile Research,* 8-6 (1938), 195.

amount of wax (see Fig. 9.15) was found to diminish steadily from the external to the internal layers of the cocoon.

The reactions of silk fibroin are similar to those of wool. The reactions toward acids and bases are of importance during manufacturing processes and during laundering and dry cleaning. The acidic and basic

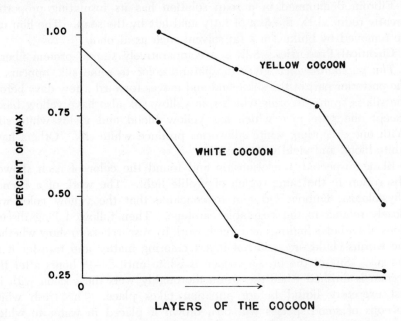

Fig. 9.15. **Distribution of wax in the cocoon.** *Source: Von Bergen,* "Distribution of Wax in Cocoon of Silk."

groups of the silk make it possible to use either acidic or basic dyes. Silk is the most sensitive of the natural fibers to photochemical deterioration.[21] It has been observed that pretreatment with almost any basic compound to neutralize the acid groups reduces the rate of deterioration. Certain reactive groups in silk react with metallic salts of tin, lead, iron, and sometimes others, to form weighting which may cause serious damage to the silk and reduces its wearing qualities. Today, synthetic resins may be used instead of metallic weighting.

Silk, like wool, is easily oxidized. Heat, sun, bleaches, and alkalies cause the fiber to become yellowed and to lose strength and wearing qualities.

[21] Henry A. Rutherford and Milton Harris, "Photochemical Reactions in Silk," *American Dyestuff Reporter,* 30-14 (1941), 345–346, 363–364.

CONSUMPTION AND USES

Silk has always been considered a luxury fiber. It is produced largely in low-income countries of the Far East but is consumed in the high-income countries of the west, especially the United States.[22] The consumption of silk in this country since 1900 has followed some remarkable phases of social and economic development. The so-called "silk-shirt era" of the late 1920s saw the highest consumption of silk in this country. Heavily weighted silks in cheap dresses and silk hosiery were characteristic of the period. Maladjusted social values were co-partners with the economic thinking popular at the time. The financial structure of 1929 collapsed, and silk consumption dropped 78 per cent by 1934–1938.[23] This drop was augmented by the increased consumption of rayon and the need to buy bread instead of silk. About 1935 over 90·per cent of the silk coming into the United States was for silk hosiery. By 1946, this use of silk dropped to 4 per cent of the previous amount. Nylon replaced silk in the high-priced hosiery field and rayon in the low-priced field. The same trend affected the use of silk in lingerie.

World production of silk has suffered a severe setback from which it may never recover. Less than three and a half million pounds were imported in 1947–1948. Apparently all the natural fibers are becoming luxury fibers, because they require more of the expensive man-hours per pound to produce than the manufactured ones.

Traditionally silk has been used in clothing because of the beauty and serviceability of the fabrics which may be made either from filaments or from staple fiber yarns used alone or mixed with other fibers to produce special textures. Silk has been used one time or another in the majority of fabrics used for clothing and to a limited extent in many of the household fabrics, exclusive of kitchen and bathroom linens. Industrial uses have included typewriter ribbons, dental floss, parachute cloth and artificial ligaments.

[22] Gerda Blau, *World Fiber Survey* (Washington, D. C.: Food and Agriculture Organization of United Nations, 1947), 112.
[23] *World Fiber Review* (Washington, D. C.: Food and Agriculture Organization of United Nations, 1948).

Chapter Ten

Rayons and Algenates

RAYONS

THE HISTORY OF RAYON is the history of the first man-made fiber. Its production has increased at a fabulous rate.

History. Rayon is the first of an indeterminable number of manufactured textile fibers. The natural fibers have long histories, the beginnings of which in many cases are lost in antiquity. Manufactured fibers belong to modern times. In the case of rayons, an idea was cultivated and developed, not a fiber-producing plant or animal. The idea, however, is not so new as it is commonly thought to be.

Manufactured fibers. A British philosopher, Sir Robert Hooke suggested in his book, *Micrographia,* dated 1664, that a more reliable job of producing fibers should be done by scientists than by the silkworm.[1] He was right from the standpoint of both production and price. About 50 years later, 1710, Rena A. F. de Reaumer, a French scientist, wrote a book on *Insects and Scientists* and again suggested that man should be able to make fibers. Nothing of significance was done until after a mechanical process for making wood pulp had been invented. In England, Schwabe experimented with filaments made by extruding solutions through fine holes into a coagulating bath. By 1855, a Swiss chemist, George Audemors, had taken out the first patent ever issued for making a manufactured fiber, British Patent No. 283. Sir Joseph Swan, British

---

[1] Charles Venable, "The Rayon Industry and Rayon Research," *Rayon Textile Monthly,* 25-6 (1944), 268–270.

inventor, while trying to make incandescent lamp filaments, succeeded in making fibers by using spinnerets and coagulating baths. The fibers which Swan was able to produce were used in cloth exhibited at London in 1885.

Count Hilaire Chardonnet (1839–1924). A pupil of the great Pasteur, Chardonnet was sent into southern France to study a disease of the silkworm which was playing havoc with the important sericulture of that region. He observed that silkworms ate mulberry leaves which contained cellulose, and produced silk.

Armed with this knowledge, Chardonnet tried to produce silk from cellulose by chemical techniques. He ended up with a nitrocellulose fiber, "artificial silk," on which he obtained his first patent in 1884. He displayed this new fiber for the first time at the French Exhibition of 1889 and was then provided in 1891 with funds for the first rayon factory, which he set up in Besancon, his birthplace.[2] He was able to produce 125 pounds of fiber per day. Even though the factory was not a success, many problems were solved in the following two years, and Chardonnet, the *Father of the Rayon Industry,* enjoyed a rare opportunity—that of seeing his efforts achieve commercial success before he died in 1924.

It was not until about 1920, when the basic patents on rayon production expired, that the industry came to the United States. The industry which had started about 1890 in Europe was at last ready to begin growing. By 1939, rayon was produced in the United States in 14 states by 17 companies. Rayon is produced in every country of the earth which is industrially important. The term *rayon* was adopted in 1924.

Production. Rayon is defined as a generic term for staple fibers, monofilaments, and continuous filament yarns made by man from regenerated cellulose with or without lesser amounts of nonfiber-forming material.[3] Estron is defined tentatively as a generic term for staple fibers, monofilaments, and continuous filaments composed chiefly of one or more esters of cellulose.[4] Cellulose acetate is at present the only estron produced commercially and is sold under a number of trade names, for example, Celanese. The modified rayons are made principally from cellulose or cellulose derivatives but may contain amounts of noncellulosic fiber-forming materials, for example, proteins. The rayons of chief commercial value at present are manufactured by the following processes: (a) cellulose xanthate (viscose), (b) cellulose acetate (estron), and (c) cuprammonium (Bemberg). A comparison of the approximate percentages produced by each process (see Fig. 10.2) shows the viscose process to be the most generally used.

[2] H. R. Mauersberger and E. W. K. Schwarz, *Rayon Handbook* (New York: Rayon Handbook Co., 1939), 2.

[3] A.S.T.M. Committee D-13, *A.S.T.M. Standards on Textile Materials* (Philadelphia: American Society for Testing Materials, 1950).

[4] *Ibid.*

The production of rayon is one of the world's largest chemical industries. Of the ten producers in the United States, the seven largest account for 98 per cent of the total rayon supply. The two chief sources

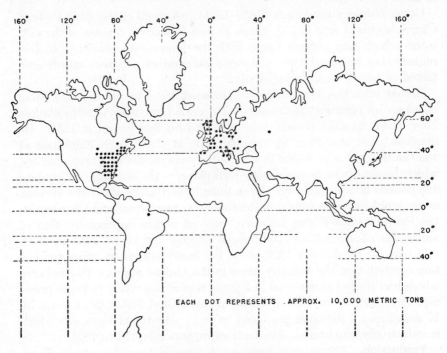

EACH DOT REPRESENTS APPROX. 10,000 METRIC TONS

Fig. 10.1. The world's rayon.

of industrial cellulose are cotton linters and wood pulp. The rayon manufacturing industry constitutes the largest single user of chemically

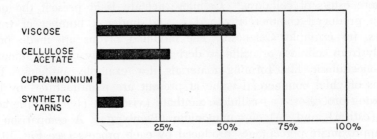

Fig. 10.2. **World rayon yarn production by process.** *Source:* RAYON TODAY (*New York: E. I. du Pont de Nemours and Co., Inc., 1941*), 13.

pure cotton which is used in cuprammonium rayon and usually in cellulose acetate. The cellulose xanthate process uses cotton linters only for high-tenacity rayons; otherwise wood pulp is used. Wood pulp is a product of the vast lumber industry. Quality pulp is obtained from hemlock in the Pacific Northwest; spruce and fir are also used. The largest pulp-manufacturing plant in the world is located in the state of Washington. Another smaller source of high-quality pulp is the Southern white pine.

In addition to the three major processes for preparing rayons, there are others of potential value. Staple fiber may be made from any filaments.

Viscose. Viscose is manufactured by the cellulose xanthate process. Charles F. Cross and E. J. Bevan discovered the reactions underlying the viscose process during their studies on alkali-cellulose-mercerization reactions and obtained British Patent No. 8700, February 6, 1893. This was the third process which got much of its early start not from interest in developing a new textile fiber, but from interest in developing a better filament for carbonization for the incandescent lamps which Edison had invented. Viscose received its name from the viscous nature of the solution from which it was spun.[5]

The Viscose Development Company was established in 1899. At that time, viscose seemed to find its chief use as a finishing material. Ireland used viscose solution to finish linen fabrics; England finished curtain fabrics, door handles, and valve wheels with it. Paper and artificial leather were sized with it. In 1900, the first viscose textile yarns were exhibited in Paris. There, by accident, the advantage of "aging" the viscose solution was discovered. Much interest centered in the process, and it grew rapidly because of its simplicity and low cost. In 1910, the Viscose Company of America was established and has since become the world's largest producer of rayon yarns. In 1938, the Viscose Company accounted for 83 per cent of world production of 815 million pounds of viscose yarns. In 1940, only about 12 million tons of viscose were produced because of the approaching war.

In the viscose process, the cellulose is swollen in a concentrated solution of sodium hydroxide. The alkali pushes the cellulose chains apart and forms an alkali cellulose. The distance between the chains is increased still more by the action of other chemicals and water until the cellulose molecules are carried into solution.

After aging the solution is extruded or spun (see Fig. 10.3) into a coagulating bath where the cellulose is regenerated.[6] Cellulose is not soluble in water. The outer surface of the fiber is coagulated first and forms a skin. Stretch spinning, widely used today, is the process of

---

[5] Emil Ott, *Cellulose and Cellulose Derivatives* (New York: Interscience Publishers, Inc., 1946).

[6] Malcom Dole, "Synthetic Fibers," *American Dyestuff Reporter*, 30-13 (1941), 327–336.

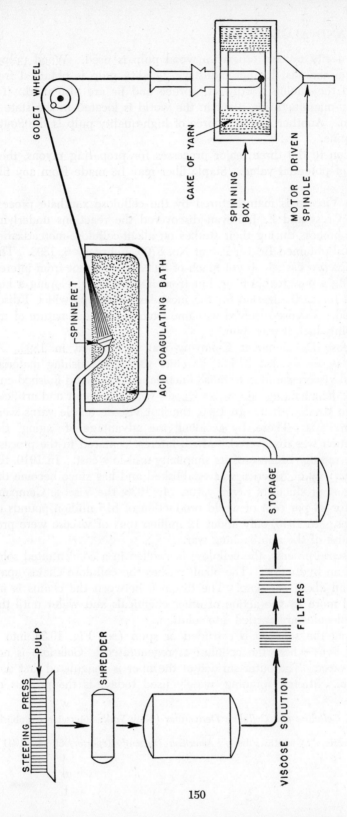

Fig. 10.3. Production of viscose rayon yarn. *Source:* RAYON FABRICS *(New York: American Viscose Corporation, 1944), 56.*

stretching the soft, partially formed fiber in order to produce very fine fibers and a greater amount of molecular orientation.[7] When wet, the fiber can be stretched greatly without breaking. When viscose swells, it swells in all directions, even in length. The swelling is reversible, and the fiber shrinks when it dries. After the fiber is spun, considerable shrinkage occurs. This causes the very shrunken, striated appearance of viscose fibers. It has been shown, however, that the cellulose particle itself undergoes no change except in length because of the chemical reactions involved in producing viscose rayon.

Cuprammonium. The United States produces limited amounts of cuprammonium (Bemberg) rayon. The production of rayon by this process was begun in Germany. In 1857, Schweitzer discovered that cellulose could be dissolved in a suitable alkaline copper reagent. Both French and German chemists were active in developing the cuprammonium process for rayon. By 1918, J. B. Bemberg had put stretch spinning of rayon on a commercial basis. Later, the American Bemberg Corporation was established in the United States.

Cotton linters are used as a source of cellulose and give a certain quality advantage. The linters are dissolved in a copper ammonium hydroxide solution (see Fig. 10.4). The solution is aged and filtered. The solution is spun into a coagulating bath. The filaments are approximately round and, as a rule, finer than those produced by other rayon processes. A very small percentage of the total amount of rayon produced is made by the cuprammonium process. The fiber is a regenerated cellulose, not a cellulose derivative.

Cellulose acetate. Manufactured by the acetate process, cellulose acetate (estron) had been prepared as a chemical in 1865. No progress resulted until 1894 when it was discovered that certain compounds catalyzed the formation of the acetate. Cross and Bevan, who had been active in developing the viscose process, obtained the first patent for the acetate process. In 1902, Little, Mark, and Walker obtained a United States patent for the production of cellulose acetate in this country. Developments continued, but it was during World War I that the acetate process really got a start as "dope" for airplane wings. When the war was over, it seemed logical to turn to producing textile filaments and yarns. By 1924, the cellulose acetate process was on a commercial basis.

In the production of cellulose acetate, highly purified cotton linters are swollen with acetic acid. After further treatments in order to achieve more desirable fiber properties, the solution is dispersed in a volatile solvent for spinning. The fiber is spun into warm air to evaporate the solvent and leave a solid fiber. Special forms of the

[7] Jack Compton, "Structural Relation of Rayon to Natural Cellulose Fibers, Study of Viscose Process," *Industrial and Engineering Chemistry*, 31 (1939), 1250–1259.

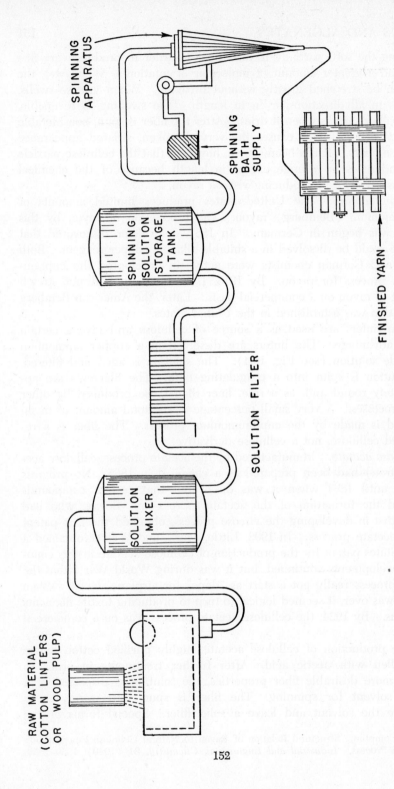

Fig. 10.4. Production of cuprammonium rayon yarn. *Source: ibid.*

fiber may be prepared.[8] The addition of plasticizers allows softening and resetting to produce unusual effects such as found in moiré. Soft, fluffy, dull fibers are prepared by incorporation of very tiny air bubbles in the solution.

England prepares high-strength acetates by stretching and partially saponifying the acetate.

Modifications of cellulose fibers. Modifications are steadily increasing. There are two types of modified cellulose: the so-called modified rayons and the cellulose derivatives (compounds made from cellulose). The modified rayons have substances other than cellulose or cellulose derivatives incorporated into the fibers. The possibilities have not been extensively developed, although the opportunity exists. Some German work was reported in 1942 in which proteins were used to lower the absorption and improve the crease-resistant properties of rayon.

Cellulose derivatives or cellulose compounds have increased greatly the service that may be expected from rayons. Cellulose acetate has been hydrolyzed to produce fibers with an acetate core but a regenerated cellulose surface. This modification incorporates the advantages of a cellulose fiber and of an acetate fiber. With the possibility of introducing both sulfur and nitrogen into rayons and cotton, it is hoped that the dyeing properties will be similar to those of wool. Fabrics with wool and rayon or cotton mixtures can then be dyed more readily in a common dye bath.

When certain changes have been made on the surface of a cellulose fiber (cotton or rayon), the mildew resistance of the fiber is greatly increased. It is not possible at this early date to foresee the extent to which modifications of the rayons may increase their value.

Merchandising Progress. The early name for rayon, "artificial silk," caused merchandising problems. The unfortunate term, as applied to regenerated cellulose and cellulose derivatives, was changed to "rayon" after much protest from the silk industry and through the efforts of the National Retail Dry Goods Association working with American Standards Association and Committee D-13 on Textile Materials, American Society for Testing Materials. The publicity attending the change in nomenclature resulted favorably for the industry. In 1926, the consumption of rayon exceeded that of silk. In 1927, the Rayon Institute was founded to promote the interests of the rapidly expanding industry. By 1933, the National Rayon Weavers' Association was chartered further to promote rayon. The first technical conference was held in May, 1937, under the co-sponsorship of the American Society of Mechanical Engineers, the American Association of Chemists and Colorists, the Textile Research Institute, Committee D-13 of American Society for Testing Materials, and the Throwsters Research Institute.

[8] Harold DeWitt Smith, "Cellulose Acetate Rayons," *Industrial and Engineering Chemistry,* 32 (1940), 1555–1559.

Aside from the consumer's right to know the content of all fabrics he buys, the greatest help which fiber identification gives is the knowledge of how best to take care of the fabric. In October 26, 1937, the Federal Trade Commission issued Trade Practice Rules for the Rayon Industry demanding complete disclosure of the rayon content in all merchandise made wholly or partly of rayon. In time, the term rayon was found to be confusing to the consumer. One reason was the difference in temperatures required in ironing. Cellulose acetate is thermoplastic and melts or fuses if ironed at a temperature above the fusion point of the acetate fiber. This and other reasons led to the adoption of estron in 1950 to identify the cellulose esters.

Rayon staple has become well established and has contributed tremendously to the growth of the industry.

No one person has been responsible for the growth of the rayon industry. The combined efforts of chemists, physicists, engineers, and other research workers, together with money and industrial knowhow, gave the world its first manufactured fibers, the rayons.

Properties. The properties of rayons, as of other manufactured fibers, may be varied within wide limits.

The physical appearance of fibers manufactured by extrusion differs from that of fibers built in nature from plant and animal cells with the exception of silk which is also an extruded fiber. The manufactured fibers are spun from solutions or mixtures which can vary in composition at the discretion of the manufacturer. Availability of raw materials, method of manufacture, and properties desired determine the composition and many of the properties of the manufactured fibers. Man, not varieties, breeds, or climate, determines the properties of the manufactured fibers. The manufactured fibers are not cellular. Rayons have, however, certain properties in common with all fibers, for example, strength, fineness, resilience, elasticity, density, and stiffness. In common with the azlons (fibers manufactured from plant and animal proteins), the rayons are weaker when wet than when dry. High-tenacity rayons lose less strength proportionately than do rayons of lower dry strength.

In general, rayons have low elasticity and recover little from crushing unless finished with crush-resistant finishes. In addition, it has been shown that cellulose acetate, viscose, and cuprammonium rayons fracture under simple tension.[9] The cracks are both internal and external. Vinyon also shows surface cracks, while nylon shows none.

The density of rayons from regenerated cellulose is approximately that of cotton. The density of cellulose acetate is less than that of cellulose. Rayons are not stiff when compared with Fiberglas, ramie, and flax.

[9] S. Simmons and F. Howlett, "Effect of Strain on Microscopic Structure of Acetate Rayon," *Journal of the Textile Institute*, 40-11 (1949), T590–T599.

In fact, rayons have a fairly good balance of the physical properties which are desirable for general use.[10]

The microscopic appearance (see Figs. 10.5, (1) and (2)) of the rayons provides a basis for comparison of surfaces and cross sections of the bright and the semidull fibers. The irregular cross section of viscose is a result of the very irregular surface.

The semidull fibers have had an opaque pigment such as titanium oxide or zinc oxide dispersed in the spinning solution. The surface of such a fiber tends to scatter the incident light and thus appears less glossy. Cuprammonium rayon (see Figs. 10.5, (3) and (4)) is a much finer fiber, has fewer striations, and has a more nearly round cross section than other rayons.

Cellulose acetate fibers (see Fig. 10.5, (5) and (6)) appear more like viscose, but they have comparatively few striations and a more regular cross section.

The physical properties, not only of rayon, but of all manufactured fibers, depend in a measure upon the degree of orientation of the molecules (see Fig. 10.6) in the fiber. The random arrangement of the cellulose molecules in solution is illustrated in A. B represents the intermediate stage after the fiber has been formed, but before stretching. C represents the orderly parallel arrangement of the molecules after stretching. The fibers in which the molecules are more highly oriented by stretching have a higher breaking strength, have less elongation, and are stiffer than the unstretched fibers.

Fibers generally produced are of two types: the regenerated celluloses or rayons; and the cellulose derivative, cellulose acetate or estron. The regenerated celluloses, viscose and cuprammonium rayons, are more sensitive to chemical reagents than native cellulose. Otherwise their behavior is similar to that of cotton. Rayons tear more readily when wet than cotton and also scorch more readily under a hot iron.

The cellulose derivatives differ from the regenerated celluloses in their behavior. All are thermoplastic and soluble in one solvent or another. Some are even water soluble.[11] Cellulose acetate is by far the most commonly used cellulose derivative and the only one commonly used as a fiber. Even so, it has had some limitations for clothing uses. It has a low moisture regain and, because of the low fusion point, may cause trouble in ironing.

[10] R. M. Hoffman, "A Generalized Concept of Resilience," *Textile Research Journal*, 18-3 (1948), 141–148.

[11] David J. Reid and George C. Daul, "The Preparation and Properties of Alkali-Soluble Metal Carboxycellulose Fibers," *Textile Research Journal*, 19-12 (1949), 794–802.

Richard Steele and Eugene Pacsu, "Cellulose Studies: XIII. Heterogeneous Hydrolysis of Trimethyl Cellulose," *Textile Research Journal*, 19-12 (1949), 771–783.

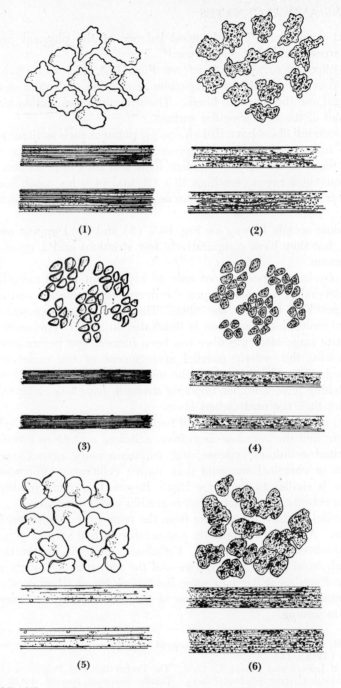

Fig. 10.5. Microscopic appearance, longitudinal and cross-sectional views of: (1) bright viscose, (2) semidull viscose, (3) bright cuprammonium rayon, (4) semidull cuprammonium rayon, (5) bright cellulose acetate rayon, (6) semidull cellulose acetate rayon.

156

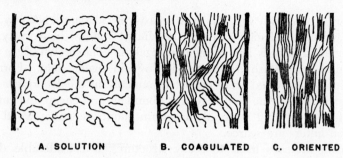

A. SOLUTION   B. COAGULATED   C. ORIENTED

Fig. 10.6. Schematic diagram of arrangement of cellulose molecules in steps of fiber production. *Source:* RAYON TEXTILE MONTHLY, *23-9 (1942), 516.*

Consumption and Uses. Improvements in quality have helped to increase the consumption and the uses of rayon fibers. Consumption has increased rapidly since the introduction of staple fibers in 1928. The export trade in rayon has grown significantly since 1934. The relative amounts of the various rayons have changed greatly since 1943. Viscose and acetate form the major part of present production. A factor which could reduce the relative importance of the rayons is the production of synthetic fibers in increasing numbers and amounts. Nylon is, at present, the most important in quantity.

The gains which have been made by the manufactured fibers are in no small part due to the fact that until recently the price has fallen as the amounts produced increased. Since 1938, the price has been comparatively stable. There is, of course, a point past which the price cannot be lowered. Costs of production and profits both must be met in any successful enterprise.

The rayons were used primarily in clothing and household fabrics until recently. At present, regenerated celluloses, modified celluloses, and cellulose derivatives are used for fibers and filaments, for finishes on fabrics, and for transparent sheets and films. Hosiery, other knit goods, broad woven fabrics, narrow woven fabrics, and tires take all of the supply of rayon except for a small but growing amount for miscellaneous uses.

By 1945, tire cord fabrics consumed one fourth of the total supply of rayons, more rayon than for any one item except broad woven fabrics. High-tenacity rayons are used in tire cords.

The American Standards Association has distributed minimum quality standards for rayon fabrics for 50 different end uses for clothing and household purposes.

ALGENATES

In 1883, an English chemist named Stanford isolated an algenate from marine algae. Today, algenic acid is derived from kelp, a seaweed that grows abundantly on the west coasts of Scotland, Norway, and Ireland, and on the Pacific coast of the United States. In Norway, various types of seaweeds are being investigated. The brown algae from which iodine and potash are extracted also yield algenic acid. Formerly 400,000 tons of seaweed were collected annually in the Hebrides. The raw material for algenic acid rayons is abundant and cheap and forms a source of fiber-forming material in certain countries where wood pulp and cotton linters are scarce.

The plant attaches itself to rocky structures at considerable depth. There are long leaf-like outgrowths from a stalk or stem. The rapid growth of the plant makes it possible to harvest several crops per year. The plant also yields a product which is widely used in foods to impart a velvety texture.

The kelp which contains 20 to 30 per cent of algenic acid is mascerated and extracted with an alkaline solution which can be extruded through spinnerets into a suitable coagulating bath as in the manufacture of viscose rayon.[12] The algenate rayon possesses a high luster and good strength, both of which can be varied to some extent by alterations in the method of manufacture. Like the cellulose rayons, the strength of the algenates is lowered as the moisture content rises. When dry, the fiber has satisfactory elasticity and can be woven or knitted into fabrics which are nonflammable because of the high mineral content.

It is thought that soluble algenate fibers may find a place in special weaving procedures to secure novel effects and in parachute fabrics to drop mines in enemy waters. Soluble algenates such as sodium algenate are used as a sizing material in weaving. Calcium algenate has been tried as a fiber, but it dissolves in mildly alkaline solutions.[13] At present, the uses for soluble fibers are limited.

[12] J. B. Speakman, "Algenic Acid Rayon: Production from Seaweed," *Textile Weekly*, 26 (1940), 636.

W. H. Cady, "Textiles from Seaweed," *American Dyestuff Reporter*, 37-9 (1948), 283.

[13] Ernest E. Tallis, "The Structure of Textile Fibres: XII. Algenate Fibres," *Journal of the Textile Institute*, 41-2 (1950), 52–55.

Chapter Eleven

Azlons

ADOPTION OF THE TERM AZLON by Committee D-13 of the American Society for Testing Materials to describe all man-made protein-base fibers is an indication of the growing importance in the textile field of these newly developed fibers.[1] Azlon fibers are manufactured from either plant or animal proteins. In the beginning, fibers made from plant and animal proteins were attempted for two reasons:

  a) the economic problem of producing a merchantable product from a farm by-product
  b) purely theoretical reasons

Stabilization of Molecular Chains. Many native proteins are fibrous, whereas others have long, folded or coiled structures which do not appear fibrous. If the latter, however, are put into solution and the long molecules paralleled by forcing them through the tiny holes of a spinneret into a curing or hardening bath, the bundles of molecules will remain in this extended form. In order to do this, it has been necessary to take advantage of the side chains located at intervals along the length of each molecular chain. After a sufficient number of the side chains of neighboring molecules has been securely bound, the filament or fiber acquires the strength and other properties necessary to a textile fiber.[2]

[1] Committee D-13, *A.S.T.M. Standards on Textile Materials*, 1.
[2] R. L. Wormell, "The Structure of Textile Fibers: XI. Fibers Made From Dispersed Proteins," *Journal of the Textile Institute*, 41-1 (1950), P16–P28.

At present, work is continuing in an effort to improve the production of fibers from such proteins as casein, peanut, zein, cottonseed, egg white, chicken feathers, and soybeans.

CASEIN, ARALAC

History. The history of casein fibers is brief and the quantity produced is unimportant. However, the significance of such fibers is great. Casein is prepared from the curd of cow's milk. It frequently happens that when man is searching for one thing he finds another. In 1890, Adolph Spitteler of Hamburg, Germany, probably did the first work on casein when he attempted to produce a white blackboard from cow's sour milk. The next work seems to have been done by Eggert Millar in 1898. The first fibers, however, hard and brittle though they were, seem to have been produced in 1903 by Todenhaupt in Germany. These efforts did not get past the laboratory stage.[3]

Apparently there were two developments that had to precede successful production of regenerated protein fibers: (1) methods of curing or hardening protein fibers, and (2) the development of the fine spinnerets so successful in the rayon industry. After these basic developments had taken place, Antonio Ferretti, an Italian, was able by 1935 to develop casein fibers successfully. They were produced in commercial quantities on rayon equipment. It was a decided economic advantage to Italy to be able to produce such a fiber during the period of sanctions. The majority of the fiber-producing countries, except the United States, licensed the Ferretti process. The fiber is still in limited production in Italy, Holland, and England.

In the U.S. Department of Agriculture, Frances Atwood, long interested in such a development, had begun research on a fiber from milk. Later, Whittier and Gould of the same department were able to solve many of the problems of producing such a fiber.[4] The first casein fibers to be produced in the United States, by a process differing from the Ferretti process, were called Aralac.[5] There followed a period in which commercial production of the fiber was discontinued. Now, however, a curled casein monofilament is being developed in different diameters and staple lengths to replace horsehair in stuffings and fabrics. Chemical treatment makes it mildew- and moth-resistant. Other modifications of casein fiber are under consideration.

[3] E. O. Whittier and S. P. Gould, "Present Status of Casein Fibers," *American Dyestuff Reporter*, 28 (1939), P641.

C. W. Bendigo, "Monofilament and Staple Azlon Produced," *Textile World*, 99-5 (1949), 106.

G. Heim, "Casein Fibre," *Journal of the Textile Institute*, 25-7 (1939), P213.

[4] E. O. Whittier and S. P. Gould, "Making Casein Fiber," *Industrial and Engineering Chemistry*, 32-7 (1940), 906–907.

[5] *Aralac* is a trademarked term coined from Atlantic Research Association, Inc., which produced it, and from *lactic* acid of milk.

Production. In general, the production of fibers from casein involves heating the milk with an acid to 90–118 F in order that the whey and casein curd can be separated. The curd is washed and the water pressed out. It is broken into small particles and quickly dried. The dry curd is then heated with chemicals to form a honey-colored viscous mass suitable for spinning into a coagulating bath. Hardening or curing of the freshly spun fiber is a complex procedure and involves a number of steps.

It was found that five million pounds of Aralac could be produced from 160 million pounds of skim milk. The raw material is obtained from various dairy sections in the United States and South America.

Properties. The properties of casein fibers are such that the fiber has had only limited use to date. When wet, neither the odor nor the strength are desirable. As is the case with any manufactured fiber, the properties of fibers from casein may be made to vary within certain limits; for example, the diameter is varied depending upon the intended use. This group of fibers lacks elasticity when dry and strength when wet. The fiber has a creamy color and a soft, wooly hand. The fibers felt readily. The specific gravity is 1.26 as compared with 1.30 for wool and 1.50 for cellulose. The moisture regain is similar to that of wool.

A comparison of the elements of which casein and wool are composed shows the chief differences to be in phosphorous and sulfur content (Table 11.I).

TABLE 11.I

ELEMENTS FOUND IN CASEIN AND WOOL

	PER CENT	
Element	Casein	Wool
Carbon	53.0	49.30
Hydrogen	7.5	7.57
Oxygen	23.0	23.66
Nitrogen	15.0	15.86
Sulfur	0.7	3.60
Phosphorus	0.8	0.00

Source: C. Diamond and R. L. Wormell, "Manufacture and Properties of Casein Fibre," *Journal of the Textile Institute,* 30-7 (1939), P224.

The molecular weight was found to be 75,000 to 100,000.[6] The heat resistance of the fiber is good, therefore the fabric may be ironed or pressed satisfactorily.

Consumption and Uses. At present, the consumption and uses of casein fibers are limited. It is thought that industrial and home furnishing uses of fibers made from casein will be more significant than clothing

[6] Heim, "Casein Fibre," P213.

uses. Early attempts to use the fiber in clothing fabrics were unfortunate. Uses which do not require high tensile strength, wet strength, and abrasion resistance are most likely to be satisfactory for the present fiber. However, since casein fibers can be successfully produced in a continuous filament and dyed in a boiling dye bath, it is thought that they may be used in knit goods. Blends with other fibers such as wool, mohair, cotton, rayon, or fur produce useful fabrics. Casein fibers have been more expensive than rayon or cotton, but less so than wool or fur.

Stiff fabrics suitable for interfacings in men's suits have been made. Curled and coiled casein bristles are being tried. The curled bristles are mixed with wool in air filters for automobile carburetors. The coiled bristles have considerable resiliency, which adapts them to use in furniture and other stuffings. A large percentage of casein fibers is used in fur felts in both North and South America. Dress and suit fabrics, blankets, neckties, some heavy underwear in Canada, and all the industrial uses, utilize only a small percentage of the nation's skim milk.

PEANUT, SARELON

History. Peanut protein has been investigated as a source of raw material for fibers.[7] The peanut fiber is very new; yet considerable effort has been centered on obtaining another outlet for this farm product. As an outgrowth of studies on wool and hair fibers, interest in preparing such a fiber had developed in England, when it was observed that in some respects vegetable protein resembled certain forms of wool and hair fibers.[8] One motive behind the early attempts to prepare fibers from such natural sources as brazil nuts, hemp seed, egg white, etc. was to learn more about the structure and behavior of the natural fibers. The protein from peanuts was of special interest.

Production. The peanut grows in Africa, Asia, South America, India, China, and the United States. About eight million tons are harvested annually in the United States, where the work on utilization of peanuts, an agricultural product of the South, has been centered at the Southern Regional Laboratory in New Orleans, one of the four government regional research laboratories. (See Chapter Twenty-two.) Merrifield and Pomes have been able to improve the spinning solution, the curing or hardening process, and the boil resistance of the peanut fiber.[9]

---

[7] David Traill, "Ardil, a Protein Fiber from Peanuts," *Dyestuffs*, 38-2 (1946), 39–45.

A. L. Merrifield and A. F. Pomes, "Fiber from Peanut Protein: I. Production and Properties of Sarelon," *Textile Research Journal*, 16-8 (1946), 369–381.

[8] W. T. Astbury, "Artificial Protein Fibers: Their Conception and Preparation," *Nature*, 155 (1945), 501.

[9] Merrifield and Pomes, "Fiber from Peanut Protein: I. Production and Properties of Sarelon," 369–377.

During the preparation of the peanut, it was found that heat over 40 to 50 C could not be used. The peanuts were therefore bleached, ground to a meal, and extracted to remove the oil at a temperature under 40 C. The proteins were extracted from the meal with a very dilute alkaline solution from which they were precipitated, dried, and made into dilute solutions for spinning. Oils, emulsifiers, and plasticizers were added to the solutions as desired. After aging, the protein solution was spun into an acid coagulating bath, then into two hardening baths of different compositions. It was found in England that one metric ton of peanuts yielded about 500 pounds of fiber.

The fiber is called Sarelon in the United States and Ardil in England.

Properties. The fibers from peanuts are too new for their properties to be well-known.

Sarelon is expected to have low wear resistance. The strength of the fiber when wet is still very low. The dry strength is of the order of 0.59 grams per denier, but the wet strength is 0.16 grams per denier (see Fig. 14.5). The fiber has a low elongation. It has a 15 per cent standard regain (see Moisture Absorption, Table 14.V), about that of wool.

Sarelon dyes readily with selected acid, vat, direct, or acetate dyes.[10] It is naturally a creamy color. The approximate composition of the peanut as given by Traill shows that up to 28 per cent of the peanut is protein (Table 11.II).

TABLE 11.II

COMPOSITION OF THE PEANUT

Type of Compound	Percentage
Arachis oil	48–54
Lecithin	0.5–0.75
Protein	Up to 28
Carbohydrate	11
Salts	2
Water	5

Source: David Traill, "Ardil, a Protein Fiber from Peanuts," Dyestuffs, 38-2 (1946), 39–45.

Consumption and Uses. Peanut fibers have not been produced in sufficient quantities for their consumption and uses to be significant as yet. Either filament or staple lengths of the fiber may be used in blends for clothing. In England, Ardil is mixed with wool in the manufacture of cloth for warm clothing. It is mixed with cotton and rayon to increase their crease resistance. It is being used in knitting yarns.

[10] Merrifield and Pomes, "Fiber from Peanut Protein: I. Production and Properties of Sarelon," 369–377.

In this country, however, the chief interest seems to be in the production of sizing and glues for paper and fabric, instead of fibers.[11]

ZEIN, VICARA

History. Zein, a corn protein, was isolated in 1821 by John Gorham, but it was not until 1935 that Swallen made zein fibers and applied for the first patent on the process.[12]

In the letter from the Secretary of Agriculture to the 76th Congress, concerning Regional Research Laboratories, it was suggested that research was needed on corn proteins. The needed studies included isolation, purification of the protein, zein, and the determination of physical and chemical properties.[13] These researches led through various stages until, in 1948, the Virginia-Carolina Chemical Corporation announced the commercial production of Vicara.[14]

Production. The potential supply of raw material for the production of zein fibers is extensive. The great Corn Belt of the United States depends to a certain extent upon the use of corn as a raw material for other products. It is possible for fibers to be one of those products. After the protein zein is isolated and purified, it is dissolved in dilute alkali. The solution is spun into an acid coagulating bath. During spinning, the fiber is stretched about 400 to 500 per cent. Then it is cured by developing bonds between neighboring molecular chains.

It was found that the wet strength and water resistance could be improved, but that shrinkage was more difficult to control.[15] An improvement of physical properties was achieved by a combination of methods of curing or hardening the fibers.

The work on the corn protein zein has been centered at the Northern Regional Laboratory at Peoria, Illinois.

Properties. At present, the properties of Vicara (zein fibers) do not permit extended use. It has a molecular weight of about 40,000, and tenacity of 1.25 grams per denier. The density is 1.29, about that of wool. Vicara is not a crystalline fiber until it is elongated almost to the

[11] R. S. Burnett, E. D. Parker, and E. J. Roberts, "Peanut Protein Hydrates," *Industrial and Engineering Chemistry*, 37-10 (1945), 980.

R. S. Burnett, E. J. Roberts, and E. D. Parker, "Viscosity Patterns of Peanut Protein Solutions," *Industrial and Engineering Chemistry*, 37-3 (1945), 276.

Jett C. Arthur, Jr. and F. W. Cheng, "Peanut Protein for Window Shade Sizes," *American Dyestuff Reporter*, 37-14 (1949), 535.

[12] Milton Harris and Alfred E. Brown, "Natural and Synthetic Protein Fibers," *Textile Research Journal*, 17 (1947), 323.

[13] Department of Agriculture, *Letter from Secretary of Agriculture on Regional Research Laboratories.*

[14] Vicara was named for Virginia-Carolina Chemical Corporation, the producer.

[15] Cyril D. Evans, C. Bradford Croston, and Cecil Van Etten, "Acetylation of Zein Fibers," *Textile Research Journal*, 17 (1947), 562.

W. P. Horst, "Vicara, New Fiber Derived from Zein," *American Dyestuff Reporter*, 38-8 (1949), 335.

point of breaking. The elongation is considered good. It is soft, has
good elasticity, and is cream to yellow in color. Because of a slick surface,
it is easier to use if mixed with other fibers such as wool and cotton.
The fiber has no felting properties; nor is it affected by mildew or moth.
It resists heat up to 310 F. The moisture regain at 65 per cent relative
humidity and 70 F is 13 per cent. A comparison between the diameters
of wool and zein fibers is shown in Table 11.III.

TABLE 11.III

RELATIVE FINENESS OF VICARA AND WOOL

VICARA		WOOL	
Denier	Width—microns	Grade	Width—microns
2.0	16.0	80s	19.5
2.5	18.1		
		70s	20.1
3.0	19.9		
		64s	21.9
3.5	21.4		
		62s	23.5
4.0	22.7		

Source: W. P. Horst, "Vicara, New Fiber Derived from Zein,"
American Dyestuff Reporter, 28-8 (1949), 335.

Early protein fibers suffered from various shortcomings: bad odor
when wet, shrinkage during dyeing, stretching of the fabric during
laundering, low strength wet or dry. Alkaline reagents in general do
not cause damage to Vicara. Therefore, fabrics containing it should be
laundered in the usual manner or dry cleaned. It is especially resistant
to inorganic acids. The strength and chemical resistance have been
increased by improving the curing process.

Consumption and Uses. At present, Vicara is chiefly of scientific interest. The production and, therefore, the consumption is limited, about
five million pounds in 1951. The best potential uses are thought to be
in drapery fabrics and in family clothing, alone or in blends. The
fabric has a soft hand and drapes well.

Soluble forms of zein fibers may be used to produce novelty effects
in weaving and lace making, in much the same way as the soluble algenate fibers are used.

COTTONSEED

Fibers made from cottonseed protein are only of scientific interest at
present. Work on utilization of proteins from cottonseed meal and cake
has been centered at the Southern Regional Research Laboratory, and
to date three methods of preparation have been patented.[16] In each

[16] Jett C. Arthur, Jr. and Hugh G. Many, "Cottonseed Protein Fiber," *Textile Research Journal*, 19-10 (1949), 605–608.

case, the proteins were precipitated with acids, washed, and air dried. It is important to remove all hulls if a good color is desired.

Information on the properties and uses of this fiber is limited. A comparison of the tenacity of cottonseed protein fibers with that of other man-made protein fibers shows the present fiber to have a low breaking strength (Table 11.IV).

TABLE 11.IV

TENACITY OF MAN-MADE PROTEIN FIBERS

Fiber	Method of preparation	Tenacity, Grams/denier
Cottonseed protein	Laboratory	0.58
Peanut protein	Laboratory	0.70
Peanut protein	Commercial pilot	0.27
Peanut protein	English pilot	0.84
Casein	Laboratory	1.15
Chicken feathers	Laboratory	0.79

Source: Jett C. Arthur, Jr. and Hugh G. Many, "Cottonseed Protein Fiber," *Textile Research Journal*, 19-10 (1949), 605–608.

EGG WHITE AND FEATHERS

Egg white and chicken feather fibers have been studied by Lundgren and associates at the Western Regional Research Laboratories at Albany, California. Again, the problem was basically one of utilization of agricultural waste or by-products. According to the 1944 estimate, there were over 170 million pounds of chicken feathers which were classed as waste products.[17] Twenty-six million pounds of inedible egg white are said to go to waste annually.

Many of the technical problems involved in the production of fibers from plant and animal proteins are similar. The structure and properties of manufactured fibers are in many ways better understood than those of the more complex natural fibers.

Lundgren has used synthetic detergents as dispersing agents for chicken feather keratin and egg white. This mild dispersing agent was used instead of the usual caustic ones in order to avoid excessive degradation of the natural protein. After spinning, the fiber molecules were oriented by drawing in steam. The tensile strength and water resistance increase with the amount of molecular orientation in the fiber.

The opportunity for the regenerated or modified protein fibers to develop commercially will probably come when they are in a more competitive position pricewise or when the need for them develops.

[17] Harold P. Lundgren and Richard A. O'Connell, "Artificial Fibers from Corpuscular and Fibrous Proteins," *Industrial and Engineering Chemistry*, 36 (1944), 370.

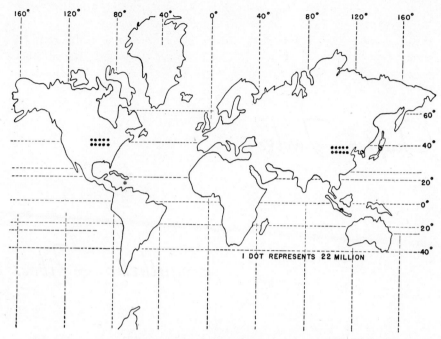

Fig. 11.1. The world's soybeans. *Source:* SCIENTIFIC MONTHLY, Feb. 1950.

SOYBEAN

The uses of the soybean have been investigated by some commercial companies as well as the Northern Regional Research Laboratory. Among other things, the soybean is a source of cheap protein for fiber production.[18] Soya proteins constitute about 40 per cent of the bean. The protein may be extracted with dilute alkali or alcohol from the dried oil-free meal. After the required viscosity has developed, the solution is stretch spun into an acid coagulating bath. The fibers are cured in a formaldehyde bath. Five pounds of soybeans are required to make one pound of fiber. In 1941, a pilot plant produced 1,000 pounds per day and by 1941, 5,000 pounds per day, but by 1945, production was still in the pilot-plant stage.

In many respects, the properties are similar to those of casein fibers. Under standard conditions of temperature and humidity, soybean fibers have a regain of 12.9 per cent. The fibers may be bleached and dyed satisfactorily. The specific gravity is 1.31. The fiber has about 80 per cent of the strength of wool but is not attacked by moths. At present, soybeans are not important as a source of raw materials for fibers but are of potential value for this purpose.

[18] E. W. K. Schwarz, "Lecithin from Soya Beans," *American Dyestuff Reporter,* 29 (1940), 220.

Chapter Twelve

Synthetic Fibers

IN THE FUTURE, it seems probable that the world may not be able to afford the expenditure of time, energy, and land on fiber production that has been spent in the past. Slow hand processes used for planting, chopping, weeding, and harvesting are slowly giving way to mechanized procedures. If the costs of production become too great for natural fibers to be generally used, then manufactured fibers will be needed in greater amounts. If all people are to be adequately clothed, the clothing must cost less. Technological developments should provide clothing for less money. Some of the factors which greatly influence the demand for, and kind and amount of, fibers are auto travel, air travel, sports, heated houses, heated conveyances, and increasing industrial developments.[1]

A comparatively recent development of the great industrial laboratories is synthetic fibers. They are much simpler in their physical and chemical structures than the natural fibers. It has been pointed out, however, that man has made rather good fibers in the few years he has been manufacturing them. Even though nature began producing fibers centuries ago, little is known about the procedures by which she prepares her fibers. Considerable is known about the catalysts, the high pressures, the temperatures, and the stretch spinning used in preparation of the man-made synthetic products.

[1] J. B. Quig, "The Future of Man Made Fibers," *Rayon and Synthetic Textiles,* 30-12 (1949), 69–71.

168

All fibers occur either as such in nature or are manufactured by man. Of the manufactured ones, there are two big classes: those in which the fiber molecule is a modified form of a natural product, e.g., rayons and azlons; and those in which the fiber molecules are built in the laboratory from small beginning units. The latter group constitutes the synthetic fibers which are especially adapted to certain uses by highly specialized properties.

Trade names of these fibers are numerous, but their structural relationships remain like family characteristics.

NYLON

History. The history of nylon and other synthetic fibers has only begun. The dream of producing synthetic fibers is by no means new, but realization had to wait for chemistry, physics, and engineering to combine forces with fibers as the objective. Walter Hume Carothers led in the research. By 1930, fiber-forming polymers had been formed, and by 1932, basic work was published.

In September, 1938, U.S. Patent No. 2,130,948 was issued to cover the new family of fibers which was even then being produced on a pilot-plant scale. In October of that year, the discovery of a new synthetic fiber was announced by du Pont. Nylon is the generic term given to this group of structurally related synthetic fibers.[2] About 3,000 different compounds related to nylon had been investigated in Germany at the beginning of World War II, but none was reported to be of economic value.[3] The best developed at that time were the Perlons which are still of interest in Germany.

Production. Nylon has helped open a new field of fiber production. There are a number of sources of raw materials for the production of nylon: petroleum or coal products, nitrogen and oxygen from the air, and hydrogen from water may be used.[4] Part of the necessary raw materials may be secured from farm by-products such as cottonseed hulls, oat hulls, and corn cobs. In addition, there are other sources of raw materials used in producing the nylon resin. The resin is melted and extruded into ribbons or made into chips for storage. When ready to produce nylon filaments, the chips are melted again, filtered, metered, and forced through spinnerets to form filaments. While the spinning is in process, it is necessary that the equipment be above the temperature at which the nylon solidifies. This in itself is a problem.

The molten nylon has to be kept under an inert gas. As the nylon

[2] A.S.T.M. *Standards on Textile Materials*, 1950.
[3] Synthetic Fiber Team, T.I.I.C., *German Synthetic Fiber Development* (New York: Textile Research Institute, Inc., 1948).
[4] E. K. Bolton, "Development of Nylon," *Industrial and Engineering Chemistry*, 34 (1942), 53–58.

is spun, the fiber is drawn four to seven times the original length in order to develop the tensile strength and elasticity characteristic of this fiber.[5] About 3,000 feet of filament per minute are spun.

An unusual property in certain of the synthetic textile fibers is that of ductility, which permits cold drawing, a process which increases the crystallinity and reduces the denier of the fiber. The denier of the filament may vary between wide limits, from less than 1.0 up to any desired size. This represents a range from the finest filaments to coarse fibers of brushes and whisk brooms. The denier is determined in part by the rate at which the filaments are drawn away from the spinnerets and by the amount of cold drawing. Nylon may either be injection molded or extrusion molded for use in sheets, rods, tubes, bristles, powders, or filaments. Both staple fiber and filaments are available.

There are many nylons possible. The problem will be to find which one is best adapted to a specific use. The quantities of nylon produced have grown steadily since the first pilot plant was established.

Properties. The unusual properties of nylon resulted in ready acceptance for specific uses. Certain of the physical properties of nylon contribute greatly to the property which is spoken of as resistance to wear. Toughness, natural pliability, and high flexing qualities contribute to a high resistance to abrasion. Nylon is about as tough as silk but three times as tough as good viscose.

The moisture regain in nylon is 3.5 per cent under standard conditions of temperature and humidity. The density is 1.14, a very light fiber. Elasticity and strength are high. Many of the clothing and household uses of nylon depend largely upon the construction of the fabric and whether staple yarns or filament yarns are used.

When the filaments are extruded, the molecules are arranged in a more or less haphazard way; but after it has been drawn, the molecules assume a generally orderly arrangement parallel to the long axis of the fiber. The orderly arrangement of molecules in the fiber accounts in part for the high tensile strength of nylon. The low denier yarns have a lower tenacity and higher elongation than those of higher denier (Table 12.I).

It is necessary that nylon fabrics be heat "set" in order to develop a soft hand and dimensional stability and to increase the ability to recover from wrinkling. Heat and moisture produce a permanent set which can only be removed by a higher temperature. Heat, moisture, and pressure cause all fibers to be plastic in varying degrees. Nylon may soften at 356 F; therefore, it must be ironed only at a low temperature. The temperature can be tested on an inside facing or extra sample of the fabric.

[5] Bolton, "Development of Nylon," 53–58.

TABLE 12.I

TENSILE STRENGTH AND ELONGATION OF NYLON YARNS

Denier	Filament count	Type	Average tenacity range gm./den.	Average elongation range (%)
15	1	200	5.2–5.5	25–28
20	7	200	4.6–5.0	19–22
20	20	109	4.2–4.6	45–55
30	10	200	4.8–5.2	20–25
40	13	200	4.5–4.8	20–25
50	34	200	4.9–5.3	20–25
60	20	200	5.0–5.4	20–25
70	23	200	4.8–5.2	20–25
70	34	300	6.0–6.4	17–22
70	34	400	6.2–6.6	17–20
100	34	300	6.4–6.8	16–19
100	34	400	6.4–6.8	16–19
150	68	300	6.1–6.5	18–21
150	68	400	6.0–6.4	19–22
200	34	400	7.3–7.7	14–16
200	34	500	5.1–5.5	19–22
210	34	300	7.3–7.7	14–16

Source: Gordon Hazlewood, "Nylon, Some of Its Properties and Applications," *American Dyestuff Reporter,* 37-9 (1948), P295–P299.

Nylon is remarkably resistant to most chemicals.[6] It is inert to alkalies but is sensitive to most acids. Phenol or hot glacial acetic acid will dissolve nylon and may be used in fiber identification.

Certain insects such as clothes moths, cockroaches, black carpet beetles, firebrats, and some ants cut their way out of both nylon and silk but seem not to eat it for food. Microorganisms do little if any damage to the fiber, although certain finishes may support mildew.

Nylon is readily dyed with certain classes of dyestuffs. The acetate dyestuffs are satisfactorily used but are not so light fast as the acid dyes. Sunlight seriously reduces the strength and elongation of dull or semidull nylon. Nylon which is not delustered is about as resistant to sunlight as linen.

Consumption and Uses. The consumption of nylon has had a miraculous growth. The consumer learned in the years between 1910 and 1938 to accept manufactured fibers. The producer had learned much, since rayon was introduced, about the properties that make a fiber especially acceptable for specific purposes. It was not by accident that nylon was introduced in hosiery. The properties which made nylon especially adaptable to use in hosiery were a high elastic recovery and

[6] G. P. Hoff, "Nylon As a Textile Fiber," *Industrial and Engineering Chemistry,* 32 (1940), 1560–1564.

a high resistance to abrasion, combined with much desired sheerness. In addition, comparative figures show that nylon is easier to stretch than silk, wool, cotton, or rayon. It launders easily and dries quickly. The consumption of nylon has grown rapidly and steadily since it was placed on the open market about 1940 in the form of women's hosiery. About 125 million pounds of nylon were produced in 1951.

A study on ease of snagging nylon tricot knits showed that the higher deniers snagged more readily. Some of the factors which helped reduce snagging were increased twist and increased gauge.[7] In a preference study made by the U. S. Department of Agriculture, launderability and durability were high on the list of properties preferred.[8] Nylon fabrics have both.

The uses of a material which can be both injection and extrusion molded are legion. As a textile fiber, nylon is being used in increasing amounts in clothing for all ages and in many household fabrics where the special properties of nylon are most desirable.[9] Some of the industrial uses are in tire cord, brush bristles, tents, hammocks, awnings, and carpets.

VINYON

History. Vinyon is a development of the early 1930's. Its history is neither long nor old. The first compound of this type was prepared in 1838 by Regnault. In September, 1937, United States Patent No. 2,161,-766 was assigned to cover the fibers. Germany also produced a similar fiber, Pe-Ce.

Production. Commercial production of Vinyon was begun in 1939. The raw materials may be obtained from petroleum and coal. After the Vinyon is prepared, it is dispersed in a solvent, de-aerated, and spun by extrusion.

The fibers are heated under tension to 90 to 100 C and stretched to develop strength, elasticity, and resilience. The material will stretch until a yarn of 10 filaments is 8 denier or less, finer than silk. Staple or filament fiber may be produced. The fiber may have a crimp developed by controlled heat setting or by a suitable bath.

Vinyon may be delustered by the usual procedures of incorporating pigment into the solution before it is spun or by a less destructive new process using water.

Properties. The properties of Vinyon are such that it is not likely to be widely used for clothing. Because of the water-repellent nature,

[7] R. L. Kroll and K. R. Williams, "A Study of Nylon Tricot Snagging," *Rayon and Synthetic Textiles*, 30-9 (1949), 111–113.

[8] *Women's Preferences among Selected Textile Products*, Misc. Pub. 641, Bureau of Human Nutrition and Home Economics, United States Department of Agriculture (Washington, D. C.: Government Printing Office, 1947).

[9] Bolton, "Development of Nylon," 53–58.

the physical properties are not affected by changes in humidity. The wet and the dry strengths are therefore equal. The standard regain is 0.5 per cent. Even fibers soaked in water at 77 F for 168 hours absorbed only 0.5 per cent of their weight in water.

Vinyon fibers, like all other synthetic fibers, are thermoplastic. In fact, the extreme sensitivity of Vinyon to heat limits its use. Vinyon melts at 150 C.

At elevated temperatures, it will shrink 75 per cent of the extended length. Temperatures of ordinary laundry procedures cause shrinkage and distortion. It should not be ironed. The heat of the sun at a window can spoil the fabric.[10]

The strength may be varied within limits, but an increase in strength results in a reduction of elongation. This comes about because of the basic factors contributing to the two properties. The freshly spun Vinyon is very weak. There is little evidence of orderly arrangement of molecules even after stretching, and that disappears entirely when Vinyon shrinks.[11] It is highly extensible, however, and when stretched develops elasticity and strength. The stretching is reversible.[12] The amount of elongation of a fiber when stretched is related to the internal molecular structure, and for Vinyon the range is from 18 to 120 per cent. Vinyon behaves like rubber in that it can be stretched and contracted an indefinite number of times.[13] The degree of stretching of Vinyon determines the stiffness or softness of the fiber. The elasticity of Vinyon is comparable to that of silk.

It is a nonconductor of electricity as shown by its tendency to develop and retain a static charge. This is undesirable in clothing fabrics.

Because of its inert character, Vinyon is not attacked by molds, bacteria, or insects. It does not support combustion because of its chemical nature. It is only fairly stable to sunlight. Vinyon is exceptionally resistant to acids, alkalies, and a number of other reagents. This is one reason it has been useful in industry.

The dyeing of Vinyon has offered problems similar to those of dyeing cellulose acetate.[14] Resistance to the penetration of water and lack of affinity for dyestuffs are basic causes for the dyeing problem. The water insoluble acetate dyes with certain swelling agents, and a dyebath below 65 C make it possible to dye Vinyon. Some reagents cause Vinyon to swell and permit the dye molecules to migrate into the fiber

[10] Reginald L. Wakeman, "The Chemistry of Commercial Plastics," *American Dyestuff Reporter*, 38-24 (1949), P856–P867.

[11] W. T. Astbury, "X-ray Studies of the Structure of Plastics," *Dyestuffs*, 39-3 (1946), 79–83.

[12] Karl Heymann, "Vinyon," *American Dyestuff Reporter*, 30 (1941), 575.

[13] Frederic Bonnet, "Vinyon," *Industrial and Engineering Chemistry*, 32 (1940), 1564–1567.

[14] Bonnet, "Vinyon," 1564–1567.

structure. Some oil soluble dyes are used. It is also possible to incorporate dye pigment into the liquid Vinyon before the spinning process.

There are three important factors in aging of the vinyl resins—namely heat, light, and loss of plasticizer.

Consumption and Uses. The consumption and use of Vinyon have been limited to those areas in which its inert character is an advantage and its low melting point is not a disadvantage. Some industrial uses are filter cloths, anode bags, special clothing for industry, and bolting cloth for the milling industry, sail cloth, cordage, fish lines, tennis rackets, and nets. Vinyon is also made into veils, shoes, felts for hats, hat trimmings, and gloves for wearing apparel. Because of its high crease resistance, Vinyon is mixed with other fibers for wearing apparel. Various modifications of Vinyon may be made and used as finishes for fabrics. Because of the difficulty in ironing fabrics made from fibers with low softening point, it has been thought that Vinyon would be more satisfactory in knitted than in woven apparel fabrics. The knitting properties of the fiber are said to be excellent. Vinyon is readily laundered and dried at reduced temperatures.

SARAN

Saran, as a fiber, was not dreamed of in 1922; yet at that time, Brooks observed the basic reaction for the preparation of such a fiber. Saran was studied before World War II in Germany where it was considered to be an improvement over the German Pe-Ce fiber in strength, pliability, and softening point.[15]

The raw materials are petroleum and salt. After the fiber material is formed, it has to be heated to about 350 C before extrusion.

Velon (similar to Saran) is another of the synthetic fibers which behaves as a metal and has to be drawn to about four times its original length in order to develop strength. Velon softens at 170 to 284 F. Saran has a softening point which may vary from 150 to 280 F. This property will probably limit the use of both Velon and Saran in apparel fabrics. The moisture regain under standard conditions is about 0.1 per cent. The fibers are tough, extremely resistant to fatigue, waterproof, abrasion resistant, and are not easily soiled.[16] Since these fibers are quite inert to ordinary chemical action, they are unaffected by acids and alkalies, except for strong ammonium hydroxide.

The specialized uses of Velon and Saran are numerous. They consti-

---

[15] Synthetic Fiber Team, TIIC, *German Synthetic Fiber Developments* (New York: Textile Research Institute, 1946).

Pe-Ce consisted of 80–85 per cent vinylidene chloride and 15–20 per cent vinyl chloride.

[16] W. C. Goggins and R. D. Lowery, "Vinylidene Chloride Polymers," *Industrial and Engineering Chemistry*, 34 (1942), 327–332.

H. R. Mauersberger, "Vinylidene Chloride Yarns Now Woven into Goods," *Rayon Textile Monthly*, 23-2 (1942), 615.

tute one of the largest groups of monofilaments being used to replace hemp, paper, reed, rattan, and horsehair.   Saran is used for upholstery fabrics in buses, outdoor furniture, and auto seat covers.   Velon is used for similar purposes and, in addition, is used for belts, suspenders, shoes, millinery, handbags, and filter cloths.   The multifilaments of these fibers should be useful in certain clothing and household fabrics.   At present, *also multi* only monofilaments are produced.   Yarns of other fibers such as rayon, cotton, and linen may be coated with the vinylidene polymer.

About 18 million pounds of Saran were produced in 1951.

DYNEL

The original work on Dynel was carried out in Germany, but the German processes were found not to be practicable.   The first successful process for making a textile fiber of this type was covered by United States Patent No. 2,404,714, July 23, 1946.   There are a number of related fibers of this type.   Only Dynel and Orlon are discussed here.

In order to produce Dynel successfully, new solvents had to be developed which would dissolve the compound in order to permit spinning.   The solvent was then evaporated, leaving the fiber intact. Stretching the filaments reduces the denier and increases the orientation of the molecules and the strength.   The filament sizes range from 2 to 24 denier, and lengths vary.

The fibers may be made in multifilament or monofilament yarns and in staple fibers.   The composition may be modified by incorporating other materials such as those used for nylon in the spinning solutions. The modifications are infinite.   The acetate dyestuffs are applied at the boiling point.   The fiber shrinks at 285 F.

The fibers are resistant to the action of heat, ultraviolet light, gasoline, inorganic acids, molds, bacteria, weathering, and abrasion.   Dynel retains the desirable properties of the regular Vinyon to which it is related. Like Vinyon it dries rapidly but, in addition, has increased resistance to heat and organic solvents.   Such valuable properties should be utilized in places where other fabrics fail to meet requirements.

Added to the usual things for which such resistant fibers are used, is hosiery, both seamless and full-fashioned.   Other suggested applications include industrial filter fabrics, tapes, and braids for electrical insulation, tent fabrics, protective clothing, netting, shoe fabrics, marine lines and twines, surgical sutures, fishing lines, dental floss, sewing threads for some purposes, sail cloth, awnings, upholstery and umbrella fabrics, chemically resistant hose, gasket packing, and a number of other products such as window curtains and drapery fabrics, clothing in the tropics, and bathing suits.   It will be necessary, however, to improve dyeing properties if Dynel is to compete with nylon in apparel uses. This may be done.

About four million pounds were produced in 1951.

ORLON

Orlon is very similar in composition to Dynel. The fibers are dry spun (see p. 189) and the solvent removed by evaporation and by extraction in water. Drawing the fiber to several times its length causes the molecules to align themselves more or less parallel with the lengthwise axis of the fiber. This causes the molecular chains in the fiber to become oriented (more crystalline). The oriented fibers are stiffer but have satisfactory strength, are wrinkle resisting, and are launderable.[17] Orlon fibers can be made either as continuous-filament or as staple of any desired length. The fibers can be formed into novelty yarns with other fibers, either natural or synthetic.

In general, Orlon is quite resistant to chemical action, not so much to alkalies, but especially so to acids and the action of ultraviolet light. High resistance to heat, microorganisms, acid, and outdoor exposure suggest such uses as automobile tops, awnings, curtains, sails, and tents. Other uses for this water-repellent fiber are rainwear, shirting, uniforms, laboratory coats, and beachwear. Good resistance to flexing, to sunlight, and to abrasion suggest usefulness in work clothes and children's play clothes. Most of the fibers are difficult to dye, but new pigments have helped.[18]

Monofilaments are suggested for use in the manufacture of rattan-like fabrics for furniture or for bristles and window screening, where their light weight, low water absorption, and high resistance to ultraviolet light, sulfur fumes, and salt air are important. Because of their high flexibility and durability, screens made of coarse Orlon fibers can be rolled up when not in use, thus permitting their incorporation as an integral part of the window structure.

Interest in fibers of the type of Orlon seems to be centered in a number of laboratories in the United States. About eight million pounds were produced in 1951. No comparable work was found in Germany.[19]

DACRON

Dacron is the trademarked name of a new type of fiber that has many properties similar to the preceding ones. The molten mass is spun, then drawn. The undrawn fibers have little strength, great elongation, and dye readily. The drawn fiber has more strength, less elongation, and less affinity for dyes. Wet strength is almost the same as the dry. Temperatures of 365 to 375 F are used to stabilize the fabric against shrinkage in subsequent ironing or pressing.

[17] William E. Larsen, Robert A. Schneiderbauer, and Robert E. Wilfond, "Orlon, Acrylic Fiber," *Scientific Monthly*, 69-6 (1949), 414–418.
[18] J. G. Quig, "Orlon in the Canvas Goods Industry," *Rayon and Synthetic Textiles*, 31-1 (1950), 64.
[19] Synthetic Fiber Team, TIIC, *German Synthetic Fiber Development*, 1948.

Dacron, like other synthetic fibers, has highly specialized properties and uses. Ordinary dry-cleaning solvents, hot dilute mineral acids, and bleaches have little or no effect. The fiber is reasonably stable to alkali. At standard conditions, the moisture regain is less than 1 per cent. Microorganisms do not attack it. The fabric should be useful for outdoor purposes, filter cloths, and possible tire cords. At present, Dacron is being used in sewing thread, shirting fabrics, men's suitings, doll's wigs, and even nose wipers on Arctic mittens. The fiber may be produced as either a multifilament or monofilament yarn.

As a monofilament, it has been suggested for the manufacture of chemically resistant screening and filtering media, and for mosquito and similar netting where high tensile strength must be achieved in an open structure fabric. About three million pounds were produced in 1951.

Terylene is a British fiber similar to Dacron and has a melting point of 256 F.[20] Terylene has been found very satisfactory for production of strong durable fabrics for tents to be used in tropical climates.[21]

OTHER NEW FIBERS

There are many synthetic fibers, some of which have strange and interesting possibilities. Others will be developed. The fibers described below illustrate some of the properties and uses of the new fibers.

Polythene. Fibers of this type are produced in both this country and England. The fibers were introduced in the United States about 1943. Germany had begun work on them about 1937, but the military did not realize the value of such a fiber in the war effort and allowed neither man power nor materials to develop and produce the fiber.[22] It would have served well as a substitute for jute for burlap bags because of its resistance to bacteria and rotting. A number of fibers of this type is known.

Polythene is a generic term for a fiber produced directly from liquid polyethylene under pressures of over 1,000 atmospheres. The rate at which the solution is spun as well as the pressure used determine the molecular weight of the fiber.[23] Polythene is useful for fibers only when the molecular weight is between 18,000 and 20,000.

The solid polymer may be molded by extrusion, injection, or compression. Fibers are formed by extruding the molten polymer through spinnerets. They are solidified by cooling, and are wound on spools or bobbins. The molecules are fully oriented by stretching the filament to about five times its original length.

[20] William H. Cady, "Terylene," *American Dyestuff Reporter*, 37-21 (1948), 699.
[21] K. Turner, "Terylene," *Textile Colorist and Converter*, 69-1 (1947), 22.
[22] Synthetic Fiber Team, TIIC, *German Fiber Development*, 1946.
[23] Frederick C. Holen, Maurice L. Macht, and David A. Fletcher, "Polyethylene," *Industrial and Engineering Chemistry*, 37 (1945), 526.

The physical properties are adapted only to unusual uses. There are two types of polythene fibers.[24] Fabric from Type A fibers may be stabilized to less than a 2 per cent change over a limited range of temperatures, 150 to 165 F. Otherwise, automobile seat covers would shrink in the sun to become unusable. Type B shrinks 15 to 20 per cent at 150 F. To preshrink either fabric, it is wrapped on a decating machine (see p. 315) and treated with steam at 212 F or fed through a hot water bath.[25] The melting points may range from 212 to 248 F. The fiber is insoluble in all organic solvents until about 122 to 140 F. Then it will dissolve in certain solvents. Polythene is the only fiber so far which has a density less than that of water, 0.92. Rope or fabric made from polythene fiber will float on water. Polythene fibers are tough, flexible, abrasion resistant, have good tensile strength (the same wet as dry), and good elasticity, but have a slow rate of recovery.[26] They do not absorb water, which probably explains the equal wet and dry tensile strengths.

The chemical nature probably explains the "waxy" hand of the fabric. With no reactive groups the fiber is as inert as paraffin. Dyeing does not present a serious problem, since a range of colors are made possible by the incorporation of colored pigments. No materials as chemically inert as polythene will be affected by bacteria, molds, or insects.[27]

Some advantages of polythene fibers are low specific gravity, low water absorption, and resistance to microorganisms. Some disadvantages are its inflammability and low melting point. Some of the uses listed by the manufacturers are watch straps, fabrics for sail cloth, balloon fabrics, foundation garments, brassieres, suspenders, rugs, carpets, blankets, laboratory and surgical aprons. For most of the latter uses, it would be necessary to give the fabrics a permanent fire-resistant finish because polythene itself is too inflammable to use in wearing apparel. Many uses will be found for fibers with properties such as polythene.

Teflon. Teflon is a fiber similar in structure to polythene, but it differs in composition and behavior. This fiber resists the action of heat up to 620 F and decomposes at 750 F. The fiber is naturally fire resistant. It may be used in heat-resistant clothes. It was used during the war for electrical insulation, gaskets, and piping.

The fiber is inert to most chemical reagents. As a result, it dyes poorly. It is insoluble in most solvents as well as in hot and cold water. The molecular weight varies.

[24] Synthetic Fiber Team, TIIC, *German Fiber Development,* 1946.

[25] Textile Research Department, American Viscose Corporation, "The Finishing of Polyethylene Fibers," *Rayon and Synthetic Textiles,* 30-12 (1949), 61.

[26] Holen, Macht, and Fletcher, "Polyethylene," 526.

[27] William P. Crowley, "Polythene As a Textile Fiber," *Rayon and Synthetic Textiles,* 30-9 (1949), 91–92.

Polyfiber. Polystyrene has been known for 100 years, but it has been made into fibers only recently. The polystyrene fibers known as Polyfiber were introduced into this country in 1944. Germany had little success in trying to orient polystyrene for sheets or filaments and the fibers were brittle.

Polyfiber is drawn like glass fibers from a molten mass. The fibers produced in this country soften at 220 to 230 F. The most remarkable property is its fineness. Its diameter ranges from 1/50 to 4 microns. The fiber is highly oriented, but temperatures around 220 F cause shrinkage which reduces the orientation.

Polyfiber fibers are considered to be of value in insulation, felts, shoe linings, carpets, padding, and as a substitute for kapok in emergency rescue equipment. The fiber is difficult to wet.

Chapter Thirteen

Inorganic Fibers

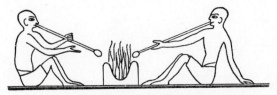

Fig. 13.1. An ancient art.

UNTIL RECENTLY, THE INORGANIC FIBERS, with the exception of asbestos, have been of limited value.

FIBERGLAS

History. According to a recent definition, glass is a "material obtained by melting oxides or combinations of oxides, or substances that yield oxides on thermal decomposition and so cooling the resultant fusion that crystallization does not occur." [1] Coarse, brittle, nonuniform glass filaments were found in tombs of early Egyptians and in the ruins of Pompeii. From this early date until the latter part of the 19th century, comparatively little was done about glass fibers.[2] Interest continued, however, as shown by the fact that patents for forming glass fibers were among the first granted by the United States Patent Office,

[1] A.S.T.M. Committee D-13, *A.S.T.M. Standards on Textile Materials*, 1944, 4.
[2] J. K. Park, "Fiberglas in Industry," *American Dyestuff Reporter*, 39-2 (1950), P59–P62.

established in 1770. About 1900, several German patents were issued.

In 1893, Edward D. Libby succeeded in drawing fibers from the end of a heated glass rod. The coarse fibers were combined with silk to make a lampshade for the Columbian Exposition in Chicago. An actress who saw the fabric decided as a publicity stunt to have a dress and umbrella made of glass. After she got the fabric, there was difficulty in getting a seamstress to make the dress and umbrella. It was necessary to line the dress before the actress could wear it, even then she could not sit in the dress. A Spanish princess saw the actress and was so pleased with the novelty that she also ordered a dress. It is said to have cost her $30,000. One of these two dresses is reported to be in existence today.

Production. There is not just one glass. There are many glasses. Nor is glass a chemical compound. It is a mixture. Usually glass is 60 per cent or more sand, chiefly silica (SiO_2) with various percentages of two or more oxides of sodium, calcium, potassium, lead, gold, magnesium, or aluminum. The oxides are added until a bubbling liquid mass is formed at a blinding white heat of about 2,700 F.[3]

Special formulae had to be developed so that the very fine fibers would resist weathering and corrosion. It should be of interest that since 1880, over 50,000 different formulae for glass have been melted, and the properties of each melt studied systematically. Of the 600 different glasses melted commercially to make thousands of things for thousands of uses, the different glasses can all be classified into five types (Table 13.I).

TABLE 13.I

EARLY USE OF GLASSES

Type	Date
1. Soda-lime	2000 B.C.
2. Lime	1674 A.D.
3. Boro-silicates	1910
4. Fused silica	1910
5. 96% silica glass	1939

It is the 96 per cent silica glass that tends to have the greatest mechanical durability and is of special interest in a study of fibers. When it was learned that the flexibility of glass is a function of its diameter, and the glass filaments were drawn finer and finer, fibrous glass fabrics became useful articles, not just novelties.

Interest in producing fibers from glass was increased when fibrous glass was accidentally produced in 1931 while fusing colored glass on

[3] H. G. Vogt, *The Evolution of Modern Glass*, Walker Announcer 49, (Minneapolis: Geo. T. Walker and Co., 3–34).

milk bottles. The possibilities of a glass fiber industry were explored. Experimentation soon put production of fibers for air filters and thermal insulation on a commercial basis. By 1935, fibers suitable for weaving were possible. The following year, a plant was set up for production of glass fibers for textile uses. In 1938, the companies concerned formed a joint corporation for producing fiber and named it Fiberglas.[4]

The Fiberglas fabric of today, made from the high percentage silica glass, bears slight resemblance to those early pieces of cloth. The fabrics may be made soft, and they drape well. Today, Fiberglas is produced by feeding marbles of specially refined glass into an electrically heated oven. As the molten glass is forced through spinnerets under

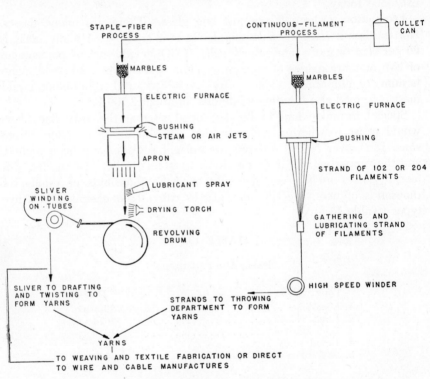

Fig. 13.2. Production of glass fiber yarns.

high pressure, the fibers are caught on a rotating wheel or if blown by steam under pressure are then passed through a burst of flame to dry them.

Properties. The properties of Fiberglas are those of the most brittle, the least resilient, and the least flexible of the textile fibers.

Physical properties. Even though man knew glass over 5,000 years ago, there is still lack of agreement on some of its properties. Some of

---

[4] "Fiberglas Textiles," *Textile Research*, 12-5 (1942), 11.

the properties of glass are not found in other fibers to the same extent. Glass fibers, manufactured from inorganic material, will not burn but will melt. They may be manufactured either as continuous filaments or as staple fibers of spinnable length, usually 8 to 15 inches long. Any diameter may be produced from about 22/100,000 of an inch to as large as desired.

The tensile strength is higher than that of metals (see Table 14.VIII). The specific gravity is 2.5, therefore Fiberglas fabrics are heavy. Fiberglas is one of the best electrical insulators. The fiber has no cellular structure. It is readily cleaned, but handling the fabric may cause damage to the brittle fibers.

It is now possible to heat set glass fibers with temperatures from 1200 to 1250 F and to follow by a resin finish which produces a softer hand and adds abrasion resistance to the fabric. Temperature-resistant fibers have been produced. These fibers soften at 2000 F instead of 1000 F as is usual for ordinary glasses. They lack resiliency and elongation. They are fairly brittle and break when bent.

Chemical properties. Glass, when so finely divided as it is in fibers, is sensitive to the action of reagents which normally have minor or no effect.[5] Strong alkalies will disintegrate glass fibers. Microorganisms and insects, however, can do no harm. The fibers cannot burn; nor can they rot or rust. They resist the action of all acids except hydrofluoric and phosphoric. Dirts and stains stay on the surface of the fiber because the fibers are not absorbent. For this same reason, the fibers do not dye well. Special pigmented resin applications have added to the range of colors possible. Color is applied to glass after it is spun (or to the cloth) because of the optical illusion that color comes with depth or thickness. Applied colors can now be permanent.

Consumption and Uses. It is expected that the consumption of glass fibers will be confined chiefly to industrial uses, possibly to drapery in public buildings, and some household uses. It is not considered promising as a fiber for clothing.

With few exceptions, the only uses of glass fibers, until 1931, were in such items as neckties, small mats, and baskets. Fiberglas is used extensively today in filter cloths, anode bags, tapes and ribbons, yarns, parachute flare shades, awnings, sandbags, lamp shades, insulation, curtains, and chiefly draperies. It can be woven, laminated, or braided but is not suitable for knitting.[6]

During the war the production of glass fibers was increased by the Germans to provide a substitute for asbestos and materials for electrical insulation.

This country produced about 40 million pounds of Fiberglas in 1951.

[5] *Loc. cit.*
[6] James Slayter, "Fiberglas," *Industrial and Engineering Chemistry*, 32 (1940), 1568–1571.

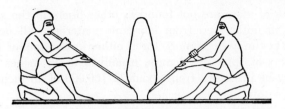

Fig. 13.3. Theban glass blowers.

ASBESTOS

Asbestos is a fibrous silicate which occurs naturally in various combinations as white, grayish, or greenish masses of compact or long silky fibers.[7] The fiber is in the form of rock which is mined from the earth. Asbestos is found in widely scattered places but is of commercial value in Canada, Vermont, Arizona, Russia, Cypress, and South America. Asbestos is already thousands of years old when it is mined from the earth. Canada supplies as much of the fiber as all the rest of the earth together. There are two principal varieties: chrysotile and crocidolite. Chrysotile fibers, found chiefly in Canada and Russia, are long and silky ones and are of most value for spinning and weaving. They also withstand higher temperatures than the other type and are chiefly magnesium silicate. Crocidolite, found in South Africa and Australia, is an iron silicate.

The first step in production is mining the rock. The fibers are then partially separated by machinery, straightened to a satisfactory degree, and blended before carding and rolling mechanically into a roving.

Specifications of the American Society for Testing Materials cover the properties of asbestos products for different uses. Fiber obtained from rock from different sources has different properties and, for that reason, is to a certain extent designated for specific uses. The Canadian fiber has a high magnesium content and is especially temperature resistant. The nonferrous types are better where high electrical resistance is required.

Although asbestos constitutes only a very small percentage of our total fiber supply, it is a most essential one. Its uses are varied. Safety garments such as leggings, gloves, hats, aprons, hoods, and even suits are widely used. Asbestos had many industrial uses before the war and has a limited use in curtains, even dish towels! It is claimed that the advantage of such a dish towel is that it can be cleaned by burning. The idea, however, is not new, as history records the use of asbestos sleeve ruffles for a similar reason and probably better cause—early methods of laundering were crude.

[7] Ingo W. Hackh, *A Chemical Dictionary* (Philadelphia: P. Blakiston's Sons & Co., 1929).

METAL

As early as the Middle Ages, the drawing of silver and gold into fine threads for weaving was a recognized industry.

Today, steel and aluminum as well as gold and silver are made into fibers. Aluminum in various colors is being used in narrow strips with cottons and rayons to produce decorative yarns. Very thin sheets of aluminum foil are coated on both sides with a colored film before cutting into the very narrow strips used in fabrics and yarns. Although the yarns do not tarnish and are washable, they are sensitive to abrasion, high ironing temperatures, and certain solvents.

Fabrics made entirely from metals have only specialized uses. Stainless steel may be made with a diameter of 0.0011 to 0.0021 inches with a strength of 119,000 pounds per square inch. It can be made into fabric with 40,000 interstices per square inch. It has 200 steel filaments per inch in each direction.

It is of historic interest that the golden damask curtains of the Metropolitan Opera House fell for the last time when the season ended in 1940. The fabric, however, still had value, both sentimental and commercial. It was sold for covers for spectacle cases.

Chapter Fourteen

Summary and Comparisons of Fiber Properties

AT PRESENT, it is not possible to compare systematically all of the properties of any of the fibers. There are a number of reasons for this. No exhaustive studies have been made in which the properties of fibers have all been tested under comparable conditions. For example, unless the strength of fibers is tested under uniform conditions of temperature and humidity and the data are calculated on the same basis, comparisons are not valid. It is to be hoped that suitable materials, methods, equipment, money and personnel will soon be available for such a comprehensive piece of work.[1]

In the meantime, some comparisons of properties of fibers can be made including the general methods of spinning the manufactured fibers to produce the fiber or filament yarns. There are three general methods by which manufactured fibers are spun. Fibers such as viscose and cuprammonium rayons are spun from a water solution and are said to be wet spun. Fibers such as cellulose acetate, Vinyon, and Orlon are spun from a dry solvent and are said to be dry spun. Fibers such as nylon and Dacron are melted and extruded in the molten state and are said to be melt spun. The method of spinning depends in part upon

---

[1] William D. Appel, "A Survey of the Synthetic Fibers," *American Dyestuff Reporter*, 34-1 (1945), P21.

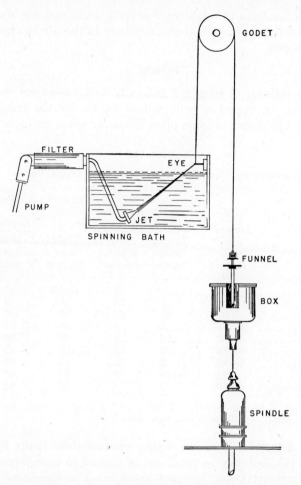

Fig. 14.1. Wet spinning. *Source: Claude Diamond,* "The Manufacture of Modern Textile Fibers," RAYON TEXTILE MONTHLY, *28-4 (1947), 123–126.*

the chemical and physical nature of the material being spun and in part upon the economy of the process.

The fundamental properties of fibers are the same for all and are: [2]

    a) properties of form
    b) physical properties
    c) chemical properties

When these properties are measured, characteristic values are found for each kind of fiber. Comparisons of the fiber properties and selection

[2] Harold DeWitt Smith, *Textile Fibers, An Engineering Approach to Their Properties and Utilization* (Philadelphia: American Society for Testing Materials, 1944).

of fabrics on the basis of relative value for a given end use should lead to greater consumer satisfaction and economy in the use of clothing and household fabrics.

FORM

The characteristics of form are generally well known for the natural fibers but can be varied at will, within limits, for the manufactured fibers. The dimensions of some plant fibers are given in Table 14.I.

TABLE 14.I

QUANTITATIVE COMPARISON OF CERTAIN COMMON FIBERS

| Fiber name | Approximate staple, inches | SINGLE CELL (data by A. Herzog) | | | Approximate area | |
| | | Approximate linear dimensions (limits or averages) | | | | |
		Length, millimeters	Width, microns	Thickness, microns	Wall, per cent	Lumen, per cent
Cotton	½–2¼	..	25	10–25	97	3
Kapok	Up to 1½	..	20	20	19	81
Flax	2–24	30	25	20	98	2
Manila	72–144	2	25	25	87	13
Italian hemp	40–80	25	25	18	96	4
Jute	48–84	3	20	20	89	11
Mexican sisal	30–48	3	25	25	91	9
Ramie	2–24	140	55	30	96	4
New Zealand hemp ..	40–60	4	15	15	92	8

Source: Edward Robinson Schwarz, *Textiles and the Microscope,* 1st ed. (New York: McGraw-Hill Book Co., Inc., 1934).

Length. Length is confined within characteristic limits for natural fibers, even silk, but may be produced as desired in manufactured fibers. The manufactured fibers, in most cases, may be produced either as filaments or as staple fibers. All of the natural fibers except silk are staple fibers. Wild silk and silk from cocoons from which the moths have escaped, however, can be used solely for staple production. The fiber cells of flax, Italian hemp, and ramie are long enough to spin into yarns.

Cross Section. The cross sections of fibers are generally characteristic except for certain of the manufactured fibers. Some quantitative measurements of the single cells of seed hairs and of bast fibers provide a basis for comparisons of the cross sections of these fibers (see Table 14.I). The diameters (widths) of the cells of bast fibers are as great as or greater than that of cotton fibers. Except in kapok, the cell wall occupies most of the cross-sectional area of the fiber. Kapok has a very thin cell wall and a large lumen. The thickness differs from the diameter in flattened cells only.

The cross-sectional area and the density of a fiber are related to fineness, which is the mass per unit length and may be expressed in a number of ways—grex and denier are familiar (see p. 32, fn 14).

Crimp. Crimp is a natural characteristic of wool fibers. Attempts are often made, with varying degrees of success, to produce a permanent crimp in the manufactured fibers in order to make them like wool.

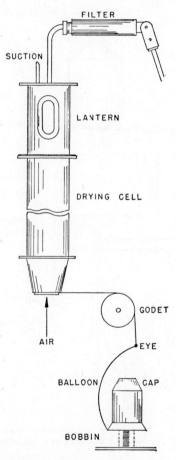

Fig. 14.2. Dry solvent spinning. *Source: Diamond, loc. cit.*

Surface Characteristics. The microscopic appearance of the surface of certain of the fibers, e.g., wool and cotton, are a guide to their origin.[3] It is necessary for many fibers to be distinguished chemically.

[3] A.S.T.M. Committee D-13, *A.S.T.M., Standards on Textile Materials*, 1950, 72–91.

Werner Von Bergen and Walter Krauss, *Textile Fiber Atlas* (New York: American Wool Handbook Co., 1948).

Frequently, both microscopic and chemical examination have to be made.

It is only, however, by the use of the microscope that the surface characteristics can be examined in detail. The manufactured fibers have some longitudinal and cross-sectional markings which are characteristic (Table 14.II).

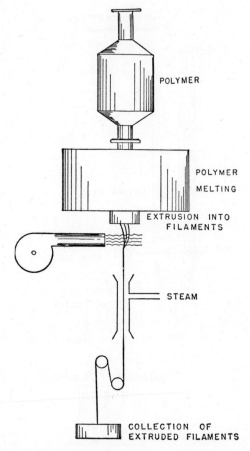

POLYMER

POLYMER

MELTING

EXTRUSION INTO FILAMENTS

STEAM

COLLECTION OF EXTRUDED FILAMENTS

Fig. 14.3. Melt spinning. *Source: Diamond, loc. cit.*

The bast fibers have much in common in appearance because of their similar origin in plant stems. Identification is not always definite (Table 14.III).

Cotton is usually easy to identify.

Animal fibers such as wool, mohair, and camel hair are identified microscopically by observing "the size and shape of the scales, presence or absence of color granules in the cortex, presence and size of the medulla, and the diameter of the fiber." [4]

TABLE 14.II

MICROSCOPICAL APPEARANCE OF MANUFACTURED FIBERS

Fiber	Longitudinal appearance	Cross-sectional appearance
Acetate rayon; saponified acetate	Broad striations	Smoothly rounded lobes
Cupra rayon	No markings	Small, nearly round
Viscose rayon	Numerous striations	Shape variable, edge serrated
High-tenacity viscose rayon	Indistinct striations	All shapes, indistinct striations
Vicara	Smooth or faintly grainy surface, occasional faint striations	Nearly round
Nylon	Smooth, rod-like	Round
Vinyon, Vinyon N	Broad striations	Dumbbell shape
Dynel	Broad striations	Irregular lobes
Orlon	Broad striations	Dumbbell shape, sometimes clover leaf
Dacron	Smooth or faintly grainy surface	Round
Fiberglas	Smooth	Round

Source: American Association of Textile Chemists and Colorists, *Technical Manual and Year Book, Test Methods, XXVII* (New York: Howe Publishing Co., Inc., 1951), 111.

TABLE 14.III

MICROSCOPICAL APPEARANCE OF BAST FIBERS

	Joints	Lumen	Natural ends	Cross-section shape	Cross-section lumen
Flax line	Present	Narrow	Pointed	Sharp polygons	Small, round
Flax tow	Present	Broad	Pointed	Sharp polygons	Larger, oval or round
Ramie	Present	Broad	Blunt	Elongated rounded polygons	Polygons with radial cracks
Hemp	Present	Broad, indistinct	Blunt	Rounded polygons	Cleft-shaped
Jute	Absent	Broad, variable	Blunt	Sharp polygons	Oval or round

Source: American Association of Textile Chemists and Colorists, *Technical Manual and Year Book, Test Methods, XXVII* (New York: Howe Publishing Co., Inc., 1951), 111.

The microscopic appearance of various fibers and standard methods for their identification have been described by Committee D-13 of American Society for Testing Materials.

[4] American Association of Textile Chemists and Colorists, *Technical Manual and Year Book, Test Methods, XXVII* (New York: Howe Publishing Co., Inc., 1951), 110.

PHYSICAL PROPERTIES

The fundamental physical properties of fibers largely determine the beauty, wear, and uses of the fabrics made from them.

Density. The density of a fiber is the ratio of the mass of the fibers to that of an equal volume of water (Table 14.IV). Density of fibers affects the weight of fabrics.

TABLE 14.IV

DENSITY OF FIBERS

Fiber	Density
(Water	1.00)
Polythene	.92
Nylon	1.14
Orlon	1.17
Dynel	1.2
Tussah silk	1.27
Vicara	1.29
Wool	1.30
Soybean	1.31
Camel hair and mohair	1.32
Estron, cellulose acetate	1.33
Silk, raw	1.33
Silk, degummed	1.35
Vinyon	1.35
Hemp and jute	1.48
Flax	1.50
Ramie	1.51
Cuprammonium rayon, Bemberg	1.52
Fortisan	1.52
Viscose rayon	1.53–1.56
Cotton	1.55
Saran	1.68–1.75
Calcium algenate	1.78
Teflon	2.1–2.2
Asbestos	2.1–2.8
Fiberglas	2.56
Steel	7.7
Silver	10.5
Gold	19.3
Platinum	21.4

Note:

$$\text{Density} = \frac{\text{Weight of substance}}{\text{Weight of an equal volume of water}}$$

The present fibers vary in density from polythene, which is lighter than water, to Fiberglas, which is over twice as heavy as water.

Moisture Absorption. The absorption of moisture is a characteristic property of most fibers. The mechanical behavior of fibers is affected by the moisture content as well as by time and temperature. It is necessary, therefore, that standard conditions of temperature and humidity be used for testing these properties. In this country, standard conditions are 65 ± 2 per cent relative humidity [5] and 70 ± 2 F. The international standards are within these limits but not exactly the same as those used in the United States. In Europe, laboratories are usually colder than in this country.

Moisture regain under standard conditions varies greatly among the fibers (Table 14.V).

TABLE 14.V

MOISTURE REGAIN OF SOME FIBERS AT 65 PER CENT
RELATIVE HUMIDITY AND 70° F.

Fiber	Per cent regain
Velon	0
Saran	0
Dynel	0.4
Vinyon	0.5
Orlon	1–2
Nylon	4
Estron	6.5
Cotton	7
Flax	8
Fortisan	9.8
Mercerized cotton	11
Viscose	11–12
Silk	11
Wool	13–16
Vicara	13
Peanut	15
Soybean	13–16

Source: G. Lousby and H. O. Puls, "Effect of Moisture on Nylon Yarns and Fabrics," *Journal of the Textile Institute*, 38-1 (1947), 30.

Those fibers whose regain is highest also swell the most readily in water. Likewise they are the most readily dyed.[6]

Fiber	Regain	Dyeability
Peanut	14.8	Good
Casein	13.6	Good
Corn, zein	13.0	Good
Soybean	12.9	Good
Nylon	4.2	Moderate
Orlon	0.9	Poor
Terylene	0.4	Poor
Vinyon	0	Poor

When fibers absorb moisture to an appreciable extent, several changes occur, among them lateral swelling which may be observed with a microscope fitted with an eyepiece micrometer (Table 14.VI).

[5] % relative humidity $= \dfrac{\text{pressure of water vapor present in air} \times 100}{\text{pressure of saturated water vapor at same temperature}}$

[6] R. W. Speke, "The Dyeing of New Fibres," *Fibres*, 11-1 (1950), 28.

TABLE 14.VI

COMPARATIVE DATA ON THE SWELLING OF FIBERS IN WATER

Fiber	Cross-sectional swelling, per cent	Longitudinal swelling, per cent
Vinyon CF	0.2	
Nylon	1.6–3.2	
Vinyon CN	4.3	
Orlon	5.1	
Acetate	7.9	
Aralac	19	
Silk	19–20	1.3–1.7
Cotton	20–26	1.3
Fortisan (high-tenacity acetate)	22	
Wool	22–26	1.2
Mercerized cotton	24	
Ramie (bleached)	37	
Rayon	44–86	0.7–7.0
Flax (tow)	47	
Viscose (high tenacity)	50	
Viscose (regular tenacity)	51–65	
Cuprammonium	56	

Source: Frederick F. Morehead, "Cross-sectional Swelling of Textile Fibers," *Textile Research Journal*, 18-2 (1947), 96.

The amount of moisture absorbed by fibers frequently determines their end uses. Undergarments, shirts, and socks are, in general, thought to be more comfortable when made of rather absorbent fibers. Diapers and dish towels should be made from fibers which rapidly absorb large amounts of water. Both the rate and amount of absorption are important. Rain coats should be made from fibers such as Dynel, which does not absorb moisture, or from fabrics treated with water-repellent finishes.

Stress-strain Behavior. The stress-strain behavior of fibers is described by the five basic mechanical (physical) properties of fibers. These properties help to produce the service qualities of fabrics (Table 14.VII).

TABLE 14.VII

BASIC MECHANICAL PROPERTIES OF MATERIALS

Properties	Service rendered
Strength	To carry a dead load
Stiffness	To carry a load without deformation
Elasticity	To undergo deformation and return to original shape upon cessation of deforming force
Resilience	To absorb shock without permanent deformation
Toughness	To endure large, permanent deformations without rupture

Source: Harold DeWitt Smith, *Textile Fibers, An Engineering Approach to Their Properties and Utilization* (Philadelphia: American Society for Testing Materials, 1944), vol. 44.

Strength is an important property of fibers and can vary within wide limits for the majority of fibers. The strength of a fiber is a measure of the force necessary to rupture it and is dependent to a certain extent upon the rate at which the load is applied.[7]

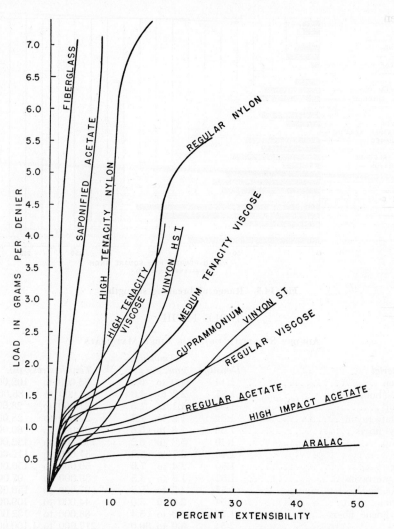

Fig. 14.4. **Typical stress-strain curves of manufactured fibers.**

[7] Harold DeWitt Smith, *Textile Fibers, an Engineering Approach to Their Properties and Utilization* (Philadelphia: American Society for Testing Materials, 1944), vol. 44.

Irving J. Saxl, "Some Fundamentals of Textile Physics," *Textile Research*, 7-1 (1936–37), 25.

Strength may be expressed as either tenacity (breaking strength per unit of fineness, usually grex or denier) or as tensile strength (breaking strength per unit of cross section, usually grams per square centimeter or pounds per square inch) (Table 14.VIII).

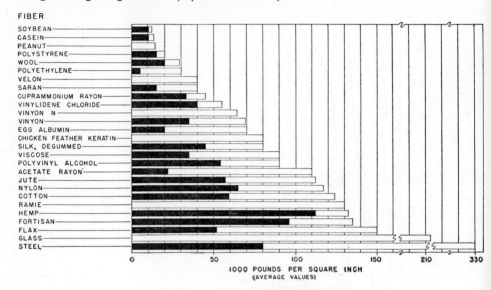

Fig. 14.5. Range of breaking strength.

TABLE 14.VIII

AIR-DRY STRENGTH OF SOME FIBER MATERIALS

Material	Density	Tenacity, gms. per grex*		Tensile stress, psi.**	
Nylon	1.14	4.0 to	6.3	55,000 to	102,000
Silk (boiled-off)	1.35	2.2 to	4.6	42,000 to	88,000
Wool	1.32	1.1 to	1.5	21,000 to	28,000
Acetate rayon	1.32	1.2 to	1.5	22,000 to	28,000
Vinyl fibers	1.35	1.8 to	3.6	35,000 to	69,000
Hemp	1.49	5.3 to	6.2	112,000 to	132,000
Jute	1.49	2.7 to	5.3	57,000 to	112,000
Flax	1.50	2.4 to	7.0	50,000 to	150,000
Viscose rayon	1.52	1.8 to	4.5	39,000 to	97,000
Saponified acetate rayon	1.52	4.5 to	6.3	97,000 to	136,000
Cotton	1.54	2.0 to	5.0	44,000 to	109,000
Vinylidene fibers	1.72	3.6 to	5.4	88,000 to	132,000
Glass	2.54	6.0 to 30.0		217,000 to	1,100,000
Steel (structural)	7.8	0.4 to	1.1	50,000 to	125,000

Source: Harold DeWitt Smith, *Textile Fibers, An Engineering Approach to Their Properties and Utilization* (Philadelphia: American Society for Testing Materials, 1944), vol. 44.

* A grex unit is equal to the weight in grams of 10,000 meters of a yarn or other material.

** Psi, pounds per square inch of cross section.

Strength is determined in part by

    a) degree of orientation of molecules and the resulting degree of crystallinity, orderliness of arrangement of fiber molecules within the fiber

    b) length of the molecular chains up to a certain length

    c) intermolecular forces which hold the fiber molecules together in the fiber wall

The incorporation of other substances into manufactured fibers affects the breaking strength; for example, pigment is used to dull the luster of some of the manufactured fibers, but the pigment reduces the fiber strength.

    A comparison of wet and dry strengths reveals the remarkable fact that the plant fibers are stronger when wet than when dry.

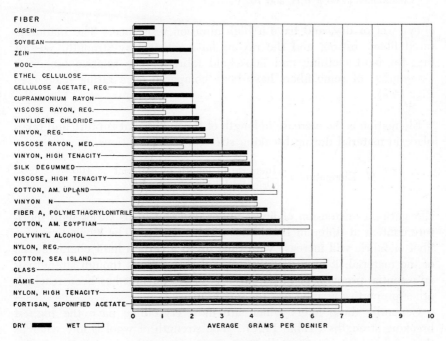

Fig. 14.6. Wet and dry strength.

All other fibers either lose strength when wet or remain unchanged. Those fibers which do not wet with water or do not absorb water are not affected by it.   A comparison of the wet and dry strengths of some protein fibers shows the greatest difference in values for degummed silk and the least difference in values for domestic wool (Table 14.IX).   The wet strength of the regenerated protein fibers, when used in woven fabrics, has to be reinforced by blending with stronger fibers.   The new synthetic fibers, nylon, Dacron, Orlon, Dynel, are extremely strong,

TABLE 14.IX

STRENGTH OF PROTEIN FIBERS

Sample	Dry*	STRENGTH grams/denier Wet	Loss
Wool, domestic	0.22	0.10	0.12
Silk, degummed	0.74	0.26	0.48
Peanut	0.25	0.027	0.223
Casein	0.24	0.016	0.224
Soya bean	0.28	0.006	0.274
Egg-white	0.34	0.006	0.234
Zein	0.23	0.036	0.194

Source: Milton Harris and Alfred E. Brown, "Natural and Synthetic Protein Fibers," Textile Research Journal, 17-1 (1947), 327.

* Conditioned at 65% R.H. and 70° F.

either wet or dry, and have a high abrasion resistance. The manufactured fibers, estron, and the rayons have satisfactory strength, wet or dry, for most clothing and household fabrics. The relative tenacities (strengths) of some fibers have been compared on a rating scale (see Fig. 14.7).

Elongation is the increase in length of the material at rupture and takes place in material during breaking strength determinations.

$$\% \text{ Elongation} = \frac{\text{Increase in length of material} \times 100}{\text{Original length of material}}$$

Elongation or extension of fibers under different loads varies with moisture content at different humidities (Table 14.X). The elongation of a fiber or fabric will increase with time up to a certain limit characteristic of the material; it often determines end uses. Even though strength is an essential property of fibers, after a certain amount has been reached, other properties assume greater importance.[8]

Generally those fibers which are most crystalline have the highest breaking strengths (Table 14.X). The strength of wool is low whereas that of flax is high. Crystallinity increases strength, elasticity, and stiffness or rigidity and decreases flexibility, elongation, crease resistance, and setting properties.[9]

Rayon fibers, which show a high degree of crystallization, show a fibrillar structure. The manner in which rayon filaments break down mechanically and chemically depends primarily upon the orientation of

[8] E. H. Freund and H. Mark, "Internal Structure of Synthetic Fibers and Its Influence on Their Physical Properties," Rayon Textile Monthly, 23-2 (1942), 605.
[9] Ibid.

the molecular chains.[10]   Rayon fibers can be made in which the molecular orientation approaches that of ramie.

The relationships between properties such as tenacity and stretching

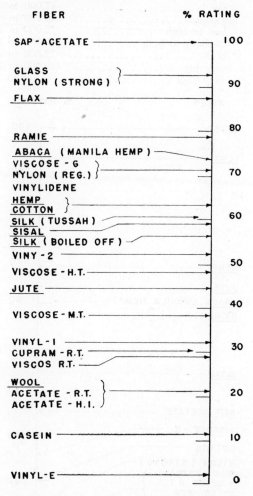

Fig. 14.7.   **Relative tenacity.**   *Source: Smith,* Textile Fibers, An Engineering Approach to Their Properties and Utilization.

at breaking point, and the degree of orderly arrangement of cellulose molecules are well illustrated by rayon yarns which differed only in moisture content and in the percentage of orientation as measured microscopically (Table 14.XI).

[10] L. M. Welch, W. E. Roseveare, and H. Mark, "Fibrillar Structure of Rayon Fibers," *Industrial and Engineering Chemistry,* 38 (1946), 581.

TABLE 14.X

CRYSTALLINITY AND BREAKING STRENTH OF SOME FIBERS

Fiber	Degree of crystallinity	Breaking strength, psi	
Wool	low	17,000 to	25,000
Silk	medium	46,000 to	74,000
Rayon	low to high	22,000 to	110,000
Cotton	medium to high	40,000 to	111,000
Nylon	high	72,500 to	100,000
Ramie	very high	129,000 to	135,000
Flax	very high	up to	156,000

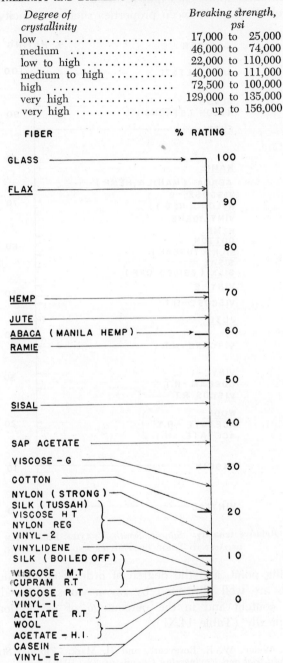

Fig. 14.8. Relative average stiffness. *Source: Harold DeWitt Smith, op. cit.*

TABLE 14.XI

SOME PROPERTIES OF RAYON SKEINS

	TENACITY GMS./DENIER		STRETCH AT BREAKING POINT %		
Sample	Dry	Wet	Dry	Wet	Orientation %
Bright 100/40	1.66	0.75	22.7	24.8	36.1
Bright 100/40	3.03	1.74	13.1	15.3	58.2

Source: D. R. Morey, "Micellar Arrangement in Various Cellulose Fibers," *Textile Research*, 4-11 (1933–34), 491.

Stiffness is that property which enables fibers to carry a load without deformation. It varies over a wide range. Within a measure, the stiffness of a fiber reflects the relative amount of crystallinity of the fiber structure. The more highly crystalline a given type of fiber, the stiffer it is. Jute and glass are the stiffest fibers; wool, casein, and elastic vinyl fibers are the softest. The degree of stiffness of fibers helps determine their use.

Elasticity is that property which enables fibers to return to their original shape at once upon release from a deforming force.

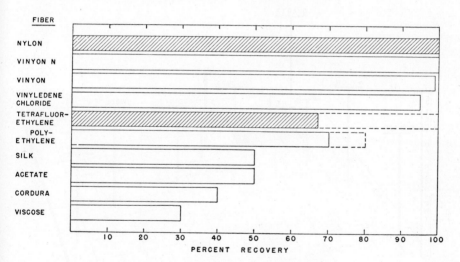

Fig. 14.9. Recovery from a deforming force.

Resilience may be thought of as lazy elasticity. Resilience is the capacity of a fiber or fabric to return to its original state at some time after the removal of the deforming force.[11] To the engineer, resilience is the ability of a material to absorb work without suffering permanent deformation. When a force or stress is applied, work is done.

[11] Smith, *Textile Fibers, An Engineering Approach to Their Properties and Utilization*.

Elastic deformation is related to the wrinkling of fabrics. Force (stress) applied to a fabric produces deformation (strain). For example, if a fabric is folded or crumpled, wrinkles appear. The extent to which the fabric recovers from the wrinkles depends upon a number of factors, such as

a) time allowed for recovery
b) physical properties of the fibers, the yarns, and the fabrics
c) amount of crushing, size of force (stress) applied
d) time during which force (stress) applied

Any study of fabric resiliency has to consider stress, strain, and time. The stress is the deforming force, and the strain is the result of the action of the force. The force may act in a number of ways

a) tension, as in measuring tensile strength or bursting strength
b) torsion, as in twisting fibers to produce yarns
c) bending, as over an edge of hem or pleat
d) compression, as in measuring filling capacity of fibrous materials for furniture stuffing

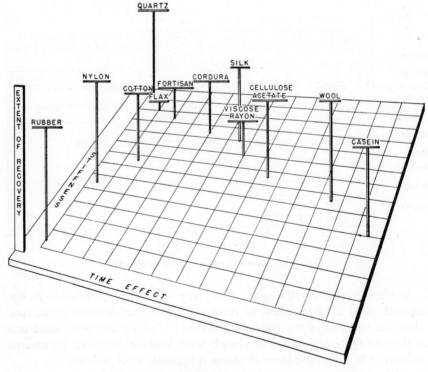

Fig. 14.10. A generalized concept of resilience. *Source:* R. M. Hoffmann, TEXTILE RESEARCH JOURNAL, 18-3 (1949), 141–148.

It has been pointed out that there are four different kinds of resilience.[12] A map (Fig. 14.10) has been designed to indicate the kinds and amounts of resiliency which exist.

It should be noted that stiffness is related to elasticity and resilience. The general-purpose fibers occupy a space in about the center of such a diagrammatic spacing of fibers. The fibers which are located farthest from the center of such a scheme are highly specialized in their elastic behavior. Such fibers are more specialized and less general in their uses.

Fibers and fabrics suffer from fatigue. If creases are repeatedly ironed into fabrics, as in edges of pleats or hems, the fibers bent over the edges suffer from fatigue and fail more readily than they would otherwise. Over a period of time, fabrics either fail to take a press readily or else lose the ability to hold a press. This may be observed as one of the differences between new wool and reused wools. Stiff fibers such as ramie and flax break at folded edges much more readily than soft fibers such as wool or rubber.

Toughness is a measure of the work required to break a fiber or fabric. A comparison of the relative toughness of fibers shows that the stiffest fibers are the least tough.

The toughest fibers are the synthetics.

Interfiber Friction. Interfiber friction is a necessary phenomenon in the spinning process. The very smooth, tube-like cells of kapok offer insufficient friction to be spinnable. Cotton fibers, on the other hand, have a shape and surface which provide satisfactory spinning properties. Some cottons are more spinnable than others. Wool scales offer a different type of interfiber friction.[13] Not only is wool easy to spin, but it felts readily because of its peculiar surface structure.

Mercerization of cotton reduces the interfiber friction by swelling the fiber. Most of the work which has been done on measuring the friction between fibers has been done on wool.

Color. The color of raw plant fibers is that of associated plant materials. Raw cottons are creamy from waxes on the surfaces. Bast fibers are creamy, brown, or greenish until bleached. Wool and hair fibers may be white, cream, tan, gray, brown, red, or black; silk, white, tan, yellow, or green. Varieties and breeds determine the color. Most fibers are white after bleaching.

Unless fibers are to be used white or in their natural color, they must be dyed.

Luster. The luster of fibers varies widely. In some fibers, it is de-

[12] R. M. Hoffman, "A Generalized Concept of Resilience," *Textile Research Journal*, 18-3 (1949), 141–148.

[13] Joel Lindberg and Nils Gralen, "Measurement of Friction between Single Fibers: IV, Influence of Various Oxidizing and Reducing Agents on the Frictional Properties of Wool Fibers," *Textile Research Journal*, 19-4 (1949), 183–201.

sirable, e.g., silk and linen.   In other fibers, luster is less desirable, for
example, some rayons.   The luster of manufactured fibers may be varied
at will in production by the use of pigments or by other means.   The
luster may be increased or decreased in fabrics by variations in yarn
construction, by fabric construction, and by finishes.   No quantitative
studies have been made on luster and its value in different end uses of
fibers.

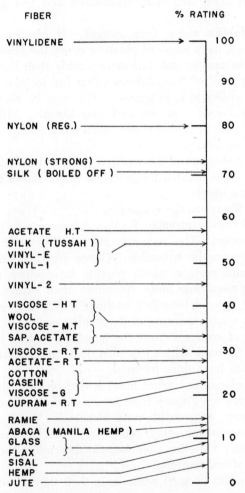

Fig. 14.11.   Relative toughness index.   *Source: Smith,* Textile Fibers, An Engineer-
Approach to Their Properties and Utilization.

Softening Range.   The range over which the thermoplastic fibers
soften is of considerable consequence to those who care for fabrics.
Ironing and pressing involve a range of temperatures which must be

kept safely below the softening or scorching points in order to avoid losses (Table 14.XII). The construction of some fabrics is more satisfactory than others.

TABLE 14.XII

SOFTENING RANGE OF SOME THERMOPLASTIC FIBERS

Trade name	Composition	Range for softening	
		F	C
Saran	Vinylidene-vinyl chloride	150– 280	65– 120
Polyfiber	Polystyrene	220– 230	428– 446
Polythene	Polyethylene	248	80– 120
Velon	Vinylidene chloride	170– 280	77– 138
Vinyon	Vinyl chloride, 88–90% and vinyl acetate 12–10%	290	167– 176
Orlon	Polyacrylonitrile	375– 428	190– 220
Estron	Cellulose acetate	400– 445	204– 229
Nylon	Polyamide	450– 480	232– 249
Vicara	Zein	482	250
Teflon	Tetrafluoroethylene	620	327
Fiberglas	Silica and other oxides	1000–2000	538–1093

Some of the manufactured fibers such as Saran and polythene are especially susceptible to shrinkage by heat. Others, such as Fiberglas and Teflon are extremely heat resistant. The temperatures at which some other fibers lose strength are given.

Fiber	Temperature F
Casein	212
Viscose	300
Cuprammonium	300
Cotton	300

Specific Heat. Specific heat of a substance is the number of calories required to raise one gram of the material one degree centigrade. The heat retaining value of clothing depends more on the fabric and garment construction than on the fibers used. This is contrary to popular opinion. The specific heats of fibers are much alike (Table 14.XIII).

TABLE 14.XIII

SPECIFIC HEATS OF SOME FIBERS

Fiber	Specific heat
Asbestos	0.251
Cotton	0.319
Linen	0.321
Rayon	0.324
Wool	0.326
Silk	0.331

Hand. Hand has been defined as "the characteristic of a fabric determined by a mental correlation of all the stimuli induced by those phys-

TABLE 14.XIV

Terms Relating to Hand of Fabrics

Physical property	Explanatory phrase	Terms to be used in describing range of corresponding component of hand
Flexibility	Ease of bending	Pliable (high) to stiff (low)
Compressibility	Ease of squeezing	Soft (high) to hard (low)
Extensibility	Ease of stretching	Stretchy (high) to nonstretchy (low)
		Springy (high) to limp (low).
Resilience	Ability to recover from deformation	Resilience may be flexural, compressional, extensional, or torsional.
Density	Weight per unit volume (based on measurement of thickness and fabric weight)	Compact (high) to open (low)
Surface contour	Divergence of the surface from planeness	Rough (high) to smooth (low)
Surface friction	Resistance to slipping offered by the surface	Harsh (high) to slippery (low)
Thermal character	Apparent difference in temperature of the fabric and the skin of the observer touching it	Cool (high) to warm (low)

Source: American Society for Testing Materials, *Standards on Textile Materials* (Philadelphia: American Society for Testing Materials, 1950), 35.

206

ical properties of a fabric appreciated by the sense of touch" (Table 14.XIV).[14] Equipment has been especially designed to evaluate certain of the properties of hand which are considered to be most characteristic of clothing and household fabrics, for example: flexibility, surface friction, and compressibility. The planoflex, the friction meter, and the compression meter respectively were developed to measure these properties.[15] The properties are described in Table 14.XIV and result in part from physical properties of fibers, yarns and fabrics. The pleasantness of touch and human comfort are related to the hand of fabrics.

CHEMICAL PROPERTIES

The fundamental chemical characteristics of fibers consist of composition, structure, and behavior toward reagents such as acids, alkalies, oxidizing agents, dyes, and solvents.[16]

Composition. The composition of the organic fibers varies widely, yet all contain carbon. Most of them also contain hydrogen and oxygen; the proteins and related compounds contain nitrogen and sometimes sulfur. Silicon and fluorine each form a vital part of the structure of some fibers. Other elements are relatively unimportant. The inorganic fibers are Fiberglas (chiefly silicon and oxygen), asbestos, and metal (chiefly aluminum, at present).

Plant fibers and rayons are chiefly cellulose.

Bast and leaf fibers of commercial importance have been analyzed at the Linen Research Institute of England (Table 14.V). Similar con-

TABLE 14.XV

CHEMICAL COMPOSITION OF BAST AND LEAF FIBERS

Fiber	Cellulose	Hemicellulose	Pectin	Lignin	Water solubles	Fat & wax	Moisture
Flax (unretted)	56.5	15.4	3.8	2.5	10.5	1.3	10.0
Flax (retted)	64.1	16.7	1.8	2.0	3.9	1.5	10.0
Ramie	68.6	13.1	1.9	0.6	5.5	0.3	10.0
Hemp	67.0	16.1	0.8	3.3	2.1	0.7	10.0
Sunn Hemp	67.8	16.6	0.3	3.5	1.4	0.4	10.0
Jute	64.4	12.0	0.2	11.8	1.1	0.5	10.0
Sisal	65.8	12.0	0.8	9.9	1.2	0.3	10.0
Abacá (Manila, hemp)	63.2	19.6	0.5	5.1	1.4	0.2	10.0
Phormium (New Zealand Hemp)	45.1	30.1	0.7	11.2	2.2	0.7	10.0

Source: A. J. Turner, "The Structure of Textile Fibres: VIII, The Long Vegetable Fibres," *Journal of the Textile Institute*, 40-10 (1949), P972–P984.

[14] A.S.T.M. Committee D-13, *A.S.T.M. Standards on Textile Materials, Tests for Properties Related to Hand of Fabrics* (Philadelphia: American Society for Testing Materials, 1950), 503.

[15] Edwin C. Dreby, "Physical Methods of Evaluating Hand of Fabrics," *American Dyestuffs Reporter*, 31-21 (1942), 497.

[16] Smith, *Textile Fibers, An Engineering Approach to Their Properties and Utilization.*

stituents were found in all of the bast and leaf fibers but in different amounts.

Animal fibers are protein fibers. Proteins from either plant or animal sources are all built from similar small units. Nylon is related to proteins in composition and structure.

Synthetic fibers vary in composition.

Structure. The structure of fibers will explain many similarities and differences in their behavior toward reagents. The largest group of fibers consists of the plant fibers and rayons. They are chiefly cellulose and hence have many reactions in common. The second largest group of fibers, based on chemical structure, is the proteins (plant and animal) and nylon. The proteins are complex and vary in composition along their molecular chain because of the side chains. Nylon and other synthetic fibers have comparatively simple structures when compared to the natural fibers.

An interesting similarity among the plant and animal fibers is the fibrillar structures which apparently are common to them all.[17] The fibrils in a fiber may be compared to the fibers in a yarn. The fibrils in silk are like strands of untwisted filaments, parallel to the major fiber axis. On the other hand, the fibrils in cotton twist about the walls of a cotton fiber like the fibers in a Z twist yarn. Interestingly enough the tiny fibrils (0.5 to 1 microns in diameter in cotton) are themselves composed of similar but smaller structures.

In the case of all the plant fibers, pectinous materials seem to act as cementing substances between units. It has been observed that cuprammonium solution dissolves only the cementing substances, which swell readily, and lets the cellulose chains float about in solution.

Reactions. The behavior of fibers toward chemical reagents, acids, alkalies, oxidizing agents, dyes, and even moisture is consistent with their chemical structure. The cellulose fibers, cotton, flax, ramie and the rayons, are hygroscopic, dye well, and are readily attacked by inorganic acids. The natural protein fibers, wool and silk, dye well, are especially sensitive to alkaline hydrolysis, are sensitive to oxidizing agents, have some resistance to acids, and absorb large amounts of water. Nylon does not absorb moisture nor dye as readily as the proteins. It has a simpler structure which allows for a closer arrangement of chains. The fiber is also unlike proteins in that it is exceptionally sensitive to acids but has fair resistance to alkalies and oxidation. Vinyon and Saran have low fusion points, are quite resistant to acids and alkalies, and do not support combustion. Polythene fibers are exceptionally flammable but are as inert otherwise as paraffin. Teflon

---

[17] Smith, "Structure of Cellulose," *Textile Research*, 7, 453.

is composed of carbon atoms already largely oxidized and is, therefore, highly resistant to burning.   The inorganic fibers do not burn.

The physical and chemical properties of fabrics are, in part, a summation of the properties of the fibers from which they are made.   Differences in fiber properties help to produce variations in properties of the numerous fabrics used in the many items of clothing for men and women as well as for the miscellaneous household fabrics.

Part Two

Fabrics

Chapter Fifteen

Yarn Construction[1]

YARN IS DEFINED by the American Society for Testing Materials as "a generic term for an assemblage of fibers or filaments, either natural or manufactured, twisted or laid together to form a continuous strand suitable for use in weaving, knitting, or otherwise intertwining to form textile fabrics."

YARN PRODUCTION

Yarn making is generally the second step in the production of fabrics. Texture, appearance, and service qualities are dependent on the characteristics of the yarns as well as on the fibers, the construction of the fabric, or the finish.

Methods and machines used in yarn production differ from mill to mill. This variation depends somewhat on the type of fiber used and on the type of yarn produced.

Cotton Yarns. The steps involved in the production of carded and combed cotton yarns are similar except that combed yarns are both carded and combed.

Opening and picking. As the bales of cotton are delivered to the mill, the cotton has been so compressed that it is necessary to loosen it up and separate the fibers before continuing with other processes in the making of the yarns. The fiber from selected bales is mixed and put

---

[1] The material in this chapter was assembled by Elvira Lindquist, Chairman of the Textile and Clothing Department, College of Home Economics, The State College of Washington, Pullman, Washington.

through bale breakers—machines which pull the fiber bunches apart by drawing the cotton onto aprons set with pins. Opening machines which have beaters then continue the loosening and mixing of the fibers and the removal of dirt. The picking machines have beaters, which continue the mixing, and screen cylinders, on which the fibers are then collected by using air currents. Dust is blown out. The soft sheets of fibers, known as laps, formed on these screens are drawn into rolls which weigh 40 to 50 pounds and are about 40 inches wide. Mineral oil is applied in opening and picking processes to prevent fiber breakage, to make fibers more flexible, and to reduce trouble from static electricity and dust later in the yarn-making processes.

Carding. The cotton fibers are separated and distributed more evenly by carding which also removes dirt and short fibers. The lap from the picking machine is set at one end of the carding machine. The fiber from the lap is drawn up over the main cylinder of the machine. This cylinder is covered with card clothing which consists of three or four layers of strong fabric into which are set numerous bent wires. Card clothing also covers the flats which move slowly over the top of the carding machine. Since the wires on the flats are bent in the opposite direction from those on the large cylinder, these wires act against the movement of the cotton and so separate the fibers into a very thin sheet. At the end of the carding machine, this thin sheet is then drawn together through a trumpet-shaped tube into a sliver, a soft, fluffy, untwisted strand of fibers. The carding sliver is coiled into a large can to be transported to the next machine.

Combing. The cost of yarns is appreciably increased by combing. It is done only when finer, more uniform cotton yarns are wanted in order to give sheerness, smoothness, or luster to the appearance of the fabric, or when greater strength is wanted for industrial fabrics. When yarns are to be combed, the longer cotton fibers are selected—those 1⅛ to 2 inches in length. Sliver lapper and ribbon lapper machines precede the combing machine. These straighten the fibers so that there will not be a high loss of long fibers in the comb waste. They again put the fiber into a lap, this time a narrow one. Sliver lappers arrange several slivers side by side and put the lap thus formed through drafting or drawing rolls which straighten and parallel the fibers somewhat by stretching the lap. The ribbon lappers by means of rollers continue the drawing of four or six laps and then superimpose the thin sheets one upon the other to form the finished lap. The combing machine has several heads. Each head combs the narrow lap from a ribbon lapper. Nippers in each head hold a bunch of fibers while the combs straighten the fibers and remove short fibers and neps, known as the noils. Each bunch of fibers thus combed is laid with some over-

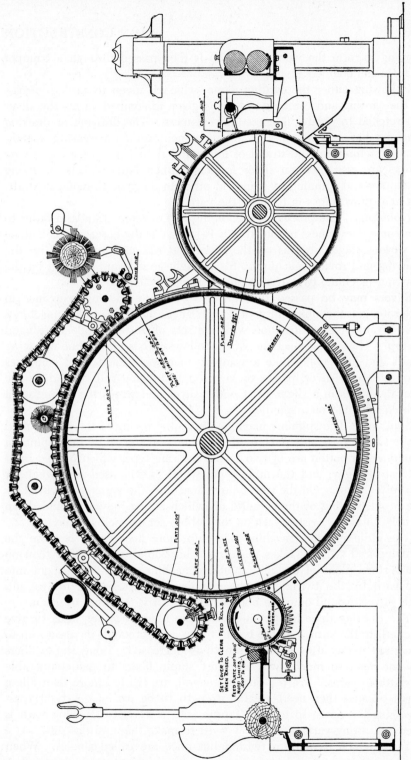

Fig. 15.1. Diagram of cotton carding machine. *Source: Merrill, Macromac, and Mauersberger,* AMERICAN COTTON HANDBOOK.

lapping to form the web. The web is then passed through a trumpet to form the combed sliver.

Following either the carding alone—which is given to carded yarns—or the carding and combing—which is given to combed yarns—the sliver is stretched to greater fineness and evenness. The drawing or drafting machine has several pairs of rollers which run at increasing speeds, thus stretching out the strand of fibers and reducing its size. Drawing rollers are also used on sliver lappers, ribbon lappers, combs, roving machines, and spinning machines in order to do some drawing or drafting at various stages in forming the yarn.

Doubling. The process of combining two or more strands in order to overcome unevenness in the strands is known as doubling. This is done at various stages also, as on the sliver and ribbon lappers and on the drawing and roving machines. Six or eight strands are doubled on the drawing machine, two strands on the roving machine.

Slivers may be passed through two or more drawing machines in order to get the uniformity of yarn size desired. Drawing machines have a table-like construction with the sets of drawing rollers arranged on top. The roving machine, which follows it, has a long line of roving heads and looks much like a spinning machine. Each head combines two strands of sliver, passes them through drawing rolls to reduce the size, then puts in a slight twist with a flyer and winds the roving on a bobbin mounted on a spindle.

Spinning. The spinning machine draws the roving to the size wanted for a single yarn and puts in the desired amount of twist. Spinning machines for cotton are of two kinds: the ring type, which is used most extensively now; and the mule type, which is still used somewhat for the softer yarns. On the ring type of machine, the yarns are twisted by the rapid twirling of the spindles on which a ring moves up and down to help wind the twisted yarn on the bobbin set on each spindle.

The mule spinning machine takes up more floor space because the drawing and twisting takes place on a horizontal plane rather than on the vertical plane of the ring spinning machine. The twist is put into the yarn by the twirling of the spindles as the carriage moves out. The yarn is wound onto the bobbins as the carriage moves in again.

The twisting done in spinning binds the fibers together so as to give strength to the yarn. As the twist is increased, strength increases, up to a certain point, after which strength is decreased. Long staple fibers do not need so much twist as short staple fibers to get comparable strength in yarns. Warp yarns, in general, are twisted more than filling yarns because they need greater strength to be woven. A tight twist gives harder yarns; so to keep fabrics soft, a lower-twist filling yarn is used. Knitting yarns have a low twist to make these fabrics soft.

Yarns which have been twisted but once are called singles. When two or more singles are twisted together, a ply yarn is formed. Such twisting of ply yarns increases the binding strength within each single, and consequently the strength of a ply yarn is greater than the combined strength of its singles. When two or more ply yarns are twisted together, a cord is formed which has greater strength than a ply yarn of comparable size.

The direction of twist in yarns is indicated as S or Z. Yarns have Z

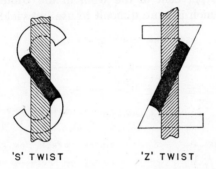

'S' TWIST   'Z' TWIST

Fig. 15.2. **Direction of twist in S and Z yarns.**

twist when the angle of the spiral twist of the fibers is that of the center line of the Z. Likewise yarns have S twist when the angle of the spiral of the fibers is that of the center line of the S. A ply yarn is usually twisted in the opposite direction from the singles of which it is composed. Twist is then indicated as S/Z or Z/S, the first letter showing the single twist and the second the ply twist. A ply yarn may have "twist on twist," S/S or Z/Z. The direction of twist for cords is given below (see p. 234).

Wool Yarns. Wool comes to the mills in fleeces which have been packed in bags or bales. The fleeces have been graded before bagging. When they arrive at the mill, a sorter separates each fleece into sections according to the fineness, length, color, and cleanliness of the wool. In order to reduce the operation costs, 75 per cent of the wool in the United States is sorted into only two parts: the outer edges of the fleece, which are of lower quality and have come from the lower parts of the body; and the central part of the fleece, which is of better quality and has come from the back and sides of the sheep. Mills which manufacture high-quality fabrics will do more sorting, making about ten sorts from each fleece (see Chapter Seven).

From 10 to 70 per cent of the weight of raw wool are the impurities, which are removed in the scouring and other cleaning of the wool. This loss in weight is referred to as shrinkage (not to be confused with shrinkage in fabrics). Natural impurities include the oils and fats, and the suint, which is the water-soluble salts from perspiration. Other impurities include sand and dirt, burrs and other parts of plants, and the tar, pitch, and paint used for identification marks. Many of the larger particles are removed by putting the wool into dusters, machines which beat the wool against screens.

Scouring. The process of removing impurities from raw wool by the use of water and detergents is called "scouring." It is done mainly by two methods: the soap, alkali, and water process, which is used for cleaning about 90 per cent of the wool in the United States; and the solvent process, which is more difficult to use but yields a superior wool.

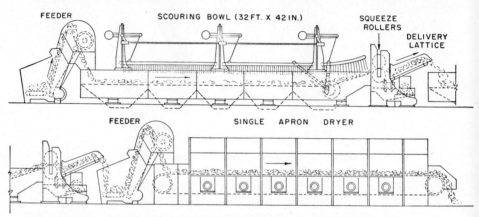

Fig. 15.3. Scouring with a continuous scouring train—the feeding end and the drying end.

In the soap, alkali, and water scouring process, the wool passes through several long vats. It is moved along by rakes with little agitation in order to minimize felting. The first vat may have warm water only, for removing the suint salts and some dirt. The second and third vats have water at a higher temperature and also have alkali and soap in order to remove fats as well as other impurities. Sodium carbonate or soda ash is the alkali used, because it is cheap, effective, and mild enough not to harm the wool if carefully handled. The alkali emulsifies the wool fat and dirt and partially saponifies the free fatty acid of the wool grease to form natural soaps. Considerable quantities of regular soaps are added to help suspend the dirt particles. Rinsing is done in the fourth and fifth vats.

In the solvent scouring process, organic solvents, such as benzene or petroleum naphtha are used. About three washes are made with the solvent. Then the solvent is thoroughly removed and the wool is given a warm-water treatment to remove water-soluble impurities. Greater strength and softness of fiber and a more open condition which facilitates carding and combing with less fiber breaking results from this process.

Burrs, seeds, leaves, straw, or similar plant particles are not all removed in scouring. If these are present in the wool in quantities which will interfere with good carding and other processes, they are removed either by a burr-picking machine or by carbonizing. Cylinders comb loose the burrs so they are thrown from the wool in the burr-picking machine. Carbonizing consists of steeping the wool in a solution of sulfuric or hydrochloric acid or salts, such as aluminum chloride, then baking at 200 to 220 F, crushing the charred plant particles and dusting to remove them. The wool is then rinsed and neutralized. If burrs are not removed by either of these methods, a burr cylinder may be used just before the carding of the wool.

Woolen yarns—carding. Woolen yarns are carded but not combed.

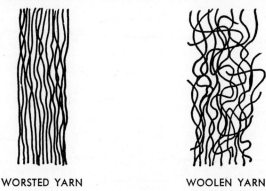

WORSTED YARN   WOOLEN YARN

Fig. 15.4. Arrangement of fibers in worsted and woolen yarns.

After wools have been scoured and dried, various new wools, and sometimes reused and reprocessed wools, or cotton and other fibers, are blended together. Reused and reprocessed wools are run through garnetting machines having cylinders set with wire spikes which open the yarns and separate the fibers. The fibers become broken in the process and are therefore comparatively short. Blending with reused and reprocessed wools must be done carefully in order to get adequate strength in the fabric, for when the fibers are more nearly the same length they can be carded together more easily. Wool is oiled and put through a blending machine before carding.

In woolen carding, an automatic feeder puts the wool into a mat which then passes onto a three-carding machine system. Each carding machine consists of a large cylinder covered with card clothing, over the top of which are arranged small rollers called workers, also covered with card clothing. As the wool passes over the large roller, the smaller rollers act to smooth out the fibers into a thin sheet. Each successive carding machine is covered with card clothing having finer wires set closer together to improve the carding done.

Woolen yarns—spinning. Spinning of woolen yarns is done either on a mule spinning machine or on a ring spinning machine. In wool spinning, as in cotton spinning, the continuous spinning machine is being used more extensively, because it uses less floor space and its production is 2 to 4½ times as great. The mule spinning machine used for woolen yarns draws yarns by moving out the carriage, and not by using drawing rollers as in cotton or worsted yarn spinning.

Worsted yarns—carding. Worsted yarns are both carded and combed during production. Fibers used for worsted yarns are longer than those

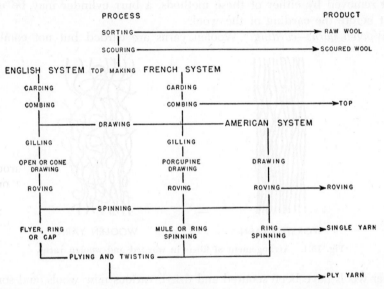

Fig. 15.5. **Flow sheet of systems for producing worsted yarns, English, French, and American.**

used for woolen yarns. More straightening of the fibers occurs in the combined carding and combing processes. When the wool for worsted yarns has been scoured and dried, it goes through one long carding machine which operates slowly, so as not to break the longer fibers. The card clothing for worsted carding machines is a thick, rubber-faced ply fabric set with the bent wires. Recently, a metal wire cloth has been used on the carding cylinder.

Worsted yarns—combing. Either of three systems for worsted yarn making may be used after the scouring and carding operations. The English or Bradford system is used for wool with an average staple length of at least 2½ inches; the French system is used for shorter wool. A third system, known as the American system, attempts to reduce the cost of production beyond the combing or top-making stage. In the American system, drawing frame, roving frame, and spinning frame used in making yarns from long staple rayon are being adapted to worsted yarn making. Fibers from 1½ to 4 inches in length are used.

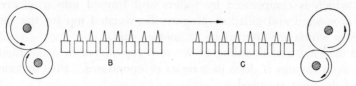

Fig. 15.6. Principles of the gill box and fallers. *Source: Von Bergen and Mauersberger,* AMERICAN WOOL HANDBOOK.

In the English system, after carding, the slivers are washed, dried, and oiled. Then they go through two gillings. In the gill box, the fibers are combed somewhat as they are passed over steel pins arranged between two sets of rollers. Since the second set of rollers operates more rapidly than the first set, drafting occurs which also helps straighten the fibers. Four slivers are rolled side by side into balls for use in the Noble comb.

Combing removes short fibers, kemps, neps, and noils. It also straightens the long fibers. Four types of combs are used for worsted combing These are:

 a) Noble or circular comb
 b) Lister or nip motion
 c) Heilmann, French, or rectilinear comb
 d) Holden or square-motion comb

The Noble comb is most used in the English system in this country. In the operation of the Noble comb, the balls of slivers are drawn into a large circular comb inside of which are two smaller circular combs whose rows of pins face those of the larger comb. As the combs keep rotating, the wool is combed and drawn into the center in four strands which unite into two and then into one sliver.

In the English system, two further gillings follow the combing. Some slivers are doubled, moisture is added to the wool, and the wool is drawn and combed over pins as it passes from one set of rollers to another in each gill box. The worsted top now formed is more uniform in size than when it comes from the comb. The top is rolled into a ball ready for the spinning processes. The top making is often done in one mill by a top maker. Then the next spinning processes may be done in another mill by the spinner or yarn maker.

In the French system of worsted yarn making, the Heilmann or rectilinear comb is preferred. Short, fine wools are used successfully, although the combs can be used for longer wools as well. The wool is gilled three times before combing. It passes into the comb as a lap or group of slivers. Nippers hold a row of fibers as a circular comb brings its pins through the fibers. Then, as the nippers let go, the drawing-off rollers grip the combed ends of the fibers as another comb goes through the other end of the wool fibers. The combed wool is laid in a layer of fibers which is compressed by rollers and formed into a sliver. The sliver is washed and gilled to prepare the worsted top for the spinning processes which are often done in another mill.

The drawing and doubling of worsted top slivers to make them into small, even rovings is done in a series of operations. Five or more systems of drawing are used:

(1) In the open drawing system, known as Bradford or English system, long coarse wools generally are made into roving for strong but fuzzy worsted yarns, although finer shorter wools may be handled on the system. By two gillings, three to five drawings, and a roving process, oiled top is made into roving.

(2) In cone drawing, long, fine wools are made into roving for fine worsted hosiery and dress fabric yarns. This is a more expensive process.

(3) In porcupine drawing, known as the French or Continental system, short wools are handled. Brass porcupine rollers adapted to short fibers and set with steel pins are used between back and front drawing rollers of a drawing frame. The yarns are smooth and soft, suitable for underwear, hosiery, dress fabrics, and men's wear fabrics.

(4) The Anglo-Continental system combines the English and French systems so as to handle various wools except very fine or very coarse ones. It can be adapted to producing yarns of various characteristics.

(5) In the American system, the top goes through three draftings on drawing machines which have been adapted from the pin-drafting machines used for long staple rayons. It then goes through a roving machine which uses two sets of drawing rollers with an apron roller between better to control fibers. The system uses less doublings and less drafting and therefore lowers costs.

Worsted yarns—spinning. Worsted yarns are spun by four methods. The first three methods to be discussed are used in the English system, the last two in the French system, and the third method in the American System.

(1) The flyer spinning machine is used for mohair, luster, and carpet-wool yarns. It is the oldest of the continuous spinning machines and, although its production is low, it is still best for long-fiber, smooth, lustrous yarns. The roving is drawn out by several sets of drawing rollers spaced far apart. Twist is put in by flyers screwed to the top of the spindles.

(2) The cap spinning machine is most extensively used in the United States for worsted yarns. It is well adapted to fine Merino and crossbred wools. On this machine, the spindle does not move, and the bobbin is rotated by a metal tube which fits over it, thus putting the twist into the yarn. Production is high on this machine.

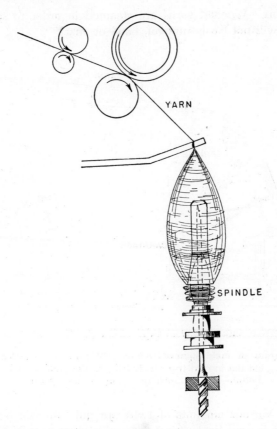

YARN

SPINDLE

Fig. 15.7. **Diagram of cap spinner.** *Source:* WOOL AND MOHAIR, *(New York:*
The Wool Bureau, Inc.).

(3) Since 1930, ring spinning has been used in English, French, and
American systems of worsted yarn production, as well as in cotton spinning. The lower cost and larger packages of yarn produced will lead
to ring spinning's replacing cap spinning. Roving led from a spool
set on a creel at the top of the frame passes through drawing rollers,
then is twisted by a traveler which goes around a ring on the spindle.
The yarn is also wound on the bobbin by the traveler.

(4) Mule spinning is the most extensively used method of spinning
in the French system. It gives an excellent soft yarn for dress fabrics
and hosiery. The roving is drawn by five pairs of rollers. Twisting of
the yarn is done by the spindles as the carriage moves out. The yarn
is wound onto bobbins as the carriage moves in again. This is known
as intermittent spinning, as compared with the continuous spinning of
the ring, cap, and flyer spinning machines.

After spinning single yarns, the singles may be twisted together to form ply yarns. Worsted yarns are steamed in order to set the twist so that they will not easily unravel, kink, or snarl.

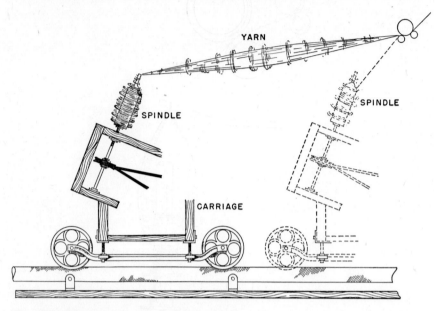

Fig. 15.8. Diagram of mule spinner. *Source:* "WOOL AND MOHAIR," *The Wool Bureau, Inc.* On the inward trip (dotted lines) the yarn is wound onto the bobbin by continued revolving of the spindle.

Twisting. Various amounts of twist are put into worsted yarns. A low soft twist is used for knitting and embroidery yarns. Normal twist is given weaving yarns. This is subdivided into warp twist and filling twist. The latter yarn has a lower twist than warp yarns but higher than the soft twist of knitting yarns. Medium twist, greater than normal twist, is used in hard or clear finished worsted. The hardest twist is used in crepe yarns. The following comparison suggests the number of turns per inch in each type of worsted yarn:

Yarns	Turns per inch
Soft knitting	5.30 to 15.87
Normal filling	7.22 to 21.63
Normal warp	9.73 to 29.18
Medium hard	13.36 to 40.06
Hard crepe	16.82 to 50.43

In general, worsted yarns, when compared with woolen yarns, have fibers in a straighter and more nearly parallel position; are smoother; often have higher twist, longer fiber, and greater fineness; and are more resilient and stronger.

Silk Yarns. When silk arrives at the yarn mills, it comes in one or another of three forms. Cultivated silk has been reeled into strands of long filament fibers, in so far as it has been possible to do so. The inside and outside of the cocoon cannot be reeled, however, and this part of the cocoons and broken cocoons which cannot be reeled are baled as waste silk. Wild silk is difficult to reel. Therefore, the cocoons are usually baled for marketing.

Reeled or filament yarns. Reeled or filament yarns are the most prized silk yarns. Raw silk for our markets is reeled into skeins. The skeins are packed 30 to a book, which is a compact rectangular package. Thirty books in turn are packed into a bale. At the mill the raw silk is sorted and then placed in a soap and oil bath to soften the gum. The skeins are placed on reels, and as many strands as desired are combined and twisted onto bobbins. If ply yarns are desired, strands are again doubled and twisted together. The process of combining and twisting silk and other filament yarns is known as throwing. It is the simplest and easiest method of yarn construction.

Single silk yarns are used for weaving yarns. Tram yarns are used for filling only and are made from two or three singles. Twist varies from very low to a hard twist in the tram yarns. Organzine yarns are ply yarns used for warp. In these, the twist of the ply is opposite to that of the single in order to give added strength. Grenadine yarns are ply yarns with a hard twist and are used for silk hosiery and some fabrics. Crepe yarns have a very high twist.

Spun silk yarns. Yarns from spun silk produce beautifully textured fabrics. Spun silk yarns are made from waste silk, some of which is known in sericulture as gum waste. Some spun silk yarns are produced in reeling and some in making the filament yarns, known as throwster's waste. Wild silk cannot be reeled and so is used in spun yarns. Pongee and shantung are typical fabrics made from spun silk yarns.

The waste or wild silk is degummed in hot soapy water. It then passes through opening machines which separate the fiber bunches and work the fibers into a lap. The fibers are combed so that they lie parallel, and the very short fibers, the noils, are removed. The strand is drawn and spun into a yarn in a manner similar to that used in the production of other staple fiber yarns. Spun silk yarns are graded according to the average length of the fibers; those with longest fibers are rated as first quality.

Linen Yarns.[1] When the flax fiber reaches the spinning mill, the first process in preparing it for yarn is roughing. The coarse fiber bundles are drawn by hand through coarse tines fastened to a bench. The

---

[1] J. L. Taylor, *Processing Domestic Flax for Textile Use: I, Decortication,* Bulletins 9 and *II, Retting and Degumming,* Bulletin 10 (Atlanta: Georgia School of Technology, 1946).

worker grasps a handful of flax first by the stem tip ends, tosses the root ends over the tines, and pulls so as to straighten the fibers and remove any remaining bark particles. He gradually works upward toward the tip, then reverses the bundle in his hand and works on roughing the tip end.

The fiber bunches are then fastened in clamps on the hackling machine, first with the root end hanging down. Traveling ladders, having bars with long sharp pins across them, come in contact with the fiber bundles so as to comb the fibers. The pins in successive parts of the hackling machine are finer and closer together. The combing gradually breaks down the fiber cell bundles into finer and finer fibers. When the root ends have been combed, the fiber bundles are reversed in the clamps so as to comb the tip end. The long, fine fibers resulting from hackling are called line. The short, broken, and tangled waste fibers separated out are called tow. The line fibers are laid in an overlapping ribbon and are pressed together. The fiber ribbon then goes through a drawing process to parallel the fibers and make the strand finer. The roving machine further draws out the strand and puts in a slight twist.

There are three methods of spinning linen yarns.[2] Dry spinning yields rough, uneven yarns. The roving passes through drawing rollers, and the twist is put in by flyer spinning. Wet spinning is used for the finer yarns. The roving is passed through hot water to soften the fiber so that drawing is done more easily to make a fine strand, which is then spun. In the third method, gill spinning, the fiber strand is passed through a gill box which combs the fibers in drawing them out to a fine strand. The gilled strand is wet spun and gives a good, even yarn.

Tow is a mass of tangled fibers as it comes from the hackling machines. Consequently, the fibers must be straightened by a carding machine. The strands may also be combed to parallel the fiber and remove bunches. They are then drawn and spun.

Rayon and Nylon Yarns. Two general types of rayon and nylon yarns are made.[3] The filament yarns are made from long, continuous fibers or filaments much like silk. Spun yarns are made from short fibers cut to different lengths for different types of fabric. Some of the fabrics look much like cotton fabrics; others look like linen, and others like woolens or worsteds. Staple fibers are frequently combined with other kinds of fibers for blended yarns.

Filament yarns. Filament yarns may be produced in any manufactured fiber. The production of rayon, nylon, glass, or other manufactured fiber filament yarns is a continuation of the production of the

---

[2] George A. Lowry, "Hemp and Flax from the Seed to the Loom," *Rayon Textile Monthly*, 18-11 & 12 (1937), 72–74 and 82–83.

[3] Herbert R. Mauersberger and E. W. K. Schwarz, *Rayon Handbook* (New York: Rayon Handbook Co., 1939).

fiber in the factory. The yarn therefore usually goes directly from fiber factory to weaving and knitting mills without going through intermediate yarn mills or yarn production rooms which are sometimes a part of the fabric production mill. Ply yarns and high-twist crepe and voile yarns may, however, go through a throwster.

Several methods are used in winding the filaments into yarn packages during the spinning process. One method used for viscose rayon yarns is that of cake or pot spinning. The group of filaments is pulled above the spinneret on to a Godet wheel which moves rapidly in order to stretch the fibers finer (stretch spinning), and then is led down into a centrifugal pot which rotates at high speed, twisting the yarn into a cake. The cake of yarn is then washed, dried, desulfured, bleached, soaped, and dried.

Another method used for viscose rayon yarns is that of pulling the group of filaments from the spinneret up through the spinning bath onto bobbins several feet above. Since these yarns have no twist, they are usually twisted in a rewinding or coning process. Cuprammonium filaments come through a funnel of water where they are stretched and are wound on a reel in a skein. Acetate rayon filaments come through

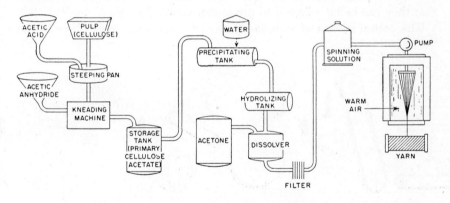

Fig. 15.9. Production of acetate rayon yarns. *Source:* Rayon Fabrics, 57.

a spinneret at the top of an enclosed column of heated air and are twisted and packaged at the bottom of the column. These are typical of the methods used to twist and wind filament fibers into yarns.

Throwing is the twisting of ply yarns and high-twist crepe and voile yarns. This may be done in a process similar to that of silk throwing, or a machine similar to the cotton ring spinner may be used, except that the drawing is omitted.

Rayon and nylon yarns are packaged on tubes, cops, cones, spools, and in skeins.

Spun yarns.   Spun yarns are produced from staple fiber obtained from filaments.   Staple fibers are made into yarns in the same manner as cotton, wool, or other short natural fibers.   Recently, however, new ma-

Fig. 15.10.   Diagram of rayon and nylon yarn packaging: tube, cop, cone, skein and spool. *Source: Mauersberger and Schwarz,* RAYON HANDBOOK, *201.*

chines have been developed which are especially adapted to rayon. These attempt to save time in making the yarns by eliminating or simplifying certain processes.   Some machines have been so successful that they are being adapted to producing worsted yarns.

The cotton system of spinning is used for the fine, short fibers in the

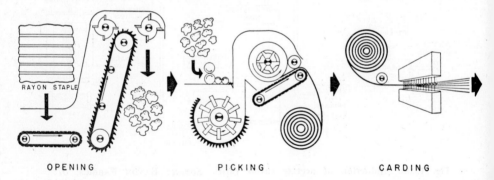

OPENING   PICKING   CARDING

Fig. 15.11.   The basic process for making spun rayon yarns.

spun yarns which are used for dress fabrics, shirtings, and sheetings. The main objective is to parallel the fibers, because the yarns can then be made finer and stronger.   The staple is blended into laps on a picking machine, and four laps are superimposed on one another.   The fiber is then carded and drawn into a sliver which is drafted, twisted slightly into a roving, and then spun.

The woolen system uses heavier and longer fibers.   Soft, lofty yarns are formed by not paralleling the fibers.   These yarns are used for

socks, blankets, carpets, and suitings.   The fibers, which may be blended
with wool fibers, go through a picker and are then carded and spun.

In the worsted system, long fibers are paralleled, but yarns are not
made as fine as in the cotton system.   The yarns are used for suitings,
coats, and sportswear.   The fibers are carded, gilled, and combed in
a Noble comb to form the top.

The American system of worsted yarn spinning was developed for
rayon yarns of long staple.[4]   A new type of pin drafter replaces the
older gilling machine.   Three of these are used, one after the other.

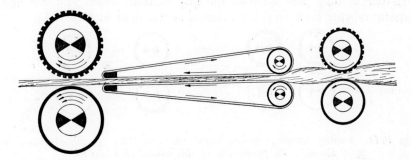

Fig. 15.12.   The American system roving frame carries the sliver by aprons or belts
at it is drawn out to finer diameter.   *Source:* "New Textile Machines
Are Ahead." *By permission of the editors of* FORTUNE.

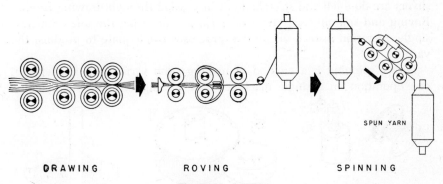

DRAWING   ROVING   SPINNING

Fig. 15.11. (*cont.*)

As shown in Fig. 15.13, several tops are doubled, passed through sets
of drawing rollers, and carried along by apron rollers to the combs
known as faller sets.   The interlocking combs move from left to right
with the strand of fibers, then return to their original positions.   The
rollers at the right move rapidly to draw the strand to much smaller
size.   The new roving machines and spinning machines are also of a

4 "Worsted Yarns—American System," *Rayon Textile Monthly,* 28-4 (1947), 75–76.

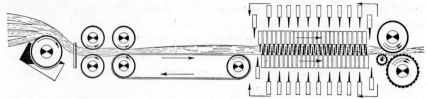

Fig. 15.13.   Diagram of pin drafter; draws the sliver small and even. *Source:* "New Textile Machines Are Ahead." *By permission of the editors of* FORTUNE.

long-draft type.[5]   These have apron rollers which help to hold fibers together as they pass between the first drafting rollers and the more rapidly moving drafting rollers, shown at the right in Fig. 15.13.

Fig. 15.14.   Another American roving frame. *Source:* "New Textile Machines Are Ahead." *By permission of the editors of* FORTUNE.

The linen or flax system may be used on rayon fibers.[6]   Carding may be shortened to one carding operation as compared with two or more on flax fibers, because the rayon fiber is already clean.   After carding, the slivers are doubled and stretched out in passing through drawing frames. Roving and spinning may then take place.   By using the gill spinner, a single operation instead of the two processes is adequate to produce the yarn.

Direct spinning is a method of making spun yarns from filaments in one operation on a single machine.[7]   In passing through the machine

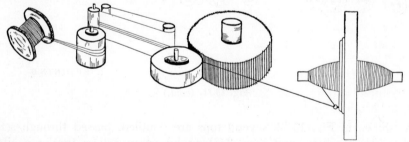

Fig. 15.15.   The direct process for making spun rayon yarns. *Source:* "Direct Spinning." *Courtesy E. I. du Pont de Nemours and Co., Inc.*

[5] "New Textile Machines Are Ahead," *Fortune,* 39-2 (1949), 129.

G. R. Merrill, A. R. Macromac, and H. R. Mauersberger, *American Cotton Handbook* (New York: American Cotton Handbook Co., 1941).

[6] D. Buchan Gibb, "Yarn and Thread Manufacture from Synthetic Fibers on the Flax, Hemp, and Jute Equipment," *Rayon and Synthetic Textiles,* 29-2 (1948), 51.

[7] "Direct Spinning," *Du Pont Magazine,* 43-4 (1949), 16.

(see Fig. 15.15), filaments are broken into staple lengths ranging from 4 to 7 inches, kept in parallel position, drawn, and spun into the yarn.

TYPES OF YARNS ACCORDING TO CONSTRUCTION

Many variations in fabrics are possible through differences in yarn structure. Thus, sheerness in fabrics results from the use of fine, smooth-combed yarns with slight spacing in weaving. Yarns may be singed to increase sheerness and porosity for summer fabrics. Warmth is given by the use of large, spongy, loosely twisted yarns with air pockets. Sometimes these loosely twisted yarn surfaces are napped to increase the air pockets and to give a feeling of softness.

High twist gives elasticity to yarns. Even nylon monofilament yarns for hosiery are twisted to give better service. Hard, firm twists may be used for rigid textures. A very high twist is used in yarns to give a crepe texture.

Since low twist gives luster, the filament warp yarns which form the surface of satins have almost no twist, whereas the filling yarns have medium or high twist for strength. Filling yarns in many fabrics have a low twist to give softness or greater absorbency. Rough and linen-like textures are given many fabrics through the use of tweed, ratiné, nub, slub, and other special or novelty yarns. Mottled and other color effects are obtained by the use of fiber-dyed and yarn-dyed yarns.

Regular or Ordinary Yarns. Among the regular or ordinary types of yarns there are the single, ply, and cord constructions.

Single. A single yarn is made of one strand of fibers with either S or Z twist or no twist.

Ply. A ply yarn is made by twisting together two or more single yarns. Most of the ply yarns have the ply twist opposite to the twist of the single, S/Z or Z/S. A twist on twist ply yarn, however, has both twists in the same direction, Z/Z or S/S.

Cord. A cord is made by twisting together ply yarns in a third twisting operation. A hawser cord has the same twist in single and ply with the opposite twist in the last process, S/S/Z or Z/Z/S. A cable cord uses the opposite twist in each twisting process, S/Z/S or Z/S/Z. In addition to these twisted types of cords, there are woven, knitted, and braided types of cords.

Novelty Yarns. Novelty, fancy, complex, or special yarns are produced to give various textures in woven, knitted, or braided fabrics. They may be made with only a single strand but frequently are made with two or three types of strands. These strands may differ in color, in fiber, in amount of twist, or in size. They may be combined with a difference in tension as the twisting is done, so that if the yarns are unraveled the length of the strands may differ. The longer strand may form loops or humps, or may be smoothly wound around the shorter strand. Extra neps or flakes may be added or the yarn may be coated. In single yarns, variations in twist are used in various ways.

As mentioned above, the novelty yarn may be a single yarn or may have two or three types of plied strands. The three frequently used parts in a novelty yarn are: (1) the ground, core, or base strand, which serves as a foundation around which the other parts are twisted; (2) the fancy or effect strands, which produce the special effect; and (3) binder strands, which are fine strands wound around the effect strands to hold them in place.

Following is a list of some of the novelty yarns, with a description of each: [9]

SLUB: soft, untwisted portions are left between twisted portions in a single yarn. Sometimes a binder is added to strengthen the yarn. The untwisted portions spread out, leaving heavier-appearing parts in the fabric.

FLAKE: portions of roving are added to form similar but larger bunches than in the slub yarn. These flakes are often of a different color and may be held by binders.

LOOP, CURL, or BOUCLÉ: the effect strand is twisted to form loops or curls and held in place by one or two binders. The effect strand is usually made of a fairly stiff fiber and usually has low twist.

NUB, KNOP, SPOT, NODE, or KNOT: at intervals the effect strand is wound many times around the base to give a rounded knot in the yarn.

COVERED or CORE: the base yarn is completely covered by having the effect strand wrapped about it. In some yarns, the covering may be a fibrous material without previous twist.

CHENILLE: a fabric is first woven on a loom which has four to eight warps grouped tightly and four to eight fillings grouped together. The chenille yarns are then cut lengthwise through the fabric, leaving the four to eight warps together. The cut filling yarns leave protruding tufts along the chenille yarn.

ZIPKNIT: a new type made by first knitting a fabric in single bar tricot. This is then raveled so as to form yarns which may be used for knitting or weaving.

RATINÉ: one or two effect strands are wound loosely around a fine base strand. One or two binders twisted about these hold the effect strands in bumpy projections along the yarn.

COMBINATION TWIST: ply yarns with one strand having a high twist and the other strand having a low twist. A crepe yarn with a high twist viscose rayon strand and a low twist acetate rayon strand is used in some rayon crepes.

[9] Werner Von Bergen and Herbert R. Mauersberger, *American Wool Handbook* (New York: Textile Book Publishers, Inc., 1948), 616.

SPIRAL or CORKSCREW: has the effect strand wound spirally about the base strand, which is either heavier or finer.

BLEND: two or more kinds of fibers are mixed together before spinning.

FROSTED, GLAZED, or LUSTER: different fibers are blended together, one of which remains white when the yarn is dyed, giving a frosty appearance. Acetate rayon is usually the fiber which remains white when blended with wool, cotton, or viscose rayon. The white fiber gives a slightly different effect when coarse or fine.

GRANDRELLE: has one or more colored singles combined with one or more white or light-colored singles in a ply yarn.

MOCK TWIST: has a colored and a white roving twisted together in a single yarn.

VOILE: hard twisted to give resilience. Voile yarns may be single yarns, but the best are ply yarns with a twist or twist construction.

CREPE: very high twist causes yarns to crinkle up easily.

PART WASTE: made with some carding waste or combing waste. They have motes, which are flecks caused by leaf or stem particles.

WHIP THREAD: a two-ply, softly twisted yarn used in lappet weaving.

THICK AND THIN or ODD AND EVEN: give an uneven texture because their rayon fibers have been spun uneven in diameter.

ABRADED: filament yarns whose surfaces have been roughened to reduce creasing.

TWEED or NEP: has little extra tufts of fibers called *neps* which may or may not contrast in color.

PLASTIC-COATED: dipped in plastic to form a protective coating or a colorful coating over them. Some are plastic-coated aluminum yarns. Others are plastic-coated glass, cottons, nylon, or other types.

MONOFILAMENT: produced from a single filament fiber. Metals and plastic synthetic fibers have been most used for monofilament yarns.

MIXTURE TWIST: formed by combining singles of different fibers in a ply yarn.

MONOCORD: made by welding together a group of nylon or rayon filaments without any twist. Nymo is the nylon yarn, and Raymo is the rayon yarn.

SEED: has extra bunches of fiber twisted in to form seed-shaped enlargements along the yarn.

Yarn Number. The yarn number is a relative measure of the fineness or coarseness of a yarn. Several systems for yarn numbering have been in use. Thus, for woolen yarns, the cut and the run are used. For worsted yarns, the worsted hank number is used. For nylon, rayon, and silk, the denier is used. For cotton, the cotton hank number is used. For linen, the lea is used. For jute, the spyndle is used. For asbestos, the asbestos cut is used.

Aside from these, there are three systems which apply to all types of yarns: the metric number, the typp, and the grex number. The grex number has most recently been recommended as the universal system to replace all of the other systems.[10]

In these numbering systems, there are two general types from the standpoint of the person who wishes to compare sizes of yarns. (1) In some systems, as the number goes up the yarn is coarser. This applies to the denier, the spyndle, and the grex number. In these, the relative measures are weights per unit length. (2) In other systems, as the number goes up the yarn is finer. This applies to the metric number, typp, runs, cuts, leas, and hanks. In these, the relative measures are lengths per unit weight.

The following list gives the relative measurements for the various number systems:

The *grex* number is equal to the weight in grams per 10,000 meters. It is also equal to the weight in grams per 10,936 yards, in ounces per 310,033 yards, and in pounds for 4,960,536 yards.

The *denier* is equal to the weight in grams per 9000 meters.

The *spyndle* is equal to the weight in pounds per 14,400 yards.

The *typp* is equal to the number of 1000-yard lengths per round.

The *lea* is equal to the number of 300-yard lengths per pound of linen yarns.

The *metric number* is equal to the number of kilometers per kilogram.

The *worsted hank* is equal to the number of 560-yard lengths per pound.

The *woolen run* is equal to the number of 1600-yard lengths per pound.

The *woolen cut* is equal to the number of 300-yard lengths per pound.

The *cotton hank* is equal to the number of 840-yard lengths per pound.

The *asbestos cut* is equal to the number of 100-yard lengths per pound.

The Yarn Count. The yarn count of a fabric indicates the number of ends or warp yarns per inch and the number of picks or filling yarns per inch. This is expressed as warp x filling (for example, 64 x 60) or as a total number (for example, 124).

To take yarn count, the ends or picks are counted in five or more locations on the fabric, and an average number is calculated. The same yarns should not be counted twice, and the yarns counted should be at least 1/10 of the width of the fabric away from the selvage.

Designation of Yarn Construction. Standard methods of designating yarns have been proposed by Committee D-13 of the American Society for Testing Materials.

[10] A.S.T.M. Committee D-13, *A.S.T.M. Standards on Textile Materials* (Philadelphia: American Society for Testing Materials, 1950), 38.

The mark / indicates plying.

The first number before the mark / indicates the yarn number of the single.

Example: 30/1 Nylon.

In filament yarns the number of filaments may be indicated after a dash placed after the yarn number.

Example: 30–10/1 Nylon.

The type of yarn numbering system may be given in parenthesis after the yarn number.

Example: 30–10 (Denier)/1 Nylon.

The S or Z twist may follow the yarn number.

Example: 30–10 (Denier) Z/1 Nylon.

The number of twists per inch (tpi) may follow the yarn twist.

Example: 30–10 (Denier) Z5/1 Nylon.

If different types of singles are combined in a ply yarn, the ampersand is used to join the two types of singles.

Example: 30–10 (Denier) Z5 Nylon & 50–20 (Denier) Z5 Viscose/2.

The number of singles may be indicated before the designations for each single enclosed in parenthesis.

Example: 2 (30–10 Z 5) Nylon & 1 (50–20 Z 5) Viscose / 3.

The number of ply is given after the / for ply and cord yarns. The twist and twists per inch may follow.

Example: 30Z5/2S5/3Z5 Nylon.

TYPES OF YARNS ACCORDING TO USE

Yarns are commonly referred to by naming them according to the intended purpose of the yarn.

Weaving Yarns. Weaving yarns are classed as warp yarns or ends, those which run lengthwise in a woven fabric; and filling yarns or picks, those which run across the fabric. Warp yarns are often stronger, more highly twisted, smoother, and finer than the filling yarns.

Knitting Yarns. Knitting yarns are softly twisted yarns. They are usually ply yarns for hand knitting and either single or ply for machine knitting. The following list describes some of the types of yarn used for hand knitting:

KNITTING WORSTED: a popular heavy yarn, used for sweaters and afghans, made of soft wool in a firm twist, sturdy and durable.

GERMANTOWN: a medium-weight yarn, made from soft wools, used for blankets and sweaters for women and children.

FINGERING YARNS: light- and medium-weight yarns, smooth and evenly twisted, 2- or 3-ply, used for children's wear and various other garments.

SOCK YARNS: especially constructed yarns for making hand-knitted socks.

BABY YARNS: light- and medium-weight yarns in 100% virgin wool or wool with rayon for novelty effects, used for infants' wear.

SHETLAND FLOSS: also a light-weight fluffy yarn used for infants' and children's sweaters and girls' light sweaters.

ZEPHYR YARNS: 100% virgin wool yarns of very fine, soft texture.
DRESS YARNS: plain types and novelty types, all wool, blends, or mixture
twists with rayons and cottons.

150 DENIER   150 DENIER   150 DENIER
3 TURNS   10 TURNS   25 TURNS

Fig. 15.16. Variation in the amount of twist in some knitting yarns. Three turns
per inch produces a soft yarn, 10 turns produces a medium soft yarn, and 25 turns
produces a hard twist resilient yarn.

Sewing Threads. Sewing threads are yarns specially made for that
purpose. Besides the regular sewing threads used for most garment
construction, special sewing threads are made for sewing shoes, carpets,
saddles, gloves, baseballs, upholstery, luggage, awnings, flags, umbrellas,
and book binding. Sewing threads are evenly spun, smooth, firmly
twisted, and finished to resist abrasion. Since strength is an important
requisite, the yarns have either ply or cord construction. These ply
threads are made by twisting together three or more already twisted
single strands. The six-cord thread is made by twisting together two
strands and, then combining three of these double threads. The six-
cord construction gives a stronger thread and is used mostly in white
and black threads. The ply construction gives a smoother thread and
is used mostly in colored threads. The label at the end of the spool
indicates which spools have a six-cord thread. Mercerization increases
smoothness and dye affinity of cotton threads. The size of sewing
threads is indicated by numbers on the labels. As the number goes up,
the thread becomes finer. The following table suggests uses for various
sizes of cotton sewing thread and the sizes of sewing needles to use with
them:

COTTON THREAD SIZES	SILK THREAD	NEEDLE SIZES		STITCHES PER INCH	PURPOSE
		HAND SEWING	MACHINE SEWING		
8, 10, 12		1-4	19	8	Canvas, Heavy Coatings
16, 20, 24		4-5	18	10	Bed Ticking, Awnings, Buttons on Work Jackets
30, 36, 40 and Heavy Duty	D	5-6	16	10-14	Draperies, Quilts, Work Clothes, Play Clothes, Sports Clothes, Buttons, Buttonholes, Suits and Light Weight Coats
50, 60, 70	C	6-8	14	14-18	Dresses, Dress Shirts, Curtains
80, 90, 100	A, B	8-10	11	18-20	Dainty Children's Dresses, Sheer Dresses, Sheer Curtains
100, 120	A	10-14	9	20-25	Georgette Chiffon, Batiste Infant's Dresses
150, 200		10-14			Fine Lace, Fine Handwork

Fig. 15.17. Sizes of thread and needles used with various fabrics.

BUTTONHOLE TWIST: thread specially made for that purpose, put up on small spools with only a few yards of thread to a spool.

MENDING AND DARNING THREADS: softly spun yarns sold in balls, on spools, or on cards.

HANDWORK THREADS: crochet, tatting, and embroidery yarns. Embroidery floss is a low- or medium-twisted yarn in ply or cord construction. Perle cotton is used for various purposes, such as knitting or embroidery. Rug-weaving yarns are made for home weaving.

TYING AND PACKAGING TWINES AND CORDS: various types, sold in balls, are made of cotton, hemp, jute, glass, nylon, and rayons.

Chapter Sixteen

Woven Fabrics[1]

WEAVING is the process most used for the manufacture of textile fabrics.[2] In weaving, two or more sets of yarns are interlaced at right angles to each other. The lengthwise yarns are known as warp or ends, and the crosswise yarns are known as filling, weft, or picks.

Fabrics of various widths are woven on different-sized looms. Narrow goods are 35 inches or less in width. Broad or wide goods range from 36 to 58 or more inches. Some fabrics, such as felts, velvets, carpets, and draperies, may be made wider, up to 540 inches in width.

Gray and Converted Fabrics. Fabrics woven from unbleached yarns are known as gray goods. These are converted by bleaching, dyeing, and other processes into finished fabrics. Some fabrics are sold in the gray state, as are muslin and unbleached sheeting, but most fabrics are converted before being sold. The names of gray goods are sometimes distinct names, e.g., fine, plain, and print cloth. However, the gray-goods name may be retained as the converted name, for example, *broadcloth*. Yarn-dyed fabrics are known as mill-finished fabrics, since they are not made up as plain gray goods, though the white yarns may be bleached after the fabric has been woven.

Selvages. Plain selvages are usually woven in the same weave as the

---

[1] The material in this chapter was assembled by Elvira Lindquist.
[2] John Hoye, *Staple Cotton Fabrics* (New York: Hoye Publishing Co., 1942).
Mauersberger and Schwarz, *Rayon Handbook*.
Merrill, Macromac, and Mauersberger, *American Cotton Handbook*.
Von Bergen and Mauersberger, *American Wool Handbook*.

fabric, although the warp yarns of the selvage are often more compact.

Tape selvages are wider and firmer to give added strength to the edges of towels, sheets, and drapery and curtain fabrics.

For narrow fabrics, the cloth may be woven twice its finished width with two extra selvages woven into the center. The wider fabric is then cut through the center, leaving split selvages which will ravel if they are not hemmed.

Yarn Count and Balanced Strength. Having an equal yarn count in warp and filling of a fabric does not mean that warp and filling are necessarily of equal strength. In order to facilitate weaving, warp yarns are frequently stronger than filling yarns. In the process of weaving, the wear and tension on the warps are greater than on the fillings. On the labels of sheets, as well as other utilitarian fabrics, it is desirable to have the tensile strength stated for both the warp and the filling directions. Yarn count alone is a somewhat vague indication of durability.

Balanced strength is attained in a fabric when the tensile strengths of warp and filling are equal. Sheets usually tear in the lengthwise direction as they are wearing out. This would indicate a need for better balance between the tensile strengths of the filling and the warp yarns in this fabric. A drapery fabric has more strain on warp than filling yarns. It would, therefore, seem better to have the greater strength in the warp of drapery fabrics. Balanced strength is often desirable in clothing fabrics because the strain is often as great on one set of yarns as on the other, especially in work and play clothes.

Preparation of Yarns for Weaving. At the mill where the weaving is to be done, the yarns, both warp and filling, need to be prepared for the loom. Below are the general procedures in these steps preliminary to the weaving.

Spooling. The individual yarns are prepared for warping by the spooling process. Warp yarns are generally shipped to the weaving mill on various types of small spools or cones. From the smaller spools, yarn is wound onto large cones or cheeses. Rayon and other manufactured fiber yarns are sometimes shipped on cones which necessitate no rewinding. During the rewinding, the yarn is measured and is also inspected for weak places, slubs, and kinks which may be removed. If the fabric is to be yarn dyed, some yarns are wound on hollow perforated jackspools or made into skeins; other yarns are wound into balls for the dyeing. Processes, such as the tying of the weaver's knot and replacement of spools, are being done automatically more than formerly.

Warping. Winding all of the warp yarn to be used for a fabric onto a warp beam in an even, smooth sheet is the process known as "warping." The cheeses or large cones which have been prepared are placed on creels holding from 300 to over 1,000 cones each. From these, the yarns are led through reels and combs in order to be arranged smoothly as they are wound automatically onto the warp beam. Sections may be warped from each creel and then combined to give the complete width of the fabric, or the yarns from several creels may be wound onto the warp beam at one time or in successive sections.

Sizing or slashing. A solution of certain substances is applied to warp yarns to decrease breakage during weaving. Surface fibers are smoothed down, and the yarn is also made more compact and stronger, so that it will better stand the friction of the heddles and reed.

As the solution is applied, the yarns go from warp beams through a slash box, between squeeze rollers, over drying cylinders, and onto another warp beam which is then ready to be set on the loom (see Fig. 16.1).

Recently a hot-air drying unit has been produced which cuts in half the time of slashing. The sized yarns pass through a box-like compartment where they are allowed to remain round instead of being flattened by the drying cylinders. This produces stronger yarns.

If fabrics are to be dyed after weaving, a sizing must be selected which can easily be removed before the dyeing. If, on the other hand, the fabric has been yarn dyed, the sizing may remain on the fabric and will give a desirable hand.

The substances used in sizing differ for cotton, woolens and worsteds, rayons, and other fabrics. Following is a list of the general types of substances used:

a) Adhesives hold the fibers together. Starches from corn, potatoes, tapioca, rice, wheat, sago, and sweet potatoes are used mostly on cotton fabrics. Gums are used to toughen the starch film. Dextrines, gums and glues, and some starches are used on wool fabrics. Gelatins are used most on rayons.

b) Softeners give pliability and lubricate the yarns. Various fats, waxes, and oils are used on cotton fabrics for softening. Soaps, sulfonated oils, and surface active materials increase penetration. Sulfonated oils and coconut oil are used on rayons.

c) Deliquescents, such as glycerine, are used in dry climates to keep the yarn adequately moist.

d) Antiseptics are used to prevent mildew, molds, and bacterial destruction.

Drawing in the warps. Warp yarns are laced through the harnesses (see Fig. 16.2). After the warp yarns have been sized, the warp beam is put into place on the back of the loom (a). The warp yarns are then drawn through the heddles (c,c') of the harness (b,b') according to a drawing-in draft. This draft depends upon the yarn count and weave of the fabric to be woven. Drawing-in is usually done by hand with a hook when a loom is first set up for a new type of fabric. After the loom has started operating, however, the warps of each succeeding

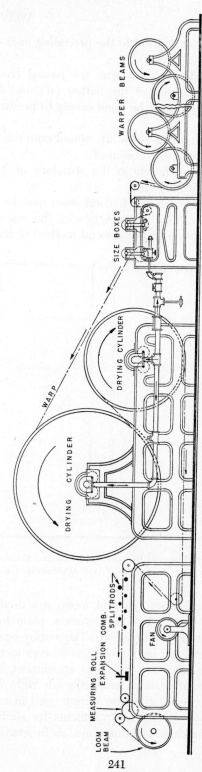

Fig. 16.1. Slashing equipment Warp yarns go from warper beam through size boxes, to drying cylinders, measuring roll, and loom beam. *Source: Von Bergen and Mauersberger, American Wool Handbook, 635.*

241

warp beam may be tied or twisted to the preceding ones either by hand or mechanically.

Reeding the warp. The warp yarns are passed from the heddles through the dents in the reed of the batten (d) and then on to the cloth beam (g). Reeding must be done evenly to prevent warp streaks in the finished fabric.

Bobbin winding. The filling yarns are wound onto the bobbins which fit the shuttle (e) of the loom to be used.

Weaving Looms. By variation in the structure of looms, plain or figured weaves may be produced.

Two-harness loom. A plain two-harness loom may be used for making a plain weave. Fig. 16.2 is a diagram of the essential parts of a plain loom and a description of the general method of its operation.

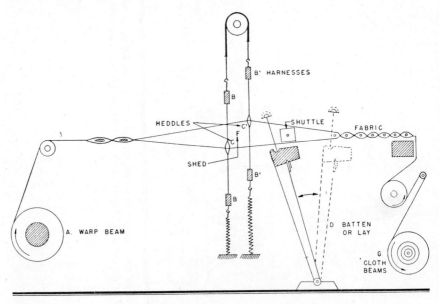

Fig. 16.2. Parts of the loom essential to weaving the cloth. *Source: Von Bergen and Mauersberger,* AMERICAN WOOL HANDBOOK, *635.*

Other looms. Several other types of looms are used in addition to the plain two-harness loom. For twill weaves, plain looms with three to eleven or more harnesses are used. The dobby-head loom weaves small-figure designs, and the jacquard loom weaves large-figure designs such as those in table damask. The leno attachment is a special type of harness which alternately skips warp threads right and left so that they cross each other, giving the leno design used in marquisettes. In a box loom, a box with several compartments for shuttles permits the use of several colors or kinds of filling yarn, as in weaving plaids. The box moves up and down by a set mechanism so as to place the shuttle with the color of yarn desired ready for use at the right time.

A new loom does not use the older types of shuttle to insert filling. A thread carrier, which weighs only an ounce (see Fig. 16.3), pulls the filling yarn across from a large cone at the side of the loom. The yarn is cut off, and the ends are tucked in on both sides. Then the carrier returns to pick up another filling yarn. This Sulzer loom operates two to three times as fast as the older type of loom.

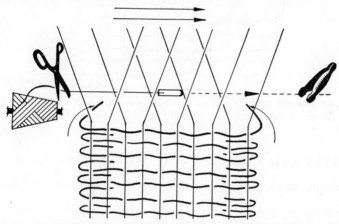

Fig. 16.3. **The new one-ounce shuttle pulls picks across the fabric from a yarn package.** *Source: "New Textile Machines Are Ahead." By permission of the editors of* FORTUNE.

Weaving Motions. The three primary motions used in weaving are shedding, picking, and beating-up or lay motion.

Shedding. To form a shed (f) or opening for the shuttle to pass through, one harness is lifted while the other is lowered. Then, to form the next shed, the opposite harness is lifted. For plain weave, alternate warp yarns have been laced through the heddles (c,c') of two harnesses (b,b').

Picking. Picking is the propulsion of the shuttle from one side of the loom to the other to put in the pick or shot, as the filling yarn is known. An automatic battery or magazine at the side of the loom replaces the bobbins in the shuttle as the yarn is used up.

Beating-up or lay motion. The batten or lay (d) moves forward automatically after the shuttle has carried the pick through the shed, to push the pick close to the fabric previously formed.

As these three primary motions follow one another in rapid succession, the loom also lets off warp yarn and rolls the woven fabric onto the cloth beam. Automatic stops occur whenever a yarn breaks and needs to be repaired. Since much of the work is done automatically, one attendant operates several looms.

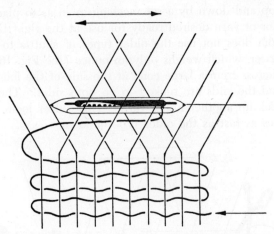

Fig. 16.4. The old bobbin-carrying shuttle moves forth and back across the fabric. *Source: "New Textile Machines Are Ahead." By permission of the editors of* FORTUNE.

WEAVES AND VARIATIONS IN WOVEN CONSTRUCTION

All woven fabrics are constructed by the interlacing of two sets of

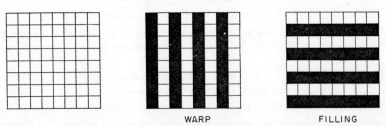

                                                       WARP   FILLING

Fig. 16.5. Woven designs are plotted on design paper. The yarns which run lengthwise in the fabric are known as warp or ends. The yarns which run crosswise are known as filling or picks. *Source:* AMERICAN FABRICS, *8 (1948), 141.*

yarns, warp, and filling (ends and picks respectively).

Plain Weave. In plain weave each warp yarn goes alternately over

           A.   B

Fig. 16.6. Plain weave, A is the design, and B is the fabric. *Source:* AMERICAN FABRICS, *2 (1947), 141 and 5 (1948), 104.*

and then under one filling yarn, and each filling yarn goes alternately over and then under one warp yarn. The next yarn goes over and under the opposite yarns from the preceding one. This weave requires the simplest threading and operation of the loom. Plain weave was the first basic weave.

Numerous types of fabrics are possible with the plain weave. Sheer fabrics, such as organdy or batiste, are made with fine yarns and low yarn count. Fabrics that are strong, yet light in weight, may be made with fine-combed or well-carded yarns and high yarn count as in balloon cloth, typewriter ribbon cloth, and percale sheeting. Strong heavy fabrics, such as canvas (also called duck), may be made with large ply yarns compactly woven. Low-twist filling yarns are used in soft-filled sheetings which are converted into flannels. Very high-twist yarns in the filling, or in both warp and filling, give crepes. Coarse, uneven yarns give crashes. Hard-twist yarns are used in transparent resilient fabrics, as in ninons, voiles, and scrims. Numerous checked, plaid, and striped fabrics, such as the ginghams and chambrays, are made from yarns which are dyed before they are woven. Thus variations in texture and appearance are given to plain-weave fabrics by the type and size of yarn and the compactness with which they are woven.

Basket Weaves. Basket weaves are derivatives of plain weave. In making a basket weave, two or more adjacent yarns are woven as one

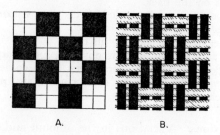

A.   B.

Fig. 16.7. Basket weave, A is the design and B is the fabric. *Source:* AMERICAN FABRICS, *5 (1948), 106.*

yarn, forming small squares over the fabric. In balanced basket weaves, both warp and filling yarns are grouped alike by twos, threes, fours, sixes, or eights. In unbalanced basket weaves, the yarns are grouped two warps to one filling, four warps to two fillings, and similar groupings in which warp and filling differ. These sometimes give a ribbed effect. Basket-woven fabrics are often more porous and loose textured than plain-woven fabrics. Interesting color effects can be achieved when they are yarn dyed. Irregular basket weaves often give interesting texture effects.

Ribbed and Corded Fabrics. Ribbed or corded fabrics have ridges running either lengthwise or crosswise in the fabric. In some fabrics, these ridges are adjacent; in others, they are spaced apart. There is a number of ways of making ribbed or corded fabrics. Sometimes one method is used alone; sometimes it is combined with another. Some of the methods for making ribbed or corded fabrics follow:

1. A larger filling yarn may be used to give a crosswise rib or a larger warp yarn to give a lengthwise rib. The larger yarn may be a ply yarn or a loosely spun yarn to give more roundness to the rib. Rep, faille, and bengaline have larger filling yarns.
2. Slub yarns, flake yarns, and other yarns uneven in diameter give or augment ribbed effects.
3. Warp and filling may have both large and small yarns grouped so as to form ribs or cords in dimities and some ginghams.
4. In broadcloths, poplins, ribbed taffetas, failles, faille crepes, and reps, a ribbed effect is obtained by using two, three, or four times as many warps as fillings. The warps are crowded together and undulate over and under the filling yarns which are spaced farther apart.
5. In piqués and Bedford cords, some of the filling yarns float across the back of the cord at a tension which shapes the lengthwise cord. Usually these filling yarns weave into the regular weave of the plain area. Stuffer yarns are extra warp yarns placed at the back of the fabric under the filling floats to round out the wider cords. In birdseye piqué, the stuffer yarns are extra filling yarns, and the back floats have been formed by warp yarns. Also, the ribs form a diamond-shaped design. In waffle piqués, the long floats of both warp and filling form the ridges of the squares on the right side of the fabric, as well as on the back.
6. Pile loops may be arranged in corded effects as in friezes, especially when the loops have been woven over wires.
7. Spacing in pile weave gives corduroy its cord.
8. Alternate slack and regular tension on groups of warp yarns will give lengthwise crinkled cords as in seersuckers. The corded effect may also be given by using alternate stripes of seersucker and piqué in the fabric known as seersucker piqué.

Crepe Constructions. Variations in the amount and direction of twist in yarns may be used in a number of ways to give a creped appearance to fabrics. Crepe yarns are very high-twist yarns which crinkle after weaving when the tension is released by removing the gums and sizings on the yarns. Crepe yarns may be used in both warp and filling, or only in the warp, or only in the filling.

1. S and Z yarns are used alternately in many crepes. These may alternate one S and one Z, two S and two Z or, less frequently larger groups may be used. A full or balanced crepe has crepe yarns alternating S and Z in both warp and filling. A warp crepe has crepe yarns alternating S and Z in the warp, with low- or regular-twist yarns used in the filling. A filling crepe has crepe yarns alternating S and Z in the filling, and low- or regular-twist yarns in the warp.
2. Combination twist yarns may be used in which one ply has a crepe twist and the other ply has a low twist. This is a variation of the plain crepe

yarn. In rayon crepes the high-twist ply is viscose rayon and the low-twist ply is cellulose acetate. These yarns give the texture we see in alpaca and moss crepes.

3. Intermittent spun yarns, in which one portion of the yarn has high twist and the next portion has no twist, are used in producing kimono crepes.

Weaves may be varied in a number of ways to produce crepe fabrics.

1. Seersuckers have crinkled stripes alternating with plain stripes. In weaving seersuckers, sections of the warp yarn are held slack while the alternate sections of warp yarn are held taut. This allows the yarns under slack tension to crinkle up. In seersucker piqué, the crinkled seersucker stripes alternate with piqué cords. Filling seersuckers, those with stripes going across the fabric, are made by weaving sections of crepe filling yarn alternately with sections of low-twist filling yarns. When moistened, the crepe yarns shrink, leaving the other sections crinkled.

2. Granite weaves give a pebbled appearance to fabrics. Floats in both warp and filling directions, usually extending over not more than two yarns, break up the surface.

3. Small dobby-figure weaves, some of which resemble basket weave by being worked in blocks, others appearing as a group of floats on the surface of the fabric, are used especially for blouse crepes. Some are made with crepe yarns, others with lower-twist yarns.

4. Matelassé crepes are woven dobby or Jacquard figures and are made of two layers of fabric which alternate in the figure and background. The background is usually made with crepe yarns, and the design is made with ordinary yarns and is puffy.

Creped fabrics may be produced by other means than the use of high twist yarns. Plisse and blister crepes are produced by chemical treatment and by embossing of resin treated fabric (see Chapter Nineteen).

Pile Constructions. Pile fabrics are those in which extra warp or filling yarns form a surface of either loops or cut yarn ends on the fabric. The weave of the backing may be either plain or twill. The length of the pile will differ in fabrics; in velvet it is comparatively short, whereas in plush it is long. Pile fabrics have soft, rich textures. Crush-resistant finishes are being applied to many of them which are being made of various fibers. Velvets are made of nylon, rayon, cotton, mohair, or silk. Velveteens and corduroys are made usually of cotton but are also made of rayon or other fibers. Velveteens usually have a clear face; corduroys are distinguished by alternating stripes of pile and plain fabric. Plushes vary, some being made of wool and others of silk.

Warp pile fabrics include velvet, plush, velours, and various pile rugs which have a cut pile. Frieze and terrycloth have a looped pile.

Most velvets are now woven as double cloth with an extra warp woven between the two layers of fabric. This pile yarn may weave under one filling yarn on each side, giving a V-construction or it may interlace with

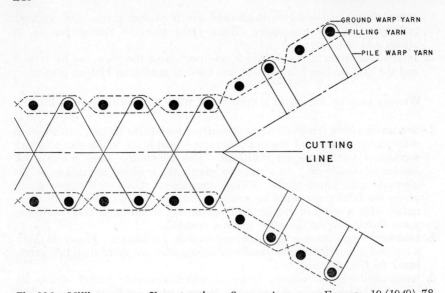

Fig. 16.8. Millinery weave, V-construction. *Source:* AMERICAN FABRICS, *10 (1949),* 78.

three filling yarns giving a W-construction which holds the pile more

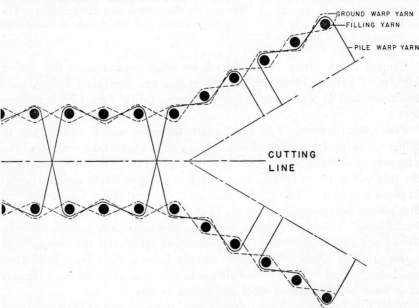

Fig. 16.9. Transparent weave, W-construction. *Source:* AMERICAN FABRICS, *10 (1949),* 78.

firmly. After weaving, the fabric is carefully cut into two pieces through the center of the pile yarns holding the two fabrics together.

Another method used for making cut-warp pile fabrics is that of weaving the extra warp over wires. In frieze, the wires are withdrawn so as to leave the loops, although sometimes some of the loops may be cut. In rugs and plush, the wires have a cutting edge at the tip so that as they are withdrawn they cut the pile yarns.

In weaving terrycloth, with its uncut loops on both sides of the fabric, a special loom is used. One set of warp yarns interlaces with the filling to form the ground; another set of warp yarns forms the loops. The ground fabric needs to be firmly woven because the strength and service qualities of the toweling is dependent on this. Ply yarns are preferable for this warp. To form the loops, the loom operates so that the tension on the pile yarn is slack as the reed pushes back every third pick. Of three picks, two go under the loops formed by the pile yarn, and one goes over the pile yarns to hold them in place. Every other warp pile yarn forms loops on the other side. The ground warps weave between these pile yarns. Loops may be made with single or double yarns. Since absorbency is dependent on the loops, the double-yarn loops should give greater absorbency if other characteristics of the towels compared are alike. The length of the loops will also affect the absorbency of the towel.

Filling pile fabrics include corduroy, velveteen, and filling plushes.

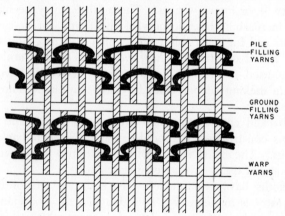

Fig. 16.10. Arrangement of filling pile yarns in weaving corduroy. Floats are cut after weaving, "W" pile. *Source: G. White, "Cotton Corduroy,"* AMERICAN DYESTUFF REPORTER, *30-12 (1941), 295.*

These are woven so that the floats across the fabric are formed by the pile filling yarn and the other filling yarn interlaces to form the back of the fabric. The floats are then cut and brushed up. In corduroys, the floats are woven so as to have spaces between the cords; in velveteen and plush the arrangement allows for complete coverage of the fabric.

Backed and Double Cloths. Backed and double cloths are those made

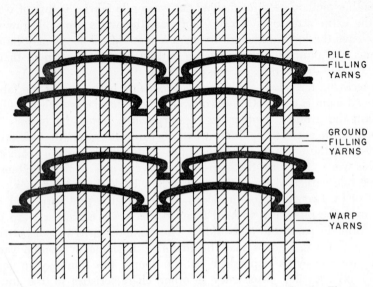

PILE
FILLING
YARNS

GROUND
FILLING
YARNS

WARP
YARNS

Fig. 16.11. Arrangement of filling pile yarns in weaving corduroy. Floats are cut after weaving, "V" pile. *Source: White,* "Cotton Corduroy."

with more than a single set of warps and fillings. They may be woven with plain, twill, or figure weaves. These fabrics may be made for the purpose of increasing the thickness of the fabric for warmth, for excluding light, and for reversible colors which give a self-lined effect.

A filling backed construction has two sets of fillings and one set of warps. It is used in making blankets, some of which have reversible colors, and in making silence cloth for table padding. These are both napped fabrics.

A warp backed construction has two sets of warps and one set of fillings. This construction is used for making French back serge and other suitings. The heavier satin ribbons are also made with two sets of warp. Some of these have reversible colors.

Double cloths have two sets of warp and two sets of filling. Upholstery tapestry is made with a face filling in the dominant color and a back filling which contrasts in color, a face warp which usually matches the face filling in color and a back warp which usually has a variety of colors. In the colored design, the back filling and the back warp are brought to the front of the fabric. In matelassé crepe, the warp and filling crepe yarns form the background on the right side of the fabric and are on the back side of the design; the warp and filling plain yarns form the puffy design on the right side of the fabric and go behind the crepe yarns otherwise. Some overcoatings made in double cloth are reversible. Others are plain-colored fabrics in which the double construction helps to give a very heavy, warm overcoat fabric.

Some triple-woven felts are made for industrial fabrics.

Leno Weaves. The leno weaves give an open-textured fabric with

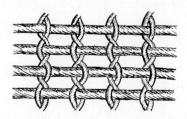

Fig. 16.12. Leno weave. *Source:* AMERICAN FABRICS, 5 (1948), 106.

less slippage and greater strength than plain weave would give in so open a fabric. In the simplest leno weave, pairs of warp yarns weave together, crossing to the right and left of each other as the picks interlace. Groups of warp yarns, instead of just the pairs of yarns, may weave in the same way. Also, plain weave and leno may be used together in a fabric. Curtain and dress marquisettes, mosquito nets, laundry nets, dish cloths, and various mesh fabrics are woven with leno weaves, some with fine yarns and some with coarse yarns.

Figure Weaves. Extra warp and filling yarns may be used in several ways for added design. In some drapery, light upholstery, and bedspread fabrics extra warps arranged in stripes, often in various colors, float along the back of the fabric until raised to the right side of the fabric for the design. When this same construction is used on dress fabrics, the back floats are often cut off, giving a clipped design.

Extra filling yarns are put in with a box loom for the clipped dots in domestic dotted Swiss and for other small designs on fabrics. This permits the use of a contrasting color for the figure. In another method, known as beat-up dot, the yarn for the dot is put in with the regular shuttle and allowed to float between figures. Floats are cut after weaving. This is a cheaper construction and does not allow for the color variation possible in using the box loom.

In swivel design, extra shuttles weave extra filling yarns around and around a group of warps to give the tied dots found in some imported dotted Swiss.

In lappet design weaving, an attachment consisting of a row of needles threaded with warp whip threads moves back and forth to produce the design which may be a continuous zigzag line or may be clipped off to a small design. The design looks much like embroidery.

The plain loom may use from two to six or seven harnesses. It is possible to use this loom for some simple figure weaving. However, the dobby loom, whose chain mechanism allows for the operation of up to 25 harnesses, is more extensively used for small figure weaves. The Jacquard loom is used for large figures and the more complicated weaves. On this loom, every warp yarn can be controlled independently. A series of large cards is punched with holes according to the pattern of the design and, as the weaving is done, the warp yarns for which holes are punched will be raised to the upper part of the shed and the rest of the warp yarns will form the lower part of the shed as the shuttle goes through. The number of cards needed relates to the number of filling yarns in the pattern repeat.

Dobby figure weaves are used on a variety of fabrics. The designs are formed by short floats in either warp or filling, sometimes both. The small designs and stripes on madras shirting and madras ginghams are typical. The background fabric often has a plain weave. Huckaback and birdseye figures, which are all-over figures, are used on towelings, drapery, and upholstery fabrics.

Jacquard-woven figures are generally larger than dobby-woven figures. They are formed by floats as in the satin weaves. In table damasks, the satin woven floats reverse in the design and background. Thus, in linen table damasks the background is made with warp floats and the design with filling floats; in cotton table damask the opposite arrangement is used, filling floats in the background and warp floats in the design.

In single damask, the yarns float over four and go under one, giving a five-leaf construction. In double damask, the yarns float over seven and go under one, giving an eight-leaf construction which makes possible a greater compactness in weaving and a smoother, more luxurious texture. When the double-damask construction is used in low-yarn-count damasks, however, the fabric is weak, because the long floats then snag and break more readily. The best table damasks are woven with fine, even, compact yarns.

Drapery and upholstery Jacquard-woven fabrics are made as damasks, brocades, tapestries, matelassés, brocatelles, and denims in various fibers and fiber combinations for those who prefer woven patterns to printed designs. As in the linen table damasks, these drapery and upholstery damasks have the floats of a satin weave in filling direction in the design and in warp direction in the background. Warp and filling may be in the same color or in contrasting colors. Brocades are similar to damasks in having a satin float design on either a satin or ribbed background, but they are usually finer and have floral patterns in multicolor formed by either warp or filling, sometimes in addition to designs formed by regular fillings. Tapestries are double cloth-upholstery fabrics in which one warp and one filling give the face background and the back warp and filling in contrasting colors are brought forward to form the design. Matelassés are also double-cloth upholstery fabrics which have a padded or quilted texture given by interlacing the coarse back filling with the face in such a way that it causes the top layer to puff up. In brocatelles the warp satin floats of the design stand out from the background because of stiff filling yarns, usually made of linen. Upholstery denims are woven on either dobby or Jacquard looms and are usually in one color, although the filling yarns may contrast and may have two or three colors. These are usually all cotton single-cloth fabrics. Most of them have rather heavy yarns.

Dress brocades, matelassés, and damasks are also woven on Jacquard looms. The damasks have filling satin designs on warp satin background. Brocades have smaller floral designs, usually on satin background, and often in several colors. Dress matelassés are crepes with puffy designs woven with regular-twist yarns and with background woven with crepe yarns in a double-cloth construction.

Twill Weaves. Twill is the second basic weave. It is recognized by diagonal lines, in some fabrics more prominent than in others, formed across the fabric by the arrangement of interlacings and floats. Twill is the most used weave in woolen and worsted suitings, dress goods, and coatings, and it is extensively used in heavy and sturdy cottons.

In weaving twills, no less than three harnesses are used on the loom. Although plain looms with three, four, and five harnesses are most commonly used, some cotton twills use up to 15 harnesses, and wool twills use up to 22 harnesses. Both plain and dobby looms are used for regular and irregular twills, and the Jacquard loom is used for large-figure woven twills.

Twills have fewer interlacings per unit area of fabric and per length of yarn than do plain-weave fabrics of comparable yarn construction. This permits the development of certain desirable characteristics in twill-woven fabrics, such as the following:

1. Twills can be made stronger than plains because more yarns per inch may be crowded together, since the floats permit some overlapping of yarns. If the same number of yarns per inch is used, however, the plain weave is the stronger.
2. Windproofing in outdoor fabrics is also made possible by this compactness and overlapping of the short floats.
3. Featherproofing is produced in tickings; the twill weaves are preferred.
4. The floats of twills, regular and broken, permit ease in napping flannels.
5. The floats of twills, as well as those of small dobby figure weaves, make for easy absorbency in towelings.
6. The twill weave is used in various ways for design, as in the herringbone and damask fabrics.
7. Twills permit various textures—the smoothness of satins, given by the long floats held close together; and the firm ridges in 9- and 11-harness gabardines, given by the compactness of shorter floats.

A number of factors affects the general appearance of twills and leads to various methods of designating types of twills. Various classifications are suggested in the following methods of comparison:

1. The yarn which makes the float on the right side of the fabric affects the appearance and essential care of the fabrics. (a) Warp-face twills are those with warp floats on the right side. (b) Filling-face twills are those with filling floats. These two types are referred to as uneven twills, because the amounts of warp and filling on the face of the fabric are uneven. Twills which have both warp and filling floats of equal length are made with an even number of harnesses, as the four-harness twills, and are called (c) even, balanced, or reversible twills. The back side of the fabric has the same construction as the right side, which accounts for its being reversible.

2. One distinction is based on the direction of the twill line. Twills in which the twill lines go upward to the right are known as (a) right twills. Twills in which the twill lines go upward to the left are known as (b) left twills.

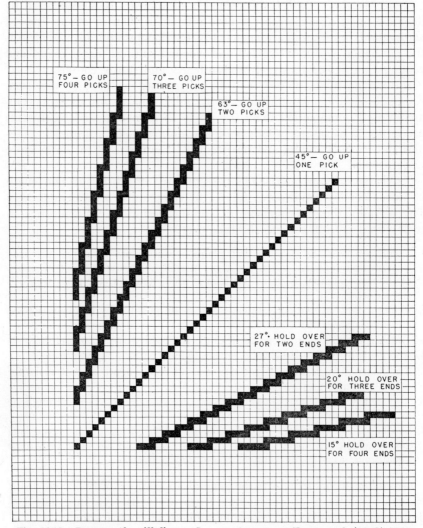

Fig. 16.13. Degrees of twill lines. *Source:* AMERICAN FABRICS, *8 (1948), 142.*

3. Another basis for differentiating twills is the angle of the twill line.   The 45° angle of (a) regular twills is the most common, since it is formed when the interlacings advance or progress by one yarn (steps up to next yarn above) in a fabric where the yarn count of warp and filling is nearly equal.   Crowding of either warp or filling will change the angle slightly. Angles of 63°, 70°, and 75° occur in (b) steep twills.   Steepness is increased some by crowding but is increased mainly by advancing the interlacings by two (skips one yarn in stepping up to the second yarn above) in a 63° twill, by three in a 70° twill, and by four in a 75° twill.   These are known as progressions of two, three, and four.   (3) Reclining twills have angles of 27°, 20°, and 15°.   Angles of 27° are retarded by two in interlacing (interlace with second yarn to right or left), 20° angles by three, and 15° angles by four.   Crowding filling yarns will recline the angle slightly in these.

4. The general character of the twill line gives a large group of types of twills, of which the following are the more prevalent.   (a) Regular twills have straight-diagonal twill lines running parallel across the whole width of the fabric.   (b) Double-line twills are similar, except that the twill lines are grouped by twos, as in cavalry twill (also called tricotine), the two twill lines held closer together than the spaces between the groups. (c) Broken twills have short twill lines going both to left and to right. (d) Herringbones have stripes formed by reversing the twill direction in adjacent portions.

5. The distinctness of twill lines ranges from (a) prominent to (b) subdued. Another classification based on the distinctness of twill lines is that of twills' being (a) smooth faced or (b) twill faced.   Twill lines may be accented or subdued in various ways such as the following:

a) High yarn counts will give more prominent twill lines in fabrics woven with the same number of harnesses.

b) High twist in yarns makes the lines prominent.

c) Combed yarns, because of their smoothness, increase the clearness of the lines.

d) Ply yarns make the diagonal line stand out more.

e) Contrasting color in warp and filling makes the lines show up better.

f) Long floats, coupled with distinct interlacing lines, give a more prominent twill.   Long floats, coupled with indistinct lines as in the satins, however, give very subdued twill lines.

g) To give distinct interlacing lines in the twills made with 5 or more harnesses, the warp may interlace with more than one yarn between the lines of floats.   In those with 8 or more harnesses, the warp interlaces in a plain weave or nearly plain weave between the rows of floats, as in an 11-harness gabardine with a repeat of $\frac{511}{121}$.

h) Progressions of one give a more distinct twill line, unless the progression of two or more is coupled with the interlacing of warp with more than one yarn between the lines of floats as mentioned in (*g*).   Satin weaves are twill variations with very subdued twill lines which produce a smooth face.

i) Another method used in weaving to make twill lines prominent is that of combining the direction of the S or Z twist in yarns forming the floats with the opposite direction in the twill line.   Thus, to make a twill line prominent these combinations are made:

(1)   An S-twist warp with a right twill in a warp face twill.

(2)   A Z-twist warp with a left twill in a warp face twill.

(3)   An S-twist filling with a left twill in a filling face twill.

(4) A Z-twist filling with a right twill in a filling face twill.

Using the opposite combinations will give subdued twill lines.

6. Another basis for classifying twills is the number of harnesses used in weaving them. The more commonly used constructions are these:

(a) Three-harness twills are the simplest. Most of them are warp-faced fabrics, $\frac{2}{1}$, including the cotton jeans, denims, and drills used for work and sport clothes, the wool and wool and rayon plainest gabardines and suitings.

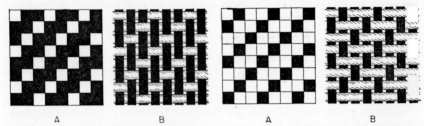

A   B   A   B

Fig. 16.14.   Three-harness twill, right hand.   The two diagrams on the right show the filling face, those on the left the warp face.   A is the design and B is the fabric. *Source:* AMERICAN FABRICS, *2 (1947) 141.*

(b) Four-harness twills include a few warp-faced, $\frac{3}{1}$, fabrics but most four-harness twills are woven in the even-sided reversible $\frac{2}{2}$ weave. Fabrics in this weave include serge, flannels, suiting worsteds and sharkskins, as well as tweeds. Some are herringbones.

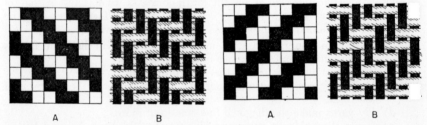

A   B   A   B

Fig. 16.15.   Four-harness twill, $\frac{2}{2}$, right hand (two diagrams on the right), and left hand (diagrams on the left).   A is the design and B is the fabric. *Source:* AMERICAN FABRICS, *2 (1947), 141; 5 (1948), 154.*

(c) Five-harness twills are mostly the smooth-faced, often lustrous satins, sateens, and damasks. The satin weaves used in weaving these are smooth, subdued twill variations.

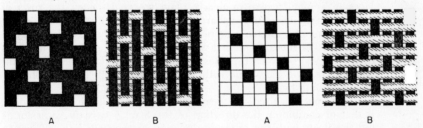

A   B   A   B

Fig. 16.16.   Five-harness satin weave.   The two diagrams on the left show the warp face, those on the right the filling face.   A is the design and B is the fabric. *Source:* AMERICAN FABRICS, *8 (1948), 143.*

(d) Eight-harness twills produce two much used fabrics: cavalry twill, also called tricotine, a double-lined twill; and double damask. Some satin and brocades are also eight-harness.

(e) Nine- and eleven-harness poiret twills and gabardines have prominent twill lines separated by interweaving the warp with six filling yarns between the twill lines.

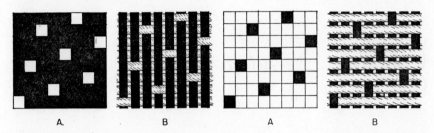

Fig. 16.17. **Eight-harness satin weave. The two diagrams on the left show the warp face, those on the right the filling face. A is the design and B is the fabric.** *Source:* AMERICAN FABRICS, *2 (1947), 141; 5 (1948), 106.*

Satin Weaves. Satin weaves are twill weave variations with long floats and indistinct interlacings and are used in weaving satins, sateens, damasks, and brocades. These fabrics are either warp or filling face. Five-harness and eight-harness constructions are most frequently used. In a five-harness weave, the warp yarn weaves over one and under four, $\frac{1}{4}$ for filling float weaves, and over four and under one $\frac{4}{1}$ for warp float weaves. The interlacings advance two yarns to either right or left and three yarns in the other directions. The result is that an indistinct twill line appears toward right and another toward left. The wide spacing of the points of interlacing and the long floats give a very smooth texture.

Sateens are cotton fabrics, either warp-faced referred to as warp sateens, or filling-faced referred to as filling sateens. Satins are very smooth, warp-faced silk, nylon, or filament rayon fabrics. Damasks are Jacquard-figure woven fabrics in which the direction of the satin floats in the design is opposite to the satin floats of the background. Brocades have colored floral designs on satin or ribbed background.

Chapter Seventeen

Nonwoven Fabrics[1]

KNITTING AND KNITS

KNITTING was invented in the 15th century, reportedly in Scotland. Knitting is the process of making fabrics with knitting needles by inter-looping the yarns to form connected chains of loops or stitches. The vertical chains of loops formed are called wales. The series of loops going across the fabric are called courses. Knit fabrics have a great deal of elasticity because the loops allow for stretching of the fabric in all directions to a much greater extent than is possible with woven fabrics.

Knit fabrics are made from various types of fibers and yarns. Yarns used for knitting must have uniform size and twist. For this reason, combed yarns are preferred. Any thin spots in the yarns would allow for pulling apart at that point. The yarns must be flexible to form the loops easily. A soft yarn with low twist is most pliable. Since the yarns must have a certain amount of strength in spite of the low twist, the yarns are often ply yarns. Fibers used are preferably the longer and the more flexible ones, as found in worsted and combed cotton yarns. Yarns must be elastic and smooth in order to be knit easily. Careful handling of the yarn in knitting is important to keep the yarns in good condition. If the elasticity is well retained by not stretching the yarn in knitting, garments will fit well and will not shrink readily to too small a size.

[1] The material in this chapter was assembled largely by Elvira Lindquist.

Besides the regular smooth yarns of cotton, wool, rayon, and nylon, some novelty yarns are used for texture effects.

Hand Knitting. In hand knitting, the needles used are quite different from those used in machine knitting. For hand knitting, the needles are pointed at one or both ends. Knitting is usually done with two or more needles but may be done with one circular needle. In using the circular needle, the knitting continues around and around, forming the fabric in a tubular shape which may, however, be fashioned to narrower or wider proportions. A tubular form as for mittens may also be made by knitting with four straight, double-pointed needles. For knitting flat pieces, two straight needles, pointed at one end and having a head at the other, are used.

In the process of knitting, the hand knitter first casts on the number of stitches or loops needed across or around the piece to be knitted. In knitting succeeding courses, she places the tip of a needle into each loop, draws another loop through the center of the loop, from the back, and continues along the course forming new loops. If the piece is flat, when the knitter reaches the end of the first course she turns the fabric in such a way that the back side is toward her. It is then necessary to lay the yarn forward before placing the tip of the needle through the loop to pull the new loop through; this process is known as purling. To make plain stitch then, one knits on the right side and purls on the back side. This is not necessary in machine knitting because the fabric is not turned over as the machine knits back on the next row. If a person could knit with both right and left hand equally well she could knit across with her right hand and knit back with her left hand without turning over her fabric. In making the rib stitch, the knitter knits one or two stitches, then purls one or two stitches, and continues alternating the two processes. The rib stitch draws together into a narrower area and gives more in length when it is stretched. This makes it desirable for cuffs, necklines, and waistbands, although it may be used for sweaters.

Machine Knitting.[2] All hand knitting is classed as filling or weft knit. This refers to the fact that the yarn goes across the fabric as it forms the loops. Machine-knit fabrics are either filling or warp knit. In warp-knit fabrics numerous yarns are used. They go in a general warpwise direction, although not straight up and down.

A knitting machine is set up with as many needles as the wales to be knit in the piece of fabric. In machine knitting, two types of needles are used. Both have a hook at the end to pull through the loops. Spring needles are used mostly for knitting fine fabrics, latch needles for the heavier fabrics which have larger yarns. The action of each of the types of needles will be described.

[2] O. Engelhard, "The Principles of Knitgoods Construction," *Rayon Textile Monthly*, 23 (1943), 205, 285, 350, 402, 475, 539, 617.

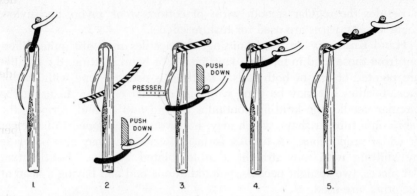

Fig. 17.1. Steps in spring needle knitting. *Source: Merrill, Macormac, and Mauersberger,* AMERICAN COTTON HANDBOOK, *605.*

In knitting, the needles may move up and down, or the fabric may be
moved up and down instead of the needles. In the latter, the general
procedure for knitting with spring needles is described. The fabric already knit is pushed down the needle below the end of the hook. The
yarn is placed under the hook by the yarn guide. A presser pushes the
tip of the hook into the eye or groove so that, as the cloth is lifted,
the preceding loop slips outside of the hook and off into the cloth. This
leaves the new loop on the hook.

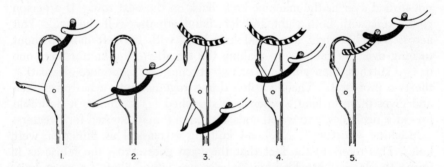

Fig. 17.2. Steps in latch needle knitting. *Source: Merrill, Macormac and Mauersberger,* AMERICAN COTTON HANDBOOK, *606.*

In knitting with a latch needle, as the fabric is pushed down it forces
the latch down and open. The yarn for the new loop is placed by the
yarn guide. As the fabric is lifted, the latch is pushed up so that the
preceding loop slips over the hook into the fabric. The new loop remains on the hook.

Basically, knitting machines are either flat or circular. However, in
order to make the variety of knit goods we have, many variations of these
two types of machines have been developed. Flat knitting machines

have one or two flat plates, also called beds, which hold the needles. Circular machines have one or two rows of needles around a circular plate. These machines knit more rapidly than the flat machines. However, the fashioning of full-fashioned hose, sweaters, and other garments is done on flat machines, as is the knitting of any shaped pieces. Flat machines also knit tubular webbing or flat yard goods from which garments are cut. Circular machines knit only tubular fabric, ranging in size from narrow braid to fabrics more than 40 inches in diameter. Wool jersey is usually purchased in this tubular form for home sewing. Rayon jersey, which is usually warp knit, is sold in a flat piece, having been knit on a flat machine.

Filling knitting. The two most frequently used stitches in filling knitting are the plain or jersey stitch and the rib stitch.

A *plain stitch* in a fabric may be recognized by the prominent wales running lengthwise on the right side and the crosswise ridges formed by the joining of two courses on the back side. The plain stitch may be knit in a tubular-formed fabric on the circular machine with one row

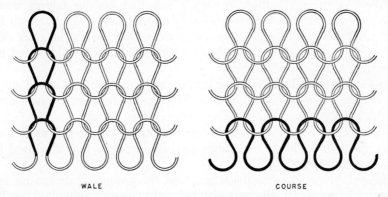

WALE   COURSE

Fig. 17.3. **Plain filling knit, wale and course.** *Source:* KNITTED FABRIC *(New York: Bemberg Corporation),* 3.

of needles, or on a flat machine with two beds of needles when the machine is so operated that it knits first on one bed and then on the next bed with the same yarn. It is also made in a flat piece of fabric on a flat machine with one bed of needles.

A *rib stitch* is recognized by the prominent wales on both sides of the fabric. In a single-ribbed fabric, the stitch is made alternately on the front of the fabric and then on the back. Stitches may also be grouped two wales to the front and two wales to the back, known as Swiss rib, or in any other combination. It is necessary to use the two rows of needles on a circular machine to make a tubular ribbed fabric. A flat piece of ribbed fabric may be made on a flat machine with two beds of needles. On either machine, the two rows of needles face each other, and the knitting is done by alternately making a stitch on one row and the next stitch on the other row of needles. This accounts for the double effect of the fabric made in rib stitch. Ribbed knit stretches more readily and draws together more than plain knit does.

A *purl stitch* is recognized by the prominent ridges formed by the courses on both sides of the fabric. In machine knitting, the purl stitch is made by drawing successive courses of loops to opposite sides of the fabric. This must be done on a special machine, called a links and links machine, which uses latch needles with hooks on both ends. The alternate rows of stitches are made with the opposite ends of the needles. A plain or rib stitch may be made on the same machine. Sweaters using all three stitches—plain, purl, and rib—are knit on the links and links machine.

Tuck stitch is made in knitting when the needle retains a loop of yarn and adds one or more loops as succeeding courses are knit, then casts off the group of loops onto another loop. The tuck stitch is used in making half- and full-cardigan knit fabrics which have a rib stitch modified by the tuck stitch in such a way that heavier fabrics result. Half-cardigan knit has tuck stitches only on the back. The loops on the front side, therefore, are short as compared with those on the back side. Full-cardigan knit has tuck stitches on both sides. The wales stand out more than in regular rib stitch.

Racking or shogging is another stitch modification applied to rib stitch. The needles of one set are moved by the other set between courses, causing the loops to be distorted either diagonally or zigzag.

Eyeletting is done by knitting adjacent stitches together so as to form small openings. This is sometimes used for lacings. It is also used for run stops in hosiery.

Designs. Numerous methods are used for producing design on knit fabrics. Jacquard attachments may be used to control individual needles by punched cards so that large designs are formed. Pattern wheels and pattern drums also act selectively on the needles to create designs. Chain pattern attachments control the knitting so as to combine various stitches in a fabric. Striping attachments make possible stripes, checks, and plaids of different yarns and colors. The float stitch attachment moves some needles out of knitting position so that yarns will float to make stripes or other designs. Extra yarns may be knit on the surface in what is known as a warp stripe pattern. This process is used in clocking for hosiery as well as all over and panel designs.

Plating or plaiting is the use of two yarns on a needle in knitting in place of one yarn. One yarn is held to the back side while the other is on the face of the fabric. The two yarns may differ in color, thus giving a reversible fabric with one color on the one side and another color on the other side. For design, the colored yarns may be reversed, known as reverse plating, so as to bring the contrasting color from the back to the front side of the fabric.   In hosiery, the extra yarn is used in the feet for added strength.   Plating may also be used throughout a fabric which is to be napped.

There are also other methods which use extra yarns in knitting. Double-knit fabrics are made by knitting two separate fabrics which are held together by an occasional stitch.   Pile fabrics are knit by feeding two yarns to each needle but drawing one loop longer on the surface of the fabric.   The pile may be napped to obscure the loops, or it may be sheared or left looped.   Some of these fabrics imitate furs.

Hosiery knitting.   Hosiery of all types is knit on special knitting machines designed for the purpose.   Men's and children's hose and all socks are knit with straight legs, either with or without rib tops, on circular machines.   The rib top may be knit on one machine and the stocking then transferred to another machine for knitting legs and feet, or all processes may be performed on one machine.

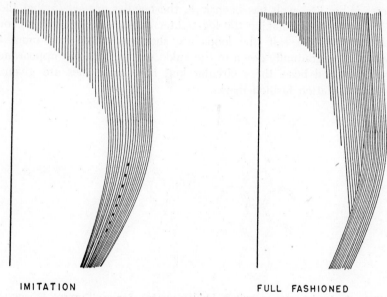

IMITATION   FULL FASHIONED

Fig. 17.4. How to distinguish women's full-fashioned hose. *Source:* KNITTED FABRIC, 11.

Women's hose are either full-fashioned or semifashioned.   The full-fashioned hose are knit on flat machines.   The knitting starts with the welt at the top of the stocking.   As the leg is knit, the number of stitches is decreased by knitting together two or more stitches several times just above the knee and along the calf.   This gives the fashion marks by which we recognize full-fashioned hose.   Shaping of the heel requires the use of additional needles which go out of action again as

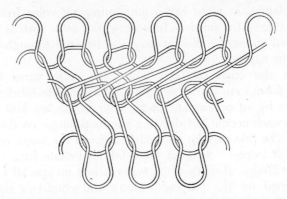

Fig. 17.5. Fashion marks in full-fashioned knitting. *Source:* KNITTED FABRIC, *10.*

the foot is knit. Seams are sewed from toe to top of the hose.

Semifashioned or women's seamless hose are knit on circular machines. When the welt has been knit, the needles are set so that they knit a shorter stitch, making the leg tighter than the welt. Throughout the knitting of the calf, the loops are shortened more and more to narrow the leg gradually down to the ankle. To imitate the appearance of full-fashioned hose, these circular knit hose sometimes are given a seam and imitation fashion marks.

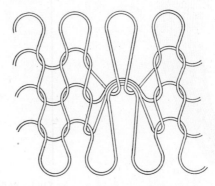

Fig. 17.6. Tuck stick used to imitate fashion marks. *Source:* KNITTED FABRIC, *10.*

Aside from style and color, women select hose by four other designations. These are size, length, denier, and gauge. Size is the length of the foot of the stocking from the tip of the toe through the center of the foot to the back of the heel, given in inches within the half inch. Thus size 9½ means the foot is 9½ inches long. The length of the leg may merely be designated as short, medium, and long or as 30, 32, 34, or 36 inches long.

Denier of the yarn indicates the fineness. As the denier goes up in number, the yarn is coarser.   Thus a 30-denier yarn is larger than a 20-denier yarn.

Gauge indicates the number, and usually also the size, of needles used in 1½ inches of needlebar in knitting the hose.   As the gauge increases, the number of loops or wales increases and the loops are smaller.   This gives a greater fineness in appearance and better elasticity.   Gauge and yarn size are related in knitting, but for a certain denier of yarn, hose of several gauge are knit.   The more commonly used gauge are 45, 48, 51, and 54.   The numbers go up or down by three points.

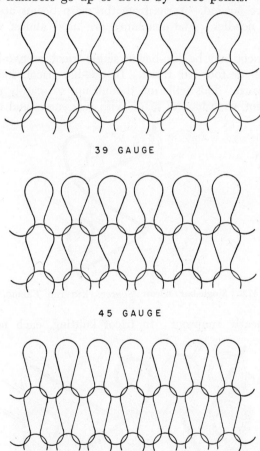

39 GAUGE

45 GAUGE

51 GAUGE

Fig. 17.7. Comparison of gauge in knitting. *Source:* KNITTED FABRIC, *10.*

Semifashioned hose are usually sold by the total number of needles used, usually around 300, rather than by gauge.   If the cut is referred to instead of gauge, cut designates the number of needles in one inch of needlebar.

Warp knitting. Warp knit fabrics have less stretch than filling knit fabrics. They run less readily, too, and some are considered to be runproof. These qualities make warp knits desirable for some under-garments, sleeping garments, and dress fabrics. Warp knits are most used for rayon and synthetic fibers whose yarns are very smooth and would run readily in filling knit.

Whereas the yarns for filling knitting are on large bobbins or cones placed on the machines, the yarns for warp knitting are wound on one, two, or more warp beams. For warp knitting, one or more yarns for each needle are needed. Yarns from the warp beams are led through guides to the needles. Flat machines are used almost exclusivly for warp knitting.

Warp-knit tricot may be one-bar or single tricot, or two-bar or double tricot, or three- or four-bar tricot. In one-bar tricot, loops are made with a single yarn. This will run, though not so readily as filling knit. In two-bar tricot, each loop is made with two yarns, and the fabric be-

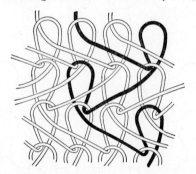

Fig. 17.8. **Single-bar tricot.** *Source:* KNITTED FABRIC, *10.*

comes more nearly runproof. In tricot knitting, each needle knits a

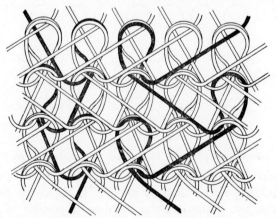

Fig. 17.9. **Double-bar tricot.** *Source:* KNITTED FABRIC, *10.*

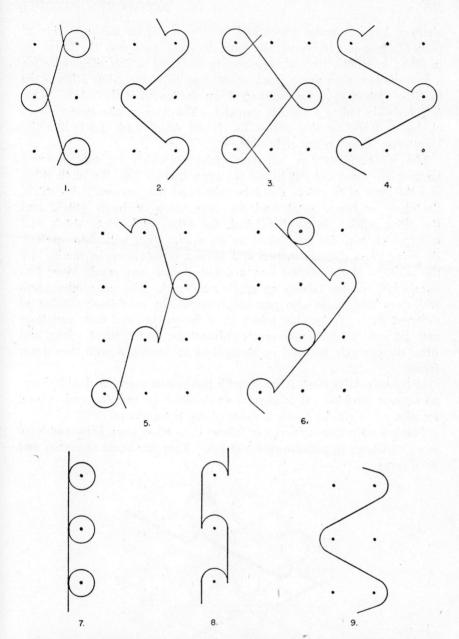

Fig. 17.10. Stitches used in tricot warp knitting: 1. the tricot stitch, 2. the open tricot stitch, 3. the cloth stitch, 4. the open cloth stitch, 5. the Atlas stitch, 6. the reversed Atlas stitch, 7. the chain or fringe stitch, 8. the open variation of the chain or fringe stitch, 9. the filling stitch. *Source: Engelhard, "The Principles of Knitgoods Construction," 402–403.*

267

chain of loops or wales which look like the wales on the right side of plain-filling knit. However, the yarn does not go across the fabric as in filling knitting. Instead, it moves to the right or left diagonally for a few stitches, then moves back again diagonally for a few stitches, so that the path of each yarn zigzags down the length of the fabric. This is not visible unless a yarn is snagged. The back of the fabric shows chains of loops running across the fabric which look much like the lengthwise wales on the right side.

The five basic stitches and their variations which are used in tricot knitting are the tricot stitch and the open tricot stitch; the cloth stitch and the open cloth stitch; the Atlas stitch and the reversed Atlas stitch; the chain or fringe stitch and the open chain or fringe stitch; and the filling stitch. In one-bar tricot, the Atlas stitch, cloth stitch, and tricot stitch may be used alone or in combination with one another. By using cross dyeing, striped and figured fabrics may be made. By the addition of the second bar, a thicker fabric may result, since two interlocked one-bar fabrics are really combined. The more open mesh and sheer fabrics are also possible, however, by combining stitches in different ways. In two-bar tricot, all of the stitches and their variations may be used in many different combinations; or the tricot, cloth, and Atlas stitches may be used by themselves or combined with their open forms.

Warp-knit Atlas cloth is made with fine cotton yarns in double loops on a tricot machine. It is given a suede finish by napping and is used for gloves. A similar fabric is made of rayon for gloves.

Raschel warp knits are coarser fabrics than other warp knits and have more variations in patterns and textures. They are made of cotton and wool yarns.

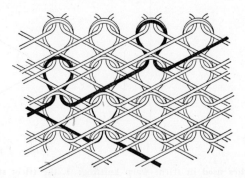

Fig. 17.11. Milanese knitting. *Source:* KNITTED FABRIC, 3.

Milanese warp knit is used only for fine silk and rayon fabrics. It looks much like tricot on both front and back of the fabric. If the yarns are irregular in size, as they are in silk yarns, a slight diagonal shadow appears.   This is because one set of yarns is guided diagonally toward the left while another set of yarns is guided diagonally toward the right, until each yarn reaches the edge of the fabric and returns diagonally in the opposite direction.

Characteristics of Knit Goods.   The quantity of knit clothing has increased greatly.   If you compare the number of knit garments with the number of woven garments you wear, you may sometimes find that you are wearing as many knit as woven garments.   The comfort of knit garments accounts for this to a large extent.   When one is active, knit fabrics will yield to stretching and bending with less strain than do woven fabrics.   Bursting strength, which is measured by applying pressure on a round area, is used as a measure of strength in knit fabrics. Sweaters give us warm garments which are more flexible, yet may be less bulky, than jackets.   For undergarments, knit fabrics shape to the body and yet allow for movement without binding.   Knit garments do not wrinkle readily and require less pressing than do woven fabrics.

Knit fabrics do have some disadvantages when compared with woven fabrics.   They may stretch out of shape and become baggy.   The loops of yarns allow for easy snagging.   The softly spun yarns show abrasion quite readily; fibers may curl up in little balls on the surface of sweaters. When a yarn is broken, hosiery runs very readily.   When laundered, knit sweaters, socks, and other garments may lose shape if they are not stretched on forms or stretched into shape on a flat surface.   Shrinkage tests for knit fabrics allow for stretching the fabric back to original size in so far as possible.   The shrinkage is the area not regained.   This area is used in calculating the percentage of shrinkage in knit fabrics.

FELTS [3]

Felt making was a primitive means of constructing fabric, older than weaving.   In felting, the fibers are made plastic with moisture and heat. Then, by the mechanical action of pressure and friction, the fibers are brought into very close contact so that they shrink together into a compactly adhering mass.   This shrinkage in the felting of fibers is undesirable when laundering clothes, but the process is useful in tailoring and in the making of felt fabrics.   Wool fiber felts readily and is most commonly used.   For the cheaper felts, reworked and reprocessed wool, noils, card waste, and yarn waste are utilized.   For hat felts, the fur fibers are most desirable.   The addition of casein fibers to hat felts has improved the strength of some felt.   Thermoplastic fibers give increased strength to hat felts.   Fibers which themselves do not bring about the adhesion in felting may be used in limited quantities with wool or fur fibers.   Kapok is combined with wool for felts used in airplanes.   Silk is

[3] Von Bergen and Mauersberger, *American Wool Handbook.*

used in making silk top hats to give the smooth, glossy appearance. Cotton, rayon, jute, and fine cattle and goat hairs are used for various types and qualities of felt.

Felt is produced in several forms. Both nonwoven felt and woven felt are made in a flat form similar to other fabrics. Nonwoven felt may be roll felt which is an inch or less in thickness when finished, or it may be sheet felt which is thicker and more highly compressed. That used for making polishing wheels may be up to three inches in thickness. Woven felts are quite thin fabrics. The felt for hat making is usually cone shaped. From this cone-shaped form the hats are blocked.

Nonwoven Felt. In the making of nonwoven felt, the wool fibers are dusted and scoured. The blend of fibers is selected and mixed. Fibers are then carded into bats which are crossed alternately to increase crosswise strength, as the bats are built up to various thicknesses, up to three feet. The completed bat is put onto the lower plate of a heavy press and is steamed to the proper saturation. The top plate is then let down onto the hot moist bat, and by oscillating rapidly it presses together the fibers so that they adhere compactly. Because of the shrinkage which occurs in the felting process, the fabric is 10 to 20 per cent thicker than the original bat of fibers.

Further compactness and strength are given to the felt by fulling. Fulling mills consist of large hammers so suspended that they drop alternately onto the fabric in a tub. When fulled, light felts are wet with warm water and soap; acid is used on heavy felt. Time of fulling may vary from 3 minutes to 12 hours. Shrinkage in fulling ranges from 10 to 75 per cent. For finishing, the felt is scoured and dyed and may be pressed and sheared for smoothness. Millinery felts may be finished with water repellents, moth proofing, mold proofing, and fire retardants, and may be stiffened with thermoplastics, resins, or other sizing.

Nonwoven felts are used for slippers and shoes, piano felts, skirts and petticoats, lining, padding, and millinery. In industry, they serve many purposes in polishing and as padding to control the effects of vibration of machinery.

Felt hats. Better felt hats are made from fur fibers because these give a soft, smooth, silky texture. Rabbit imported from Australia and Europe is chiefly used. Beaver, nutria, and muskrat give the luxury felts. After the pelts have been cleaned, the long hair fibers are clipped off because they do not felt well. The fur is then carroted by being brushed with a chemical solution with roller brushes and is dried or cured to improved felting. The skins are softened and stripped in narrow strips from the fur by spiral roller blades. The fur is sorted, blended, and put through a blower where hair fibers and foreign matter drop down because they are heavier than the fur fibers. About three ounces of fur are carefully weighed out and sent into the hat-forming, circular compartment. Here, the fiber is drawn by suction in a thin layer of fur, onto a copper cone with thousands of small holes. This layer increases in thickness from top to bottom so that the brim is thickest. Cone and felt are wrapped in wet fabric and covered with another metal cone. This is then dipped in water to make the fibers stick together so that the felt can be removed from the cones. The hat is then hardened by a kneading machine and shrunk and pressed by rollers. Although some fiber dyeing is done, the felt is most frequently dyed and sized at this stage. The cone-shaped felt is first blocked mechanically by flattening the tip and rounding out the crown and then by stretching the brim. Hand blocking may be done, especially in finishing the shaping of the hat. The surface may be given a smooth finish with sandpaper or a brushed finish with a wire brush. Suede finish has a clipped nap. In the silk finish, the nap is clipped short and is smoothed down to a glossy finish. Derby hats are stiffened with shellac.

Woven Felt. In the making of woven felt, some processes are like those used in making nonwoven felt. The wool is dusted, scoured, blended, and mixed. The fiber is carded and spun into yarn. Yarns are woven into fabrics, some of which are more compact than others to give greater firmness. The fabrics are then fulled. Although hammer mills may be used, the more modern mills full the cloth by pushing it through heavy rollers while the cloth is moist. The felt is finished by washing, napping, shearing, and pressing.

Woven felts are used for printing and lithographing, for polishing stones, glass, and wood, for tennis ball coverings, and for various other factory uses. Woven felts are durable and in general are stronger than pressed felts, especially where breaking stress can be met by the added strength of yarn and woven structure. It is not used for millinery or similar purposes, however, where much shaping is required.

LACE AND NET MAKING

The oldest laces in existence today were made of hair in Egypt about 2500 B.C. Most of the handmade laces of today are made from cotton and linen in England, Holland, Belgium, France, Italy, and Switzerland. The laces made in the United States are mostly machine made. Lace is defined as an openwork fabric of fine threads, usually figured. Although whole garments may be made of lace, it is more frequently used as edge trimming or insertion.

Machine-made Lace. Machine-made lace is generally made on a net foundation. Warp-knitted tricot net was first made in 1758 and is therefore the earliest type of machine-made net. By attempting to ravel an edge of tricot net, one can recognize the loop formation characteristic of all knitting. Also, these nets stretch more lengthwise than crosswise. They are frequently coarser than nets made on a lace loom; but some, such as a nylon net, are very fine.

In 1809, a net loom was invented which manipulated yarns in three directions, and in 1813, the loom for figured laces was made. Bobbinet, with its hexagonal-shaped mesh, is the commonest plain net of this type. Filet has square mesh. Other nets have diamond- and triangular-shaped mesh. Maline and tulle are some of the sheerest nets. Raveling an edge will reveal that the yarns are twisted about one another to form the mesh of this type of net. These nets will stretch about equally lengthwise and crosswise.

Handmade Lace. Handmade laces, known as real laces, are made by several rather distinct methods. Although some machine-made laces are difficult to distinguish, much of the real lace can be recognized by one who studies how they are made. Some of the better known methods for making lace are described briefly.

CROCHETING: a yarn is looped with a crochet hook. Filet squares and medallions are common forms of design. Irish crochet has shamrocks and roses made in units and put together with chains with numerous picots on them.

KNOTTED FILET: made with a netting needle. The older method was to knot yarns at the corners of the filet squares with the fingers. Fish net is a plain filet. Darned filet has a pattern darned in with a darning needle after the mesh has been made by knotting.

TATTING: knotting yarn with a tatting shuttle to form characteristic circles of knots and picots.

KNITTED LACES: usually made by looping cotton crochet yarn with steel needles.

BOBBIN OR PILLOW LACE: made by placing a pattern on a small, hard pillow, usually cylindrical in shape. Pins are arranged on the pattern, and the design is worked with a number of bobbins by weaving yarns about the pins and twisting yarns around each other. Narrow bobbin laces include Valenciennes or Val, Torchon, Cluny, and Binche. Among the wider bobbin laces are Chantilly, Mechlin, and Duchesse.

NEEDLE-POINT LACE: worked with needle and thread on a pattern drawn on paper or fabric. After the lace is made, the fabric is cut away, leaving the lace made of yarn. Alencon, Rose Point, Point de Gaze, and Venetian Point are needle-point laces.

CUTWORK: made on fabric. The edge of the design is buttonholed, and the background fabric is cut away from between parts of the design.

DRAWNWORK: hardanger and hemstitching, for example, are also made on fabric by drawing out some yarns from the fabric and then with needle and thread designing on the yarns left in the fabric.

CARRICKMACROSS: made in two types of lace. In the applique type, fine lawn is sewed onto net by a stitch outlining the design which is then held by an over stitch. Extra lawn is cut away to reveal the net background. In the other type of Carrickmacross lace, only the lawn is used. The outlining stitch is held by an over stitch around the design edge, and bars of thread with picots make the background. This is much like some Italian cutwork.

EMBROIDERY: not lace, but similar in decorative design and in its use. A needle and thread are used to create a design on fabric.

PLASTIC FILMS AND SHEETS

Several processes are used to manufacture plastic films and sheets. Very thin films may be made by some of these methods, all of which belong to modern times.

Cutting or Slicing. The first method used was that of cutting sheets from a pressed block of cellulose nitrate with a slicing knife. Pearl-like effects, variegated colors, or stripes may be produced by the way in which the material is put into the block before it is sliced. Other plastic sheets, such as those made of synthetic resins, may be made in this way, also.

Extrusion. Thermoplastic substances, such as cellulose acetate, cellulose acetate butyrate, nylon, vinyl resins, polystyrene, and polyethylene, are softened by heating and forced by pressure through die openings which are either flat or circular. If the die is circular, the plastic comes out as a tube which is then slit and flattened. The plastic may be extruded into air or a bath for cooling and hardening. While still soft, the plastic may be stretched by rollers to make the film thinner.

Film Casting. Solutions or dispersions of plastic substances such as cellulose acetate or ethers, the vinyls, polyethylene, nylon, polystyrene, or rubber-like compounds are used. The solution or dispersion may flow onto large casting wheels. The plastic film dries as the wheel goes around and is then stripped off. The solution or dispersion may flow onto belts or bands of metal moving over drum pulleys which carry the plastic through drying ovens. Still another method is to allow the solution to flow onto paper from which the plastic film is then stripped.

In polymerization casting, the liquid monomers of such materials as methyl methacrylate and polyesters are poured between glass molds and then heated in ovens for the length of time necessary to form the polymer.

Another type of film casting is that used to produce cellophane. A solution of cellulose xanthate, such as is used for producing viscose rayon, flows from a hopper through a long narrow slit into an acid coagulating bath which regenerates the cellulose in a film. The film is carried through purification tanks and glycerol for softening and is then dried. It may be made moisture proof by coating with resin or wax, flame proof, or given other finishes.

Calendering. Films are formed from thermoplastics, such as the vinyl resins, by pressing between huge, heated rollers. The sheets or films may be stretched thinner as they are being calendered. Heavy-gage sheets may also be pressed by applying heat and pressure to resin held between large metal plates.

Foamed sponge is extruded in strips after the plastic has been expanded by gas. Besides rubber, these may be made from neoprene and other synthetic rubbers, cellulose acetate, polyvinyls, phenolics, and polystyrene. Various thicknesses of foamed sponge are used for rug pads, furniture padding, mattresses and cushions, aircraft paneling, and luggage construction.

Plastic films have properties which make them well suited to certain purposes. Some of their properties, however, limit their use. Thus, the lack of porosity limits their use for most clothing purposes. For rainwear, such as coats, capes, hoods, and umbrellas, the water proof quality of the vinyl plastics and neoprene is useful, however. Seams may be heat sealed in thermoplastic materials for greater protection at the seam lines. Aprons and other protective garments, crib sheets, hospital equipment, shower curtains, table cloth covers, garment bags, refrigerator bags, and bowl covers made from the polyvinyls, polyethylene, glass, or neoprene are likewise impervious to water.

Plastic films are extensively used for packaging. Thermoplastic methyl methacrylate, cellulose acetate, and polystyrene may be shaped from sheets into transparent boxes for display purposes, for these substances may be made rigid or flexible. The vinyls, polyethylene, pliofilm, and other synthetic materials protect moist and dry foods, cosmetics, and drugs, because they are water proof and gas impervious. Cellophane and other cellulose plastics are inexpensive wrappings which protect from dust and dirt but not from moisture, unless they are wax or resin coated.

Durability of the different plastics varies. Shoe soles, heels, and uppers made from vinylidene, neoprene, and other synthetic rubbers have good flexing, tearing, and abrasion strength. Polyethylene has good folding endurance and is flexible at low temperatures. Some plastics crack in cold weather. Cellulose nitrate will burn readily, but others such as the vinyls melt but will not burn. Flame-proofing materials are added to some plastics. Some plastics stretch; some are elastic and will return to shape when stretched; still others hold their shape well. Backing with woven fabrics may increase dimensional stability of those which tend to stretch.

Plastic sheets and films may be transparent or opaque. They may simulate leather, may have an embossed surface, or may have a smooth glossy patent finish when used for luggage, handbags, and upholstery. They may be colored by printing, screen printing, or painting as well as by the addition of colored pigments before they are formed.

BONDED FABRICS

Bonded fabrics are considered relatively new materials. Wool felt, in which felting of the wool fibers results from applying heat, moisture, and pressure; and paper, in which wood and other fibers are made to adhere due to the presence of natural adhesives, are forerunners of bonded fabrics. Use of synthetic plastic binders to hold textile fibers together gives the newer bonded fabrics the possibility of great variations in texture, appearance, and service qualities and so has created a type of textile which somewhat fits itself between paper and woven fabrics.

Cellulose fibers, such as rayon and cotton, have been used most extensively to form the web which is the first step in production. Wool, glass, and other fibers which will not disintegrate during the bonding process may, however, be used. Long fibers give a stronger fabric, although short waste fibers give a less expensive product.

Methods of Forming Web. Several methods have been used for forming the web by either textile or paper manufacturing machinery. Carding the fibers on a textile machine aligns the fibers largely in one direction and gives greater warpwise strength than fillingwise strength. Layers of these webs may be lapped across or at an angle to increase crosswise strength. Paper machinery aligns the fibers less than the textile carding machine. An aerodynamic doffing and condensing machine gives the most random arrangement of the fibers for the web. This gives a fabric whose strength is distributed in all directions.

Methods of Bonding. Several methods are used. Thermoplastic fibers such as cellulose acetate, nylon, Vinyon, or other suitable compounds may blend either with viscose rayon or with cotton fibers. As the lap is passed through heated rollers, the thermoplastic fibers soften and become adhesive and thus hold the cellulose fibers together. Instead of heat, solvents may be used to soften the estron or vinyl fibers. However, this method is more difficult and expensive. Cellulose acetate fibers may be saponified to cellulose after the bonding process, thus making the fabric less likely to tear apart when it may come in contact with heat later. For packaging, the heat-sealing characteristic of the acetate rayon is retained, however.

Another process for bonding is to add the bonding adhesive while melted, or in a solution or emulsion after the web is formed. Resins or cellulose solutions may be sprayed onto the web in a nonporous coating. The binder may be printed on in design and may be colored by adding pigment to the binder. The binder may be applied from solution by padders or an impregnating bath. If a cellulose solution such as cuprammonium cellulose or cellulose xanthate is used, the cellulose is regenerated to give fabrics which are unaffected by water, either hot or cold. Emulsions of various synthetic resins, such as the polyvinyls, polystyrenes, and polymethyl methacrylate, rubber latex (either freshly compounded or prevulcanized), new water-soluble polymeric materials, and water-soluble derivatives of cellulose have been used commercially.

A third process for bonding is that of giving a surface treatment with a chemical bath, using such chemicals as zinc chloride, sulfuric acid, or sodium hydroxide. This method is used less in commercial production.

Properties and Uses of Bonded Materials. Bonded materials may be finished soft or stiff. Soft flexible fabrics handle like woven fabrics and are used for towels, disposable sheets, tablecloths and napkins, dishcloths, dusting and polishing cloths, handkerchiefs, diapers, bibs, shoulder pads, curtains and draperies, costumes, and graduation gowns. The stiffer fabrics are used for wrappings, pennants and banners, labels and placards. For color the fibers may be natural, bleached, or dyed. Dyestuff may be added to the binder, or the fabric may be piece dyed or printed. Embossed designs are possible. Surface textures may vary from smooth to napped or rough.

Draperies and other fabrics may be made flame resistant. Some fabrics are made water absorbent; others are water repellent and stain resistant. Warm coat interlinings may be made with wool fiber. Strong fabrics, made by cross laying the webs of aligned fibers, are suitable for work garments, aprons, protective clothing, and bag materials. Thick, strong fabrics are coated for leatherette which is used for upholstering furniture and cars and, if the coating and bonding agent are compatible, these will not blister and peel.

Noncracking wallpaper is another product. Window shades, oilcloth, and linoleum are other household uses for which bonded fabrics are being tried out as the base fabric. Bonded fabrics compete with woven fabrics for plastic laminates because they are cheaper. These construction materials are strong, lightweight, easy to fabricate, and have dimensional stability. They are useful in the construction of boats, trailers, automobiles, and airplanes.

LAMINATION

Lamination is a method of constructing special fabrics by sealing layers of fabric together with adhesives or by the application of heat and pressure.

An example of lamination is the wiltless or starchless shirt collar. The inner-lining fabric for the collar is made from cellulose acetate fibers which, when pressed or treated with solvents, adheres to the outside collar fabric to stiffen the collar.

Plastic films are laminated to foil, paper, glass, woven textiles, and other plastic films for various purposes, such as protective packaging of foods and other materials, gift-wrapping papers and ribbons, washable wallpapers, lampshades, waste-basket fabrics, and shatter-proof window glass.

BRAIDING

Braid is either a tubular or a flat fabric made by plaiting diagonally three or more strands as in winding a maypole or braiding hair. Variations in the width of fabric, in patterns for interlacing the strands, and in color and texture combinations are possible as in military braids and other trimmings. Belts may be braided in any width in interesting color combinations from ribbons or natural or plastic straws. Hats are made by braiding natural or manufactured straw and sewing it into shape. In the same manner, braided rugs are shaped and sewed from braided strands of cloth. Some other braided fabrics are shoe laces, elastic, cords for curtain pulls, tapes used for pajamas, and various other cords.

Chapter Eighteen

Color on Fabrics

LIGHT is a form of radiant energy, and energy can neither be created nor destroyed; it can only be changed from one form to another. In order to appreciate the origin and properties of color on fabrics, it is necessary to know something of the relationships between light and color.

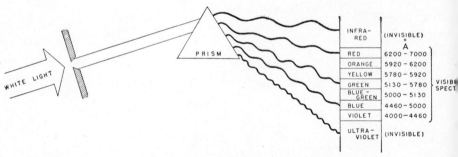

Fig. 18.1. **White light spread by a prism to show the different colors in the visible spectrum.**

Sources of Light. There are a number of sources of light:

    a) sunlight, stars
    b) fluorescent substances
    c) incandescent metals, iron, magnesium, copper (the latter two used in X-ray targets)
    d) carbon arcs (used in Fade-Ometers and other equipment)

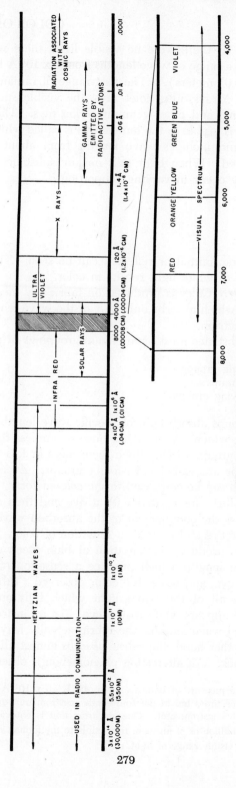

Fig. 18.2. The electromagnetic spectrum.

Origin of Color. If there were no visible light, there would be no color. Light covers a range of wave lengths from 3 x 10^{14}Å to 1 x 10^{-14}Å (30,000 to 0.000,000,01 meters).[1] The vast range of radiant energy includes cosmic rays, X-rays, ultraviolet rays, the visible spectrum, heat rays, and broadcasting and other communication rays. The portion of the spectrum which is visible to the human eye is called white light (the visible spectrum) and includes wave lengths from about 4,000 A to 7,000 Å, violet to red. When light falls on any substance, the folowing phenomena may occur in varying proportions:

  a) reflection
  b) absorption
  c) transmission

Only light that is transmitted or reflected can be seen. Therefore, the selective absorption of white light results in color.

Behavior of a Dye. Color is produced on fabrics by means of a dye or colored pigment which absorbs only part of the wave lengths of light from the visible spectrum.

  To be a dye, a substance must have certain groupings or parts.

  a) color-producing groups
  b) color-fixing groups
  c) color-intensifying groups

Color-producing groups absorb light of specific wave lengths to produce colored compounds, which are not dyes, however, unless they also contain basic or acidic groups which attach them more or less firmly to the fabric. Such groups are called color-fixing groups. Every dye has a *colorless form* which can be converted to the *colored form*.

When fibers or fabric are treated with a dye and then are observed in a pure white light, the complement of the absorbed wave lengths are reflected back to the eye and produce a sensation of color. Thus, if the wave lengths which produce the sensation of blue green are absorbed by a dye, the wave lengths which produce a sensation of red are reflected back to the eye, and red is the color observed (Table 18.I).

When practically all of the white light which falls on a fabric is *reflected,* the fabric appears white to the eye. To an instrument which records the reflected wave lengths, the fabric actually may be far from white. If, on the other hand, the fabric *absorbs* almost all the incident light, it appears black. An interesting phenomenon is observed in some

---

[1] Å, angstrom unit, a measure of length (see p. 425). 3 x 10^{14}Å to 1 x 10^{-14}Å may be read thus: three times ten to the fourteenth angstrom unit to one times ten to the minus fourteenth angstrom unit. One angstrom unit is equivalent to 3.937 x 10^{-9} inch or 0.003937 millionths of an inch; not visible to the human eye, but 4,000Å to 7000Å produce the visible range of light.

of the substances which absorb in the ultraviolet. Sometimes light is absorbed in the ultraviolet and is emitted in the visible to produce fluorescence. Those compounds which emit in the blue visible region

TABLE 18.I

ABSORPTION OF VISIBLE LIGHT

Wave length absorbed, Å	Corresponding color	Color observed
4000	violet	greenish yellow
4250	indigo blue	yellow
4500	blue	orange
4900	blue green	red
5100	green	purple
5300	yellow green	violet
5500	yellow	indigo blue
5900	orange	blue
6400	red	bluish green
7300	purple	green

Source: Alfred F. Schneid, "The Organic Chemistry of Color," *Interchemical Review*, 8-2 (1949), 35–46.

to produce fluorescence are being used to dye fabrics white. The result is a striking white produced by the fluorescent dye.

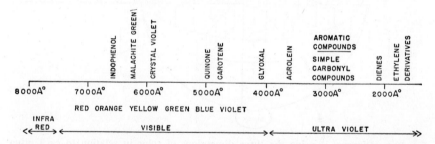

Fig. 18.3. Diagram showing absorption spectra in the visible and ultraviolet regions. Source: James B. Conant, THE CHEMISTRY OF ORGANIC COMPOUNDS (New York: The Macmillan Co., 1939), 544.

Primary colors are variously explained. The primary colors generally accepted for light consist of three different hues: red, blue, and green.[2] Their complements are yellow, magenta, and blue green. Each hue blends into the next. There is no sharp line of demarcation between neighboring hues, only arbitrarily set regions. Color photography has increased the general knowledge of light and color.

Pigment colors such as those used in water colors, oil paints, dyes, and pigment printing are considered to have the three primary colors, red,

[2] Reprinted by permission from *An Introduction to Color*, by R. M. Evans (published by John Wiley & Sons, Inc., 1948), 231.

blue, and yellow and the complements, green, orange, and violet. Complementary pigment colors mixed in equal amounts produce a neutral gray according to the Munsell color theory. Equal amounts of the complementary colors in light give a white light, not a neutral gray color.

Description of Color. One way of explaining color is to describe it as the eye's interpretation of light. Color may also be described as the mental reaction to the radiant energy that is included in the range of light frequencies to which the eye is sensitive, violet to red.

A standard method of designating color has been established by the Inter-Society Color Council and the National Bureau of Standards and is called the ISCC-NBC method.[3] The method is based upon the three

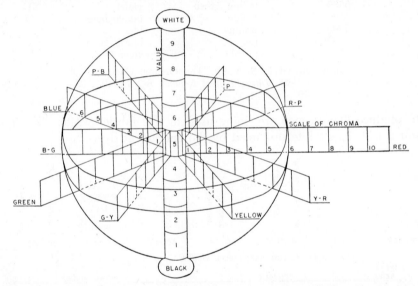

Fig. 18.4. Diagram showing the three dimensions of color in relation to each other and to the color sphere. *Source: Courtesy of Munsell Color Company, Baltimore, Md.*

variables of color: hue, value, and chroma in the Munsell System (see Fig. 18.4).[4] The hues provide the color names, e.g., blue. The average eye can distinguish about 125 different hues. The value gives the location on the axis between black and white. It gives the apparent amount of color or lightness. The chroma or saturation gives the distance from the axis at any given value. It may be defined as the per

[3] Dean B. Judd and Kenneth L. Kelly, "Methods of Designating Colors," *Journal of Research*, National Bureau of Standards, 23 (1939), 355.

[4] Dorothy Nickerson, "History of the Munsell Color System and Its Scientific Application," *Journal of the Optical Society of America*, 30 (1940).

John E. Tyler and A. C. Hardy, "Analysis of the Original Munsell Color System," *Journal of the Optical Society of America*, 30-12 (1940), 587.

cent of hue in a color. It varies from pale or weak to deep or strong.

It is a well-known fact that people do not see color alike. Observer differences are real. Two people may see differences in both kind and amount of color, or they may not. There seem to be no simple relationships between the physical properties of color and mental concepts produced by it.[5] Mental concepts of color have not been so well studied as have the physical properties.

Project No. 2 of the Inter-Society Color Council was established "to find a means of designating colors in the U. S. Pharmacopoeia, the National Formulary, and pharmaceutical literature, such designation to be sufficiently standardized to be acceptable to science, sufficiently broad to be appreciated and usable by science, art, and industry, and sufficiently commonplace to be understood at least in a general way by the whole public." The project took seven years to complete and now *Methods of Designating Color* is recommended tentatively for general use.[6]

A brief explanation should be given of the nature of the Inter-Society Color Council. It is, at present, composed of 185 individual members and 19 organizations.[7] The purpose of the council is to stimulate and coordinate the study of color for the benefit of science, art, and industry. The breadth of interest in color may well be illustrated by a listing of the member organizations, a number of which is interested primarily in the use of color on textile fabrics for clothing and household purposes.

American Artists Professional League
American Association of Textile Chemists and Colorists
American Ceramic Society
The American Designers' Institute
American Institute of Architects
American Institute of Decorators
American Oil Chemists' Society
American Pharmaceutical Association, National Formulary
American Psychological Association
American Society for Testing Materials
Federation of Paint and Varnish Production Clubs
Illuminating Engineering Society
National Association of Printing Ink Makers
Optical Society of America
Society of Industrial Designers
Society of Motion Picture Engineers
Technical Association of the Pulp and Paper Industry
The Textile Color Card Association of the United States, Inc.
U. S. Pharmacopoeial Convention

[5] Evans, *An Introduction to Color.*
[6] Deane B. Judd and Kenneth L. Kelly, "Methods of Designating Colors."
[7] E. I. Stearns, "Current Activities of the Inter-Society Color Council," *American Dyestuff Reporter*, 39-4 (1950), 109–112 and 120.

Comparison of Colors. The comparison of colors on fabrics has always been a subjective process. However, a growing consciousness of the importance of color and developments in artificial lighting have increased the demand from illuminating engineers, color photographers, decorators, and designers for an objective means of comparing colors. Colors may be compared by the following observations:

a) photometric comparisons [8]
b) juxtaposed comparisons
c) successive observations
d) time lapse or memory

Significance of Color. Usage has given significance to color.[9] Color symbolism is found in many phases of everyday life, for instance, colors in codes, traffic lights, academic robes, theatrical costumes, seasonal greeting cards, and flags. A few examples will illustrate the significance commonly attached to certain colors.

Color	Significance
Purple	Pomp, dignity, power
Yellow	Sacred color of Imperial China, sunshine, spring
Gray	Poverty, battleship, birds
Green	God Pan, jealousy, highwaymen, youth
Black	Night, death, grief, evil, judges
Brown	Peasant color, rural
Red	Sacred to Mars, God of War, danger
Blue	Sky, sea, navy, truth
White	Innocence, elegance, luxury, purity

Appreciation of the uses of color may be either intellectual, emotional, or both. An intellectual appreciation involves an understanding of the influences that give significance to color. On the other hand an emotional reaction to color may be simply that of acceptance, enjoyment, or dislike. Color has many aspects, some of which are:

a) aesthetic *e*) industrial
b) social   *f*) civic
c) healthful *g*) chemical
d) religious *h*) biological

Both practical and emotional benefits are to be had from the intelligent use of color. Color combined with textures in fabrics provides the basis for creating becoming clothing and household interiors; color gives both beauty and value to our surroundings. The first prerequisite

[8] Edward W. Rhael, "The Elements of Color and Spectrophotometry," *American Dyestuff Reporter*, 38-3 (1949), P490–P495.
[9] "Historic Significance of Color," *Textile Colorist*, 63 (1941), 587.

for clothing and household fabrics is appearance, of which color is the most important component.

The psychology of color is not clearly defined.[10] The problem is being studied by the Inter-Society Color Council, under the auspices of the Illuminating Engineering Society Research Fund, in an effort to clarify the factors involved in reactions to color. What, for example, is the effect of a given color in clothing upon the wearer? Upon the observer? Why do preferred colors and color combinations vary with individuals? Honoré de Balzac, the great French realist who gave special emphasis in his writings to the effect of environment on the development of character, once said that a woman's character always found expression in her favorite color. If so, the consumer should know about it. While little is understood about the effect of one color upon another; [11] less is known about the effects of color on people.

Some general reactions have been observed by people experienced in the use of color.[12]

Color	Reaction on observer
Blue	Soothing
Red	Stimulating
Yellow	Stimulating
Green	Cooling
Black	Quieting
White	Cheery
Orange	Stimulating
Brown	Restful, warming
Purple	Soothing

Yellow, orange, and red are the stimulating colors and are called the warm colors. Green, blue, and purple are considered to be the quiet, restful colors and are called the cool colors.

HISTORY OF DYESTUFFS

Throughout history, color has been a most prized property of fabrics for clothing and household uses.[13] Methods of securing color were uncertain and costly. Up to the middle of the seventeenth century, dyeing was considered an art. The changes which came were in part the result of papers by Sir William Petty on the *History of the Common Dyeing Practices* and by Robert Boyle in 1663 on *Experiments and Considerations Touching on Color,* both of which were published by the Royal

[10] J. H. Archibald, "The Glory of Color," *Textile Colorist,* 62 (1940), 191–193.
[11] Dr. W. D. Wright, "Color Adaptation and Color Contrast: II, Methods of Investigation," *Rayon and Synthetic Textiles,* 33-1 (1950), 84–86.
[12] W. Schweisheimer, M.D., "Effect of Color on the Eye and Mind of the Beholder," *Textile Colorist,* 68 (1946), 43.
[13] Alfred Leix, "Colors of the Ancient Orient," *Textile Colorist,* 61 (1939), 626.

Society in England. England had, at that time, a flourishing dyestuff industry based upon natural dyes. Another century was to pass, however, before modern dyestuffs became a reality.

Natural Dyestuffs. The history of natural dyestuffs includes the story of the early efforts made by man to color his body and his clothes with the juices of berries and leaves, the blood of animals, and colored earths. At a later period, the plant dyes of importance included madder, woad, indigo, and logwood. Venice was the principal trade center for scarlet dyes during the Renaissance. Tyrian purple was obtained from a small gland in a shell fish found on the Mediterranean coast. Brown was obtained from walnut juice and other plant extracts. White was even more prized than color before chlorine bleaching was discovered. Yellow was obtained from saffron. Green was produced by the chlorophyll from plant leaves. Blue was obtained from woad. Dyes from animals included cochineal (the female only), kermes, and Tyrian purple. Many inorganic salts were also used.

The use of natural dyes was backed by vast economic forces. England, in 1727, passed a law against the use of wood dyes such as logwood, because they were imported from America. The American dye resources were so great, however, that Bancroft, an English chemist, succeeded in popularizing logwood and cochineal to the extent that Parliament granted him exclusive right to sell those dyestuffs in England and Wales for fourteen years.[14] In the *Annals of Commerce*, MacPherson said that such discoveries as the American supply of natural dyes were of great consequence in commerce. The superiority of a color was considered sufficient to secure an extensive sale of goods dyed or printed with it. MacPherson further contended that durable and beautiful colors are of more importance to the prosperity of a nation than can readily be conceived.

It is of interest to consider some of the more important natural dyes of that time. Madder roots were used as a source of alizarin, a vat-type dye. The natural vat dyes were the most important dyes of the eighteenth century. In 1758, the House of Commons appointed a committee to consider the growth of madder in England in order to give more families work in the winter. A meeting of calico printers and druggists was called to decide the matter.[15] Even though they decided to raise madder in England, it was still being imported in increasing amounts as late as 1799.

Alizarin was of especial importance because so many colors could be

---

[14] C. E. Barraclough, "Historical Survey of Dyeing," *American Dyestuff Reporter*, 10 (1922), 80–84.

[15] P. J. Thomas, "Beginning of Calico Printing in England," *English Historical Review*, 39 (1924), 207.

produced with one and the same dyestuff.[16] Different metallic salts gave different colors. Chromium gave claret red; aluminum gave a cold Turkey red; calcium gave blue; iron gave violet black; and mixtures of these salts gave other colors. Alizarin was a most highly prized dye of the ancients.

Woad, another natural vat dye, was used by the early Britons to paint their bodies. The Gauls used it as a dyestuff but found it inferior to indigo. Woad was the foremost blue dye in western Europe for almost 1,200 years. During the eighteenth century, indigo completely replaced it. The introduction and spread of indigo in Europe had been long delayed because of the activities of powerful syndicates of woad growers and merchants who prevailed upon their governments to restrict the importation of indigo. The Venetians had used indigo as early as 1194 A.D.

Indigo blue, the oldest dyestuff known, was used by the Egyptians over 4,000 years ago.[17] The leaves of the indigo plant were steeped for 9 to 14 hours in order to hydrolyze the coloring matter. When the extract was aerated, the dye was oxidized to the blue form, which was water insoluble, and precipitated out. After the blue paste was dried in blocks, it was ready for shipment.

Walnut juice was used by the Roman and Grecian women as cosmetics. It was also a valuable dye in colonial America.

Synthetic Dyestuffs. A few synthetic dyes preceded the great discoveries of Perkin. In 1704, Diesbach accidentally produced Prussian blue which was used as a dyestuff for about 200 years. It is now used as a laundry bluing. The secret of how to prepare Prussian blue was kept for 50 years. Outsiders were told it was made of blood.

Picric acid was prepared in Germany by Wolff in 1771. Even though it produced an ugly yellow, it was widely used on silk for lack of a better dye.

The natural dyestuffs were, therefore, almost the only dyestuffs possible until William Henry Perkin discovered mauve, in 1856, and was granted British Patent No. 1984. Born on March 12, 1838, William Henry Perkin was at seventeen a student of the great chemist, Hoffmann, when he decided one Easter vacation to "do something" about preparing synthetic quinine. He failed to do that but did prepare the first important synthetic dye. The father had confidence enough in his son to finance his manufacturing venture, and he made a fortune even though the risks were great.

[16] Joseph H. Park and Esther Glauberman, "Importance of Chemical Developments in the Textile Industries during the Industrial Revolution," *Journal of Chemical Education*, 9 (1932), 1143–1170.

[17] Max Bender, "A Study of Vat Dyestuffs," *Rayon and Synthetic Textiles*, 20-7 (1949), 81.

England was able to maintain her supremacy in the dyestuff industry for only a short time, because she was too well satisfied with her progress. France and Germany were not so complacent. Germany soon took the lead and was able to maintain her supremacy until the 1930's when the United States surpassed her. As early as 1914, the German monopoly of dyestuffs had been questioned in the United States, but World War I delayed progress.

Since the British chemist Perkin discovered synthetic dyes in the nineteenth century, many varied and complex dyestuffs have been added annually. Today the number of dyes is so great that a new Colour Index, scheduled for publication in 1955, is being prepared by the joint efforts of the British Society of Dyers and Colourists and the American Association of Textile Chemists and Colorists. The Colour Index will list every dye about which information can be traced. Chemical constitution, properties, and methods of use are among the data which will be given. The present state of knowledge of how a dye molecule adds color to a textile fiber or fabric will be organized and presented. The forces, physical and chemical, which hold a dye molecule on a fiber, will be described in the new Colour Index.

The synthetic dyestuffs are much purer and cheaper than those that are of plant or animal origin and have almost replaced them. The story may soon be the same for our textile fibers.

CLASSIFICATION OF DYESTUFFS

There are approximately 35,000 American-made dyes which have been classified as to type. Many are included in the 1,316 types described in the present Colour Index.

Methods of Application. The dyer classifies dyestuffs according to the method of application to a fabric.[18] The following classes include the most commonly used dyes:

  a) Acid dyestuffs provide low-cost, brilliant colors of most value on silk and wool.

  b) Basic dyestuffs require the use of a mordant. They are low-cost bright colors. Silk and wool dye directly. Cotton dyed with basic dyes absorbs less moisture than undyed fibers. Apparently the basic dye lowers the affinity of cotton (cellulose) for water by blocking the relatively acidic alcohol groups.[19]

  c) Direct dyestuffs were introduced in 1884. They fade in water but have fair light fastness. They adhere to the fibers by adsorption. Fabrics dyed with direct dyes should be used where it is not important that they be laundered but need light fastness. Most of the

[18] Edward W. Pierce, *Modern Methods of Dyeing* (New York: Ciba Co., Inc., 1940).

[19] R. F. Nickerson, "Hydrolysis and Catalytic Oxidation of Cellulose Materials," *Industrial and Engineering Chemistry*, 34-2 (1942), 1480.

direct and developed colors have both light and wash fastness improved by resin finishing.

d) Developed dyes are direct dyes. They have good wash fastness and are often used in piece dyeing when discharge printing is to follow.

e) Naphthol, azoic, or ice colors form an insoluble color lake on the fabric in a manner similar to the developed dyes. These dyes have fairly good fastness and are easy to apply.

f) Pigment colors have grown in popularity because of their ease of application and comparatively low cost. They are relatively fast to chemicals, light, and washing, but are limited in their fastness to crocking or rubbing. They are bright colors. Pigment is printed on the fabric in a resin paste which on curing becomes insoluble. The paste acts both as carrier and fixing agent holding the color to the fabric mechanically. Dyes may be applied in pastes which, after they are properly set, may be soaped and washed.

g) Vat dyes are the most important class of dyestuff used on fabrics. Vat dyes acquired their name from the fact that formerly they were applied to the cloth in a large container called a vat. Today, the name applies only to the class of dyestuffs that has to be reduced to the colorless form, before being applied to the fabric, and then reoxidized to the insoluble form in order to develop the color. The dyed fabric is then aged, soaped, and washed.

h) Mordant dyes produce dull, comparatively fast colors on wool if dry cleaned, often called chrome colors from the use of chromium salts as a mordant.

Properties of Some Vat Dyestuffs. The vat dyestuffs may be classified into the three following groups:

a) Indigo, indigoids, indigosols, algosols, and related structures

b) Anthraquinoids, fastest and most expensive

c) Sulfur colors, cheapest and most commonly used, introduced in 1900 (black, best in this group)

Indigo and related dyestuffs are easily applied to fabric and have varying degrees of fastness on different fibers and in different colors. Vat dye is not synonymous with fast color; yet it is frequently referred to on labels with the implication that it is. Some vat dyes, however, such as the anthraquinoids will "outlast" the cloth; others have very poor fastness. The first vat dyestuff was synthesized in 1880 by A. von Baeyer.

Tyrian purple, which is similar to indigo, was one of the early prized vat dyes, first known about 1600 B.C. Large quantities of shell fish and much labor were required to produce the most expensive dye of ancient times. It is of interest that the priceless Tyrian purple, or royal purple as it is sometimes called, is practically unknown today.

Indigosols and algosols which are coming into general use for wool and silk are the colorless forms of vat dyestuffs.[20] They are water solu-

[20] Hans Luttringhaus, "Application of Leuco Esters of Vat Dyestuff to Wool," *American Dyestuff Reporter*, 38-4 (1949), P173.

ble. After the wool or silk is saturated with the colorless form of the dye, the color is developed in a neutral or acid bath with the aid of a mild oxidizing agent. They behave much like acid dyes. The older types of vat dyes were not used generally on the protein fibers because the alkali necessary in their use damaged the fibers.

The growing demand for washable wools has caused manufacturers to increase their use of the indigosols and the algosols in both dyeing and printing of wool and silk. Unlike the old type vat dyes, they have greater affinity for wool than for rayon or cotton.

Helidons, more of the vat dyestuffs especially applicable to wool, are applied from a dilute alkaline solution at a comparatively low temperature, 120 to 140 F.[21] Dyes are being used effectively on wool tops (carded and combed wool) and raw stock (raw wool), and the dyeing is being done with conventional dyeing equipment. The advantage of fiber dyeing is threefold: it makes the wool wash fast and light fast and does not injure the fiber. So far a fairly complete range of vat dyes in varying tints and shades has been successfully applied.

The anthraquinoid dyestuffs in general produce the fastest colors and are especially applicable to cottons. One group, the indanthrene dyes, includes the fastest dyes known. They can be removed from a fabric only by an alkaline reducing agent which reduces them to the colorless form. Some are prepared in the soluble form.

Sulfur colors are dull and have good fastness to soaping, light, and crocking. They are used on cottons and are comparatively cheap. They include blues, greens, yellows, browns, grays, and blacks. Before World War II, more sulfur black was sold than any other single dyestuff. Sulfur blacks are used in large quantities on cotton fabrics, but frequently the sulfur causes excessive oxidation of the fabric.

The vast increase in the use of vat dyestuffs would not have been possible had other developments not paralleled their synthesis. Wetting agents; dispersing agents; leveling, fixing, and thickening agents are all dye auxiliaries which have helped reduce the time and expense of vat dyeing.

Different dyestuffs have quite different effects on cotton.

  a) Resistance to weathering is produced by some dyes.
  b) Naphthol-dyed cottons deteriorate more rapidly than the undyed bleached fabrics.
  c) Direct, diazotized, and developed dyes increase the resistance of cotton to deterioration.

Light is a serious factor in aging of fabrics. Whether light is present or not, certain blues, greens, and blacks in sulfur and vat dyes ac-

---

[21] H. Luttringhaus, J. E. Flint, and A. A. Arcus, "Helidon Dyestuffs for Wool," *American Dyestuff Reporter*, 39-1 (1950), P2–P11.

celerate the oxidation of cotton cellulose when exposed to bleaching agents. Certain of the yellow, orange, and red vat dyes increase the photochemical oxidation of cotton cellulose.[22] Vat dyes may have different effects on the oxidation of cellulose in light and in a bleaching solution.

Mordant Dyes. The chrome colors are produced by mordant dyes which acquire their name from the fact that chromium is often the mordant used to set or fix the dye on the fabric. However, in special cases aluminum, iron, or tin may be used. Chrome colors are duller colors than the basic dyes but have about the same degree of color fastness, which is very poor, to washing. Because of this both are used on cheap classes of cotton fabrics and are generally not soaped, but are sold with starches and gums in them. When laundered, the colors usually fade. A few exceptions can be soaped and washed. On wool, these dyes are much more satisfactory. They are used chiefly on men's outer wear which is usually dry cleaned, not washed.

A summary of some dyestuffs with characteristic properties is given (Table 18.II).

APPLICATION OF DYESTUFFS

There are four stages of manufacture in which color may be applied to textile materials.

    a) solutions, before spinning
    b) fibers
    c) yarns
    d) fabrics

The fabric may be piece dyed or printed by any one of a number of methods.

Solutions. The manufactured fibers may have colored pigment or dyestuffs dispersed in the spinning solution. The available and practical colored pigments are limited. Technical difficulties are inherent in this process of obtaining color on fabric.

Fiber Dyeing. Loose fibers may be dyed successfully where handling of the wet mass does not involve damaging the fibers or tangling them unduly. Wool is easily dyed as raw stock, but some fibers, such as silk filaments and cotton fibers, are difficult or impractical to dye at this stage.

The improvement of machinery has greatly improved the procedure for handling raw fibers. One piece of equipment consists of a perforated drum which, when partially submerged in the dye bath and rotated, allows the dye to circulate through the loose fibers. It is possible to

---

[22] G. S. Egerton, "The Action of Light on Dyed and Undyed Cottons," *American Dyestuff Reporter,* 36-20 (1947), 561–570 and 573.

place the fibers in the drum, scour, bleach, and dye before removal. The fibers are less tangled, however, when the dye is pumped through the fibers. Good-quality yarns are produced from fibers dyed in this manner.

TABLE 18.II

A SUMMARY AND SOME PROPERTIES OF DYESTUFFS

	FIBER TYPE			
Dye type	Cellulose	Protein	Other	Qualities
Acid	. . . .	wool, silk	nylon	Bright shades, generally fast
Basic	cotton	wool, silk	. . . .	Brilliant shades, cheap, fugitive
Direct	cellulose fibers	. . . .	nylon	Bright, cheap, poor wash fastness, fast to light
Naphthol or ice colors	cellulose fibers	. . . .	. . . .	Bright, fairly good wash fastness, fair to light
Pigment colors	all	all	all	Cheap, easy to apply, relatively fast
Vat dyes Indigo	cellulose fibers	. . . .	. . . .	Fast, cheap, easy to apply
Indigoid	. . . .	wool	. . . .	Fast (use protective colloid to dye)
Indigosols	. . . .	wool	. . . .	Excellent fastness to light and washing
Algosols	. . . .	wool	. . . .	Fast to dry cleaning
Anthra- quinoids	cellulose fibers	. . . .	. . . .	Fastest dyes known
Sulfur	cellulose fibers	wool	. . . .	Good fastness to washing and light, cheap
Chrome or mordant colors	. . . .	wool	nylon	Dull, poor fastness to washing but fast to dry cleaning
Developed	cellulose fibers	silk	. . . .	Faster than direct colors to washing and light, best to light. Used in ground shades for discharge

Note: Subsequent finishing materials may change the degree of fastness. Fastness may be improved or not, depending upon the dye and the finishing material.

Even though fiber dyeing is expensive, there are certain distinct advantages. There is better penetration of the dye into the fiber, which produces a higher degree of color fastness. Direct, sulfur, vat, and developed dyes are used on the cellulose fibers. Fiber blends produce many beautiful effects which are not otherwise possible on fabrics. Fibers of different chemical composition react differently to a given dye bath. The manufactured fibers are most often dyed as yarns or fabrics, not as fibers.

Yarn Dyeing. There are three general procedures by which yarns are dyed: hank or skein dyeing, package dyeing, and beam dyeing. The yarns are usually dyed in skeins or packages.

Hanks or skeins of yarn are immersed in the dye bath. The rods or poles holding the hanks may be moved by hand, or the hanks may be dyed in revolving drums.

Package dyeing involves winding the yarns on a perforated cylinder to form the "package." In some types of machines, a number of packages or even cakes is placed on fixed perforated spindles in a large, enclosed container. The dye can be circulated from the outside of the package in or from the inside out. This insures good circulation and level dyeing. Vat dyes are used exclusively. A thousand pounds of yarn may be dyed at a time in such a machine. Most of the package yarns are used in shirting fabrics.

Beam dyeing is similar in principle to package dyeing, except that one large perforated beam instead of many small spindles is used. Several hundred pounds of yarn are wound on the beam. The tank may be open or closed. Beam-dyed yarns are used for warp yarns. Long-chain dyeing in many respects has its counterpart in the continuous processes used for scouring and bleaching. From 200 to 1,000 yarns of 1,000 to 10,000 yard lengths may constitute a load. The chain or rope of yarns is guided by rollers through the dye bath one or more times, then washed, rinsed, and wrung through squeeze rolls. This method is best adapted to large-quantity dyeing. Yarn-dyed yarns are used chiefly for gingham, chambrays, denims, true seersuckers, and madras. Those are cotton fabrics in which both wash and light fast colors are required. Large quantities of vat dyes are used, as well as limited amounts of other dyes.

Fabric Dyeing. Fabric dyeing consists of either piece dyeing or printing. Fabrics are dyed either in a jig or dye kettle, or in a pad-steam unit which make possible rapid continuous processing. Dyeing, one of the most important parts of wet processing of fabrics, is usually preceded by bleaching. Whether the fabric is piece dyed or printed, the process is followed by an aftertreatment to fix the dye.

Piece dyeing. When the woven or knitted fabrics made of cellulose fibers comes from the loom, it is probably singed to remove surface fuzz; desized to remove warp sizing and other sizings; and bleached, especially if a light color is desired. In some instances, the cotton is mercerized. Besides developing a silky luster, the fibers absorb more dye. Fabrics made of cellulose fibers, cotton, rayon, and flax, are most frequently piece dyed, a rapid and economical process, especially since continuous processes are being installed. In general, dyes are less fast when applied to fabrics than when applied to fibers or yarns.

The type of equipment used for piece dyeing depends upon the degree of fastness desired, the type of dye, and the fabric.

Jig dying is usually used for piece dyeing dark colors. Most types of dyes can be used in the jig where large rolls guide the cloth repeatedly through the dye bath until the desired shade is obtained. Jig dyeing, reel dyeing, and other continuous dyeing processes are alike in that the fabric is continuously or intermittently in the dye bath. Relatively

small batches are dyed in the jig or on the reel.   In the latter, delicate
fabrics and woolen crepes can be dyed without undue strain and distortion.   The continuous dyeing process makes it possible to dye large
quantities of fabric to uniform colors.   Details of a continuous dyeing
machine will vary somewhat with the type of dye and of fabric.   Different steps are involved in applying a vat dye from those used for a
sulfur dye, but each must be reduced to a colorless form before applying it to the fabric.   The color is then developed on the fabric.

Pad dyeing, a form of piece dyeing, as a rule, is used for light colors
where fastness is not a necessary quality.   In pad dyeing, the fabric dips
into a trough or dye bath and passes between rollers which squeeze off
the excess solution.   If the dyes are direct, the process is simple and
rapid.   If vat dyes are used, the cloth has to be transferred for finishing
after the dyeing process.   The pad-steam process is continuous but has
to be carefully controlled to produce even colors.   On the other hand,
it affords a great saving in time (one tenth the usual time), labor, and
other costs.   It is possible to pad, dry, steam, oxidize, soap, and dry at
the rate of 80 to 150 yards per minute.   Solutions or dispersions of dyestuffs are padded onto fabrics made of synthetic fibers such as nylon
and Orlon.   They are then given a high-temperature treatment in which
the dye dissolves in the fiber.

The multilap continuous process is essentially an enclosed padder and
is especially suited to delicate fabrics.   Woolen piece goods, wool mixtures, and spun rayons may be dyed on the multilap padder.   Except
for cross-dyeing and resist dyeing, piece dyeing produces a solid color
on the fabric.   Piece dyeing of fiber mixtures creates unusual effects.

Vat dyeing can now be carried out in a continuous process.   Padding
the pigment on and high-temperature fixation of the dye by the pad-
steam method have made it possible to apply colors such as direct, naphthol and sulfur, as well as the regular vat dyestuffs to fabrics in great volumes.   Small lots and dark shades are usually applied in a jig.

Printing.   Colored design may be produced on cloth by any of three
methods: by weaving or knitting, by embroidering with colored yarns, or
by printing.[23]   Printing has for its purpose the creation of design on the
cloth.   The most generally used printing processes are roller, batik,
block, screen, and spray.   Roller printing includes direct, duplex, discharge, resist, photographic, flock, and pigment printing.

The dye for printing has to be incorporated in a paste which acts as a
vehicle for transfer.   The following list includes most of the pastes in
use which require cooking:

Corn starch
Corn-starch derivatives

[23] "Print Styles," *J. Soc. of Dyers and Col.*, March 1947, 97.

Wheat starch
Gum tragacanth
British gums
Dextrines
Locust bean gums
Gum arabic

Among the pastes which do not require cooking and provide a softer hand are the following:

Some natural gums
Soluble vegetable starches
Soluble cellulose derivatives
Some synthetic resins

Roller printing, which came in with the Industrial Revolution,[24] is the most rapid printing process. About 1775 Alexander Bell fitted an engraved copper plate around a roller to make printing a continuous process. Previous to that, in 1770, Bell had invented a flatbed press on which a section of cloth was printed and then moved, much like hand blocking. The next step in roller printing was the use of engraved copper rollers. The cloth to be printed passed between two large cylinders, one padded and the other the engraved roller.

For roller printing of textiles, an inverted type of engraving is used on the rollers. The depressions are filled with a thick paste which is transferred by pressure to the cloth.

The parts of the printing machine are adjustable except for the star gear which drives the engraved rolls which in turn drive the entire machine. The central cylinder is made of cast iron or steel and is covered with a heavy fabric of wool and linen. This is covered with an endless blanket made of wool and linen, or rubber and fabric. On top of this is an unbleached or gray cotton sheeting. This sheeting protects the blanket from excess color paste as the fabric is being printed. In some instances, this protective sheet is not needed. Rubberized blankets have the advantage that they may be longer and pass through a washer where the excess color paste is removed and the blanket dried on its way back past the engraved print roller. There is a pair of rollers for each color in a design, one engraved, one padded. Each engraved roller carries only one color. Some machines print 16 colors.

The engraved print roller is usually made of chromium-plated copper, and is 16 or 18 inches in circumference. The circumference of the roller determines the repeat in a design. Even larger rollers may be used for table cloths and other special work. Pressure is used on the print roller to transfer the paste from the cylindrical roller to and into

[24] H. A. Webb, "Cotton Printing," *American Dyestuff Reporter*, 37-24 (1948), P791.

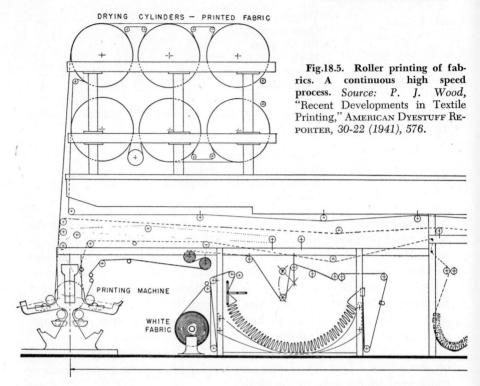

Fig.18.5. Roller printing of fabrics. A continuous high speed process. *Source: P. J. Wood,* "Recent Developments in Textile Printing," AMERICAN DYESTUFF REPORTER, *30-22 (1941), 576.*

the cloth. Under the roller is a color box containing the color paste. A wooden finish roller turns in the paste and transfers the color to the print roller. A metal doctor blade wipes the print roller clean of all paste except that in the depressions of the engravings. The excess color

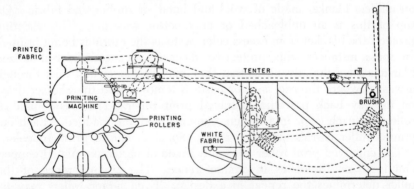

Fig. 18.6. **Roller printing of fabrics. An eight roller printing press.** *Source: Wood,* "Recent Developments in Textile Printing," 576.

flows back into the color box. Another scraper blade known as a lint doctor scrapes against the print roller as it turns from the cloth. The lint doctor prevents the accumulation of lint and excess color. When the freshly printed fabric leaves the printing machine, it goes directly to the drying cylinders or cans to be dried and aged from a few minutes to an hour. Any curing or other finishing treatment follows this. All fast colors are soaped and thoroughly washed. Recently, a new direct printing roller has been set up in England. The roller is built up of cakes of pigment in a mosaic. The damp cloth is rolled past until the roller is consumed. Beautiful effects are claimed.

Duplex printing is a direct roller printing process done either by

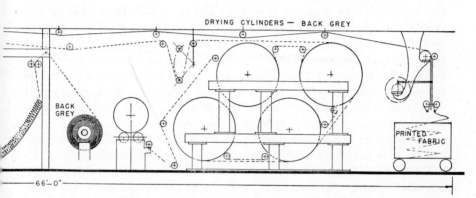

running the fabric through the printing machine twice or by using a machine which prints both sides at once. This type of printing is done to simulate a woven design.

Discharge printing is a roller printing process which bleaches areas of color on a piece-dyed fabric. If a dye is added to the bleaching paste but is not bleached by it, the fabric can be both discharge printed and direct printed at the same time. Unless the process for discharging the dye is carefully controlled, the fabric will be damaged. If the fabric is to be marketed as being washable, special dyes are used.[25]

In discharge printing, steam is used with a reducing substance to destroy the dye on the fabric. The reduction products are rapidly washed from the fabric to leave a colorless design. Discharge printing is a process requiring extreme care in every step in order to avoid oxidation of the fabric and to insure a clear white discharge. Some of the dyes used are comparatively fast to light but not to washing. Therefore, discharge printed fabrics are used chiefly for drapery, some linings, upholstery fabrics, and some clothing.

Resist printing is the reverse of discharge printing. A resist paste is printed on the fabric which is then piece dyed. Then, when the resist

[25] T. N. Patrick, "Discharge Printing," *Textile World,* 99-7 (1949), 137.

paste is removed, a white or colored design is left on the dark background. In general, this process does less damage to the fabric than does the discharge printing.

Photographic printing consists of two processes, both of which sensitize the cloth and then expose it under a film.[26] In one case, light destroys color; in the other, it develops color.

Flock printing is a fairly recent development resulting from the more general use of synthetic resins in the textile industry. Briefly, a resin design is printed on the fabric, and the finely cut flock is applied. The resin is heat cured to anchor the fiber securely in the resin and the resin to the fabric. Dyed cotton, rayon, or wool flock are used. Flock may be used for fabric or paper printing. The flock may be evenly or unevenly cut. Fabric or paper coated with evenly cut flock has the appearance of a pile fabric. This type of printing is most commonly used on cottons and rayons. There are two general methods of production. In one, the flock, very short fibers, are pressed into a plastic substance previously printed on the fabric. In the other, the flock is oriented end down in the plastic when the resin-printed fabric is passed between two electrodes. The latter process gives a velvety surface.

Wool fabrics are seldom printed in the United States but when they are, fastness to light, washing, and perspiration are desirable.

Pigment printing is, at one and the same time, one of the oldest methods of obtaining color on a fabric and one of the newest since it is again coming into prominence. The essential difference between dyes and pigments is chiefly a matter of particle size and solubility. Soluble dyes are applied from solutions. Pigments are not soluble and are applied from suspensions. Dyes are absorbed by the fibers, but pigments generally remain on the surface. Synthetic resins and light-fast pigments together with the simple mechanical process of using two or three rollers provide a simple inexpensive method of applying color and design to fabric. Medium and light colors are best. The process is especially practical for adding color to some of the synthetic fibers which are difficult to dye. Either a solid color or design may be achieved. Fabrics to which color has been added by this process sometimes crack or rub off unless the color has been skillfully applied.

Batik is a form of resist printing and is largely a hand process. In this type of printing, a wax or resin is used as the resist. This type of decoration was developed originally in Java where special oils and elaborate processes were used to develop beautiful fabrics in elaborate but primitive designs, usually on cotton.[27] Batik is characterized by a crackled effect caused by cracks which develop in the wax as the fabric is handled. A number of colors may be used.

[26] "Screen Printing," *Rayon Textile Monthly*, 27-2 (1946), 91.
[27] C. G. Hampson, "Javanese Batiks," *Textile Colorist*, 61 (1939), 623.

Block printing is an old hand process.[28] Wool was hand blocked in China and in India at an early date. The design is lacking in the fine detail which is possible and even necessary in roller printing. There is no limit to the size of design, except that it must be a usable design in the space where the fabric will be or can be used. The blocks are carved from wood but may be combined with metal to achieve fine detail in a design. The cloth to be printed is spread on an 8-to-60-foot concrete table which has been covered with a pad of cloth or woolen felt protected by another cloth. The wooden blocks are "inked" by pressing them on a pad saturated with the dye paste. The block is then placed on the fabric and tapped with a mallet to force the dye paste into the fabric. Bold, massive designs in rich colors are adapted to this type of printing. It is an expensive process.

Screen printing is a less expensive and more rapid process than block printing.[29] It is considered a hand-printing process.[30] The silk screens are cheaper to prepare than the wooden blocks but do not last as long. The same dyes may be used for both block and screen printing. The paste is thinner for screen printing than for block printing. In both cases, it is necessary that the fabric be properly scoured and bleached and usually pad dyed to a suitable background color. Fabric is stretched and pinned on long tables. The screens, which have been prepared in such a manner that only one color is applied at a time, are used in a series. After the dye for each part of a design has been applied, the screen is raised and the dye allowed to dry before the next color is added. A different screen is used for each color. To prepare a screen, the design may be reproduced photographically on a sensitized gelatine on the silk screen. Everything except the design is covered with an alkali-resistant paint, and the gelatine covering the design is washed out. The screen is then ready for use. Screens are prepared by a number of other procedures. Soluble vat or developed dyes are used with the usual thickening agents to prepare the pastes for printing. After printing, the fabric is finished just as after any other printing process.

The Peruvians practiced screen printing as early as 1531.[31] The process was not used in the United States until 1916. Screen printing is a form of stenciling. There has been a great increase in the use of silk-screen printing. There are several advantages. The designer can use a great variety of large, bold designs on fabrics to be produced in moderate quantities.

---

[28] P. Chadwick, "Block Printing," *American Dyestuff Reporter*, 38-23 (1949), 833–834 and 840.
[29] E. S. Beton, "The Screen Printing of Textiles," *American Dyestuff Reporter*, 38-19 (1949), 683–685.
[30] "Screen Printing," *Rayon Textile Monthly*, 27-2 (1940), 91.
[31] David Heritch, "Screen Printing," *Textile Colorist*, 64-757 (1942), 40.

MECHANISM OF DYEING

The physical and chemical forces involved in attaching a dye to a fiber are complex. Dyestuffs are nonvolatile substances, and a nonvolatile substance may be removed from a solution or suspension by one of three processes:

a) adsorption
b) solution in a better solvent
c) precipitation

Different fibers remove dyestuffs from such solvents as water or oil by one or another of the processes. The manner in which a specific dye is removed from any one dye solution depends upon a number of things.

Factors Involved. Some of the factors involved in the manner in which a dye becomes attached to fibers follow: [32]

a) nature of the fiber
b) nature of the dye
c) acidity or alkalinity of dye bath
d) concentration of dye in bath, very important
e) temperature of dye bath, very important
f) concentration of salts

In the latter case, salts may change the aggregates of dye molecules, or they may change the charge on the fiber.

Behavior of Specific Fibers. The shape of the dye molecule is of importance. A long dye molecule with active groups along its axis is thought to dye cellulose fibers especially well. Since viscose and cuprammonium rayons are celluloses, they dye in a manner similar to cotton, except more readily. Most dyes seem to be held to cottons and other celluloses by electrical forces. When wet, cotton is comparatively negative. Cotton fibers are structurally very porous. This allows for good penetration. It also provides a very high specific surface for the adsorption of dyestuffs. The same is true, but to a lesser extent, for viscose and cuprammonium. Fibers which swell the most are the most readily dyed (see p. 193).

Estron is not readily dyed with the usual cotton dyes but is most easily dyed with oil-soluble dyes, and a few other dyes. Certain dyes are soluble in solid cellulose acetate.

Nylons may be dyed with acetate dyes.

The protein fibers are much easier to dye than cellulose fibers. They are chemically much more reactive than cellulose. The protein fibers contain both acidic and basic groups and may be dyed with either basic

[32] R. C. Rose, "The Mechanism of Dyeing," *Rayon Textile Monthly*, 23-1 (1942), 161.

or acidic dyes. It is true, however, that different protein fibers dye differently.

Kemp and "dead wools" lack affinity for the usual wool dyes and if mixed with regular wool cause uneven dyeing. Unless such fibers are systematically mixed or used for special effects, they lower the quality of the fabric.

Mohair, which is used in knitting yarns, pile fabrics, astrakhan, and curl cloths, has a greater affinity for wool dyes than does wool itself.

Camel's hair is often dyed a richer brown before sale in order to improve the color, since the natural color is drab. Camel's hair may be used alone or mixed with wool or other of the specialty hair fibers. It dyes well in mixtures.

Alpaca fibers range in color from black, brown, red-brown, fawn, gray, tan to white and often are used in their natural color. Alpaca has less affinity than mohair for dyestuffs. It requires an excess of acid to dye well, as does camel's hair.

Common goat hair frequently does not dye well.

Angora rabbit hair is a beautiful white and is used either white or in very bright shades produced by acid dyes.

Feather fibers usually dye lighter than wool with which they are sometimes mixed. Usually acid dyes are used. It is necessary to handle these fabrics very carefully to avoid abrasion.

Casein fibers dye best at low temperatures 40 to 45 C. They become quite tender and plastic at 90 C. Wool fibers dye best at higher temperatures. Special care must be taken to insure even dyeing of mixtures. Usually the dyeing is done best when the fibers are fiber dyed and then blended if a uniform color is desired. In varying degrees, other manufactured protein fibers should present problems similar to those of casein fibers.

Some of the synthetic fibers have presented serious dye problems because of

- *a*) the inert chemical nature of the fiber
- *b*) the highly crystalline structure
- *c*) the dense compact physical structure
- *d*) the lack of absorption
- *e*) the lack of swelling which permits the dye molecule to enter the fiber structure

COLOR FASTNESS

Color is of inestimable social and economic value. It is one of the most important properties of most clothing and household fabrics, and is the dominant factor in appearance of fabrics. Market studies have shown that both garments and yard goods are selected first by appearance (color and texture) and second by other aesthetic and economic factors. Great losses are caused by colors which fade.

Factors Affecting Color Fastness. All dyestuffs can be converted into the colorless form, or the color may be destroyed by oxidation sufficient to destroy the color-forming group. In addition, the dye may not be sufficiently anchored in or on the fibers to produce a fast color. Color may be destroyed by sunlight or by laundry bleaches and stain removers. Some of the factors affecting fading are:

a) light source, the wave length, intensity of light, and length of time exposed to light
b) relative humidity, dyes fade more readily in high humidity
c) the manner in which the dye molecule is attached to the fiber
d) additional finishing materials: may not affect, may increase, or may decrease color fastness of dyes
e) type of fiber, linens usually fade more readily than cottons; small differences in the physical and chemical makeup alter dyeing properties, e.g., stretch spinning of viscose makes it less easily dyed
f) molecular structure of the dye, some less stable than others
g) some colors of some types of dyes less stable than others
h) method of dyeing important

Causes for Consumer Complaint. Color causes the bulk of complaints received by dry-cleaning establishments.[33] A recent study showed that approximately 31 per cent of the complaints were caused by dye trouble and 17 per cent were caused by stains. Almost half the complaints had to do with color, wanted or unwanted. When the six most common complaints in retail-store adjustment departments were tabulated, three out of six concerned color. Discoloration and staining, poor fastness to sunlight, and use of mixed fabric dye lots were causes of the most frequently made complaints.

A northeastern Regional Cooperative Textile Research Project studied the color fastness of certain types of dyes on 211 garments and 100 fabrics found in women's and children's wearing apparel.[34] The color fastness tests were on fastness to laundering, dry cleaning, light, and perspiration. The fibers included were cotton, wool, silk, and viscose and acetate rayons. The five dyes most frequently found were: azoid, anthraquinone, acid, thioindigoids, and developed, in that order. Lack of fastness to light and wet crocking were the two most serious deficiencies found.

Gas fading of acetate rayons is caused by the reaction of certain dyes to gases in the atmosphere.

Test Methods. The American Association of Textile Chemists and Colorists recently reclassified their standard and tentative test methods

[33] Dorothy Siegert Lyle, "Dry Cleaning Problems Brought to the Class Room," *Journal of Home Economics,* 41-3 (1949), 130.

[34] American Association of Textile Chemists and Colorists, *Technical Manual and Year Book,* vol. 25 (New York: Howes Publishing Co., Inc., 1949).

into two groups: [35] (1) methods for testing color fastness of textiles, and (2) other test methods for textiles and textile chemicals. Twenty-three separate tests for measuring the degree of color fastness of textiles to destructive agencies have been developed. The various tests cover color fastness to washing, light, perspiration, abrasion, crocking, bleaching, acids and alkalies (Table 18.III).

The methods of testing color fastness established by the American Association of Textile Chemists and Colorists are incorporated into Commercial Standard CS-59-44 and into Federal Specification C.C.C.T.-

TABLE 18.III

DEGREES OF COLOR FASTNESS RECOGNIZED BY STANDARD
TEST METHODS OF A.A.T.C.C.

	COLOR-FASTNESS RATING	
Test methods	Lowest class	Highest class
Cotton and linen		
Home and commercial laundering	1 2 3 4 5	
Chlorine bleaching	1 2 3 4 5	
Peroxide bleaching	1 2 3 4 5	
Manufactured fibers and mixtures		
Home and commercial laundering	1 3 5	
Atmospheric gas fading	1 2 3 4 5	
Silk		
Home and commercial laundry	Washing procedures described	
Mill washing	1 2 3 4 5	
Degumming	1 2 3 4 5	
Peroxide bleaching	Do or do not fade	
Wool and wool mixtures		
Home and commercial laundry	1 2 3	
Mill washing and scouring	1 2 3 4 5	
Fulling	1 3 5	
Stoving	1 3 5	
Carbonizing	1 3 5	
Textiles of any fibers		
Acids and alkalies	1 3 5	
Dry cleaning	1 3 5	
Heat, dry and wet—pressing	1 3 5	
Light	0 1 2 3 4 5 6 7 8	
Perspiration	1 2 3 4 5	
Phototropism	The dye is or is not phototropic	
Checking (rubbing)	1 2 3 4 5	
Sea water	Is or is not fast	
Weathering—tentative only		

Source: American Association of Textile Chemists and Colorists, *Technical Manual and Year Book,* vol. 28 (New York: Howes Publishing Co., 1952).

[35] *Ibid.*

191a for woven fabrics. One or the other of these standards is sometimes referred to on labels carrying information on color fastness. The
degree or class of fastness, however, is seldom mentioned, and would
mean little to the consumer buyer if it were. A simple system of indicating dye performance such as the rayon industry is sponsoring for labeling
could benefit the entire textile industry as well as the consumer.

Classes of Color Fastness. Usually five degrees or classes of color fastness are indicated. There are eight for fastness to light. The class
numbers have the following interpretations:

Light	Most properties except light	Color fastness
1		Very poor
2	1	Poor
3	2	Fair
4		Fairly good
5	3	Good
6	4	Very good
7	5	Excellent
8		Maximum

A Fade-Ometer is used for accelerated laboratory testing of color fastness to light. The hours of exposure in the Fade-Ometer may be converted into standard Fade-Ometer hours of exposure by the use of the
Bureau of Standards Light Calibration Paper No. 1554 which is provided to laboratories upon request. Standard dyed fabrics may be obtained from the American Association of Textile Chemists and Colorists
for the purpose of evaluating color fastness of fabrics tested in a Fade-
Ometer.

The Launder-Ometer, also developed by the American Association of
Textile Chemists and Colorists, is standard equipment for determining
color fastness of fabrics to laundering. Standard test methods have
been developed for its use.[36]

[36] American Association of Textile Chemists and Colorists, *Technical Manual and
Year Book.* 1952.

Chapter *Nineteen*

Finishing Processes

THE MECHANICAL FINISHING PROCESSES help to determine the hand and appearance of fabrics.[1] The type and quality of the fabric determine, to a large extent, the type of finish or finishing process used to prepare it for market.

As cloth comes from the loom, it is known as greige goods or gray goods. Some of the preliminary processes used to convert the gray cloth to a more attractive as well as more useful condition will be described.

SCOURING

The purpose of scouring is to prepare the cloth for finishing. It is a preliminary finishing process which removes foreign matter from all the fabrics concerned—wool, cotton, synthetics, silk, rayons. Scouring agents include soaps, oils, alkalies, and other agents such as the soapless detergents. Dry-cleaning agents are also used.

Piece scouring. Piece scouring removes oils, sizing, dirt, or other materials acquired or left on the fibers or fabric during spinning and weaving. Soft water is essential if soap is used in order to prevent formation of insoluble calcium and magnesium soaps on the fabric.

---

[1] Von Bergen and Mauersberger, *American Wool Handbook.*

Merrill, Macromac and Mauersberger, *American Cotton Handbook* (New York: Textile Book Publishers, 1949).

Schwarz and Mauersberger, *Rayon Handbook* (New York: Rayon Handbook Company, 1939).

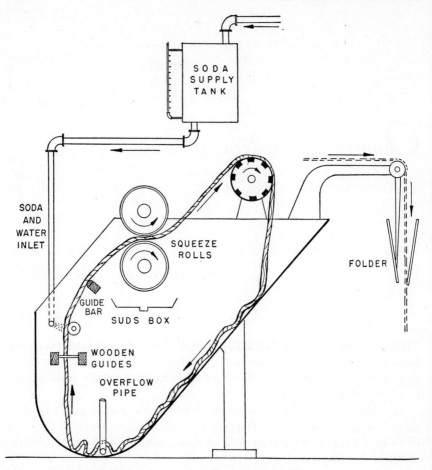

Fig. 19.1. **Scouring cloth with a string, rope, or dolly washer.** *Source: Von Bergen and Mauersberger,* AMERICAN WOOL HANDBOOK, *816.*

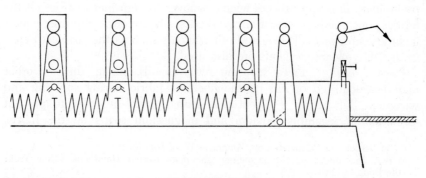

Fig. 19.2. **Continuous cloth washer.** *Source: Wood,* "Recent Developments in Textile Printing," *576.*

Scouring agents are usually soaps and weak alkalies. Silk fabrics are degummed in a mild soap solution. The synthetic detergents are relatively unaffected by hard water and rinse more readily than soaps. This makes them of value when felting is to be avoided or in scouring light yarn-dyed fabrics. They have the advantage of being nonalkaline and, for this reason, are less harmful to certain dyes and to wool and silk fibers.

Several types of machines are used for scouring. The string washer, also called rope or dolly washer, is most common. Pieces of cotton are sewed into several endless ropes which pass side by side over rollers placed at the bottom and top of a tank of scouring solution. The rollers keep the cloth moving continuously for one to four hours. The scouring liquid is drained out, and rinse water is run in.

A broad washer, which is similar to a string washer except that the fabric remains open, handles fabrics which are likely to crease.

A continuous piece washer, which is much more rapid than the string washer, has four wash bowls and seven rinse bowls. The last one contains cold water. Strips of fabric are sewed in a continuous line. Each strip goes through in about 20 minutes.

A regular laundry wheel may be used to scour crepes and light-weight dress fabrics. One to two hours are required.

Dry Cleaning. Dry cleaning may partially replace scouring in water (see chapter fifteen). Dry cleaning removes oils and other impurities which are on the fabric as it comes from the loom. The cloth enters the enclosed machine, goes into a soaking compartment containing the dry solvent, and passes over rollers. The solvent enters the soaking compartment and flows countercurrent to the direction of the cloth. It is redistilled before it is used again. The fabric then enters a drying compartment where it goes over drying cans (see Fig. 19.3).

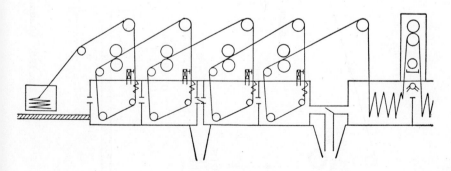

Fig. 19.2 (cont.).

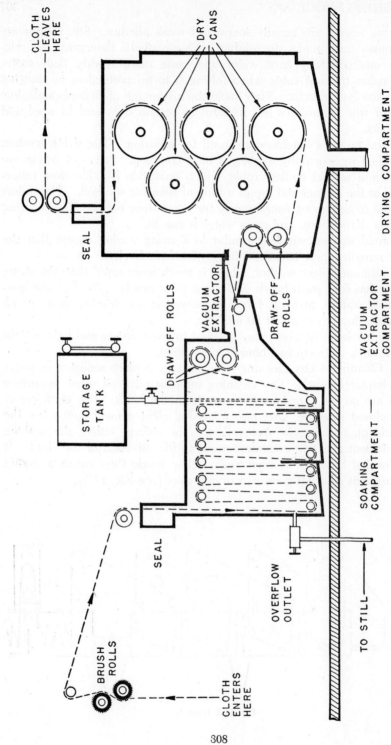

Fig. 19.3. Continuous dry cleaner. *Source: Wood,* "Recent Developments in Textile Printing," 576.

308

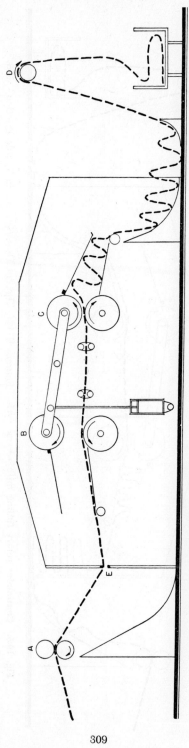

Fig. 19.4. Continuous rotary fulling mill: forward cycle. *Source: Wood*, "Recent Developments in Textile Printing," 576.

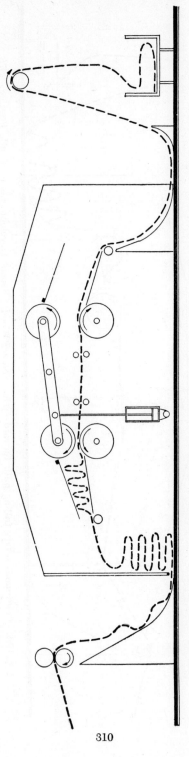

Fig. 19.5. Continuous rotary fulling mill: reverse cycle. *Source: Wood,* "Recent Developments in Textile Printing," 576.

SHRINKAGE PROCESSES

Shrinkage processes for producing dimensionally stable fabrics are common to most fabrics.

Fulling or Milling. Fulling or milling is peculiar to the woolen industry. Three factors are involved: moisture, friction, and heat. Moisture causes the fiber to swell and produces an increase in elasticity. As a result of friction or pressure, the wool fiber travels in the direction of the root until it contacts other fibers and becomes entangled with them in a compact mat or felt. Heat assists the movement of the fibers and increases their plasticity. The fabric is moistened in a soap solution. A 5-per-cent solution is used if slight felting is desired, a 10-per-cent solution for heavier felting of fabric. If color bleeding occurs with soap, other solutions may be used.

Two types of machines are used: the stock or hammer fulling mill and the rotary fulling mill. In the stock or hammer fulling mill, the fabric is fulled in bulk. Two sets of hammers pound the cloth. The amount of shrinkage, which occurs in both warp and filling direction, depends on the length of time the fabric is pounded. This machine is used for felts and fabrics where only slight fulling is wanted.

In the rotary fulling mill, the fabric travels in rope form. Two felting rollers, exerting considerable pressure, pull the cloth through the machine. From the rollers, the fabric is crammed into a crimping box which compresses the fabric so that the warp shrinks. Another device assists the shrinkage of the filling as the fabric moves on into its throat. The fabric is again brought back to the felting rollers and continues around the mill again.

A continuous rotary fulling mill has recently been made. It consists of two sets of fulling rollers. One set of rollers acts on the fabric as it moves in one direction. Then the 60-yard length of fabric moves back and is pushed by the other set of rollers. Several pieces of fabric side by side move back and forth automatically until adequately fulled, when another length of fabric is drawn into the mill.

Crabbing. Crabbing is a shrinkage process that sets the warp and filling by removing strain. In the English system of crabbing, the cloth is passed in full width through boiling water onto a roller. A second and third unit improves the finish; the last unit contains cold water to complete the setting. In continuous crabbing, the cloth passes through a series of tanks equipped with immersion rollers, sprays for rinsing, and squeeze rollers to remove the water.

Stabilization of Fabrics from Cotton and Manufactured Fibers. For cottons there has long been a procedure for mechanically shrinking the fabrics during finishing so that they could be guaranteed to shrink or stretch no more than 2 per cent. It has not been possible to stabilize rayon fabrics by so simple a procedure as is used for cottons. Chemical means have been used, however, with some success and will be discussed in Chapter Twenty. Fabrics made of a number of the heat-sensitive fibers as yet need further improvement before they can be ironed without special caution or without undue shrinkage or other damage.

NAPPING AND GIGGING

These procedures are used to bring one end of many of the fibers in the filling yarns to the surface of the face-finished fabrics in order to produce a nap or fuzzy surface. Napping is more commonly used in finishing fabrics than gigging. There are four systems of raising nap by wire-covered rollers or by teasels.

> a) moist napping
> b) dry napping
> c) moist gigging
> d) wet gigging

A napped surface is considered desirable for various reasons.

> a) improve appearance, soften pattern, blend color
> b) cover defects, conceal weave
> c) give softness, sponginess, lofty hand
> d) produce warmth

Finishes on wool fabrics may be divided into (1) clear finish, (2) face finish, and (3) modification of clear or face finish.

In clear-finished fabric, the weave and color are prominently developed. The fabric receives no fulling or only enough to give firmness. Most fabrics belong in this class.

Face-finished fabrics have a nap or pile. The weave is subdued. The weave may even be completely concealed by the nap. Nap or pile may stand erect or may be brushed or pressed to lay in one direction. This gives a lustrous or smooth, soft appearance. Face finish is often applied to woolens, and less frequently to cottons, rayons and nylons.

Modifications produce finishes between the clear and face finishes. Unfinished worsted have a surface fuzz, because they have not been sheared. The hand is soft and flannel-like. Another modification is found in fabrics with a clear-finished face and a napped back.

Napping. Wet napping is done on fulled fabrics, dry napping on those fabrics which are not fulled. Napping is done extensively on spun nylon and rayon fabrics and occasionally on fabrics made from filament yarns. Wool and cotton fabrics are often napped. Moist napping and dry napping are done by fine steel wires when a thick lofty nap is required. The action is greater than that of gigging. The machine for napping consists of a large cylinder around which are arranged a number of small rollers covered with card clothing. Fine wires in the card clothing lift the fibers. In double-action napping, there are

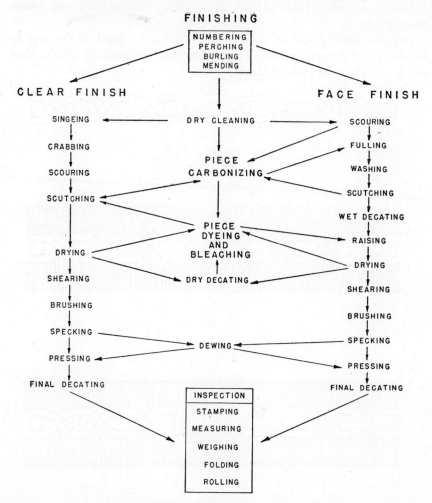

Fig. 19.6. **Clear and face finishes on wool fabrics.** *Source: Wood,* "Recent Developments in Textile Printing," *576.*

36 small rollers, 18 revolving clockwise and 18 counterclockwise. The wires in the card clothing are bent slightly so that the wires on one set of rollers pull the surface of the cloth in one direction and the wires of the other set of rollers pull in the other direction. The action is not a tearing out of fibers but a fluffing or raising due to the vibration of the wires in contact with the fabric. The rollers revolving with the cloth give a long nap, and those revolving against the cloth give a short nap.

The speed of the two sets may be adjusted to differ. In a single-action napper, the rolls all revolve in the direction of the fabric. The nap may be varied in depth and amount, sometimes by shearing. Some fabrics have only a trace of nap, while others have a thick nap resembling plush.

Different effects may be obtained by variation in depth of the nap, by brushing and raising the nap, by pressing flat, by finishing with a gloss, or by causing it to curl or ripple.

A.

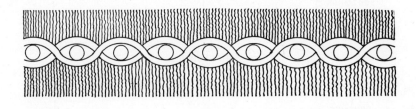

B.

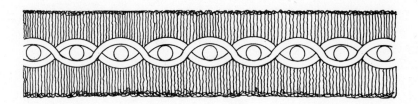

C.

Fig. 19.7. Steps in napping: A. cloth before napping, B. napped on both sides, C. finished. *Source: Courtesy of St. Mary's Woolen Manufacturing Co., St. Mary, Ohio.*

Face-finished or napped fabrics include blankets, coat fabrics, outing flannel, wool flannel, wool broadcloth, canton flannel, and brushed rayon and nylon knits.

Gigging. Gigging or teaseling, a mild form of napping, is carried out with teasels which come from a thistle plant cultivated in Oregon and New York in the United States, and in France. The teasels are set in frames on a drum. In order to raise the fibers slowly, used or old teasels are used first, and then new ones. The fibers are first raised by moist gigging. Then wet gigging lays the fibers in one direction. The result is a nap with a lustrous appearance. Fine woolens may be finished in this manner.

SHEARING AND SINGEING

These procedures are designed to produce a smooth uniform surface on the fabric.

Shearing. Shearing cuts the nap to a smooth, uniform surface. It also cuts off ends, knots, lumps or fibers, and some other defects in cloth. Gray goods are sometimes sheared before bleaching and finishing fabrics previous to inspection. Clear-finished fabrics such as gabardines are sheared to remove all surface fibers. The closeness of the shearing on napped fabrics will differ for broadcloths, duvetyns, or suedes. The nap must be cut gradually. The machine is set to cut high at first and is lowered gradually. This gives a more evenly sheared surface. Shearing machines have revolving blades like those on a lawn mower.

Fancy shearing may be done by lifting and lowering the cutting device. Another method uses an engraved metal roller as the bed on which the fabric rests in order to produce cut designs.

Singeing. Clear-finished fabrics are singed to remove all projecting fibers. Fibers are burned either by gas flame or heated plates. In gas singeing, the fabric passes rapidly over open gas flames. Plate singeing gives luster to mohair linings.

DECATING

Decating, a blocking or shaping process, is accomplished by applying heat, moisture, and tension. Steaming shrinks the fabric and also conditions it by loosening up the fibers and removing excess glaze. Decating improves the color, hand, and finish of rayons. Unevenness in crepes may be overcome by decating. In many instances, fabrics are set so that they will not shrink. After the fabric has passed through the steam box a brush lays the fibers on such fabrics as wool broadcloths.

Wet Decating. This process is used to set fibers permanently and to give some luster. There are various types of machines for decating, all of which have the following parts: a metal trough with one or several perforated metal cylinders, a pump for circulating water or steam through the cylinders, and a tensioning device. Cotton leaders are stitched to each end of the fabric. As fabric and cotton leaders are wound on the perforated cylinders, the cotton leaders cover the cylinder on the inside and cover the fabric on the outside, thus protecting the fabric. After the cylinder is rolled with cloth, it is placed in the trough. Water ranging from 140 F to boiling is circulated in and out of the cylinder for

5 to 20 minutes, or steam is blown from the inside for 5 to 20 minutes. Cold water or cold air is then drawn through with a vacuum pump to cool the fabric.

Dry Decating. In dry decating the cloth is wound on the roller under tension. Then hot steam is forced through it. The wool becomes plastic so that creases and folds are removed. As cold air is drawn through the roll, the fabric cools and sets permanently. It is left on the roll for a few hours. Luster is given to such fabrics as the broadcloths. The highest luster is developed by repeated wet and dry decating.

In final decating, the fabric is rolled around a large perforated cylinder with a thick-napped cotton leader if shrinkage is wanted or on a small cylinder without a leader if no shrinkage is wanted. Steam is forced through the perforations for one to five minutes, then is removed by a vacuum pump. One decating machine has the cloth passing through decating tables. This allows greater shrinkage than the use of a cylinder where the fabric is more firmly held.

CALENDERING AND RELATED FINAL FINISHING PROCESSES

Following starching or resin finishing, most cotton goods are calendered to give final smoothness to the cloth. This gives the same results as ironing or pressing of clothing. The type of calender used will depend upon the finish desired. Calenders consist of three to eleven heavy rollers, 8 inches to 12 or 15 inches in diameter, set one above another. These usually are arranged so that polished metal rolls alternate with soft, wrapped rolls. The wrapping may be cotton cloth, linen, paper, or other suitable fabric.

By threading a calender in different ways, different types of finishes may be obtained, as in the three ways shown in the diagrams in Figs. 19.8, 19.9, and 19.11.

Swissing. The swiss finish makes cloth less porous and open, develops a smooth finish, and tends to increase its strength. The slightly dampened fabric passes from the batch roll over four guide rolls, and then between the large calendering rolls and onto a batch roll. This is preliminary to friction calendering, shreinering, embossing, or mangle finishing. A three-roll calender will give only a light finish; a seven-roll calender will give either heavy or light finish, depending on the speed. The finish is also affected by the construction of the fabric, amount of moisture, and composition of starch mix or resin, as well as by the surface of the rolls, their composition, and the pressure used. The swissed calender finish is used on cotton fabrics such as dress goods and shirting.

Chasing. On the chasing calender, the cloth enters the pressing rolls as in swissing. When the cloth reaches the top rolls, it passes over guide rolls and again enters the calender rolls. Then it continues over the

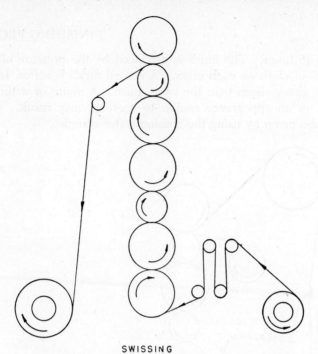

SWISSING

Fig. 19.8. Seven-roll calender threaded for swissing. *Source: Merrill, Macromac and Mauersberger,* AMERICAN COTTON HANDBOOK, *705.*

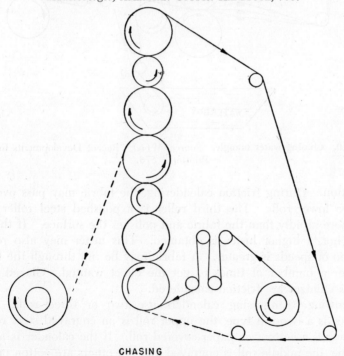

CHASING

Fig. 19.9. Seven-roll calender threaded for chasing. *Source: Merrill, Macromac, and Mauersberger,* AMERICAN COTTON HANDBOOK, *705.*

rolls 3 to 15 times. The finish is produced by the pressure of the several layers of cloth on each other. A chased finish is softer, fuller, and has a less glossy sheen than the swiss finish. A moire or a thready appearance, or an appearance similar to beetling, may result. A chased finish is also given by using the chasing water mangle.

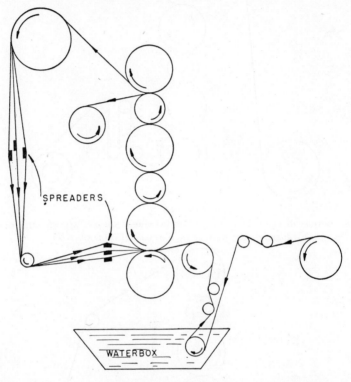

Fig. 19.10. Chasing water mangle. *Source: Wood,* "Recent Developments in Textile Printing," *576.*

Friction. During friction calendering, the fabric may pass over only the two lower rolls. The third roller is a polished steel roller which goes more rapidly than the fabric and polishes the surface. If the third roll is hot, a higher luster is obtained. This luster may also result if the ratio of speeds is greater. A fabric may be run through the friction calender a number of times to get the effect wanted. Glazed fabrics such as chintzes are friction calendered.

Embossing. Embossing calenders use two or three rolls. If the calender is a two-roll type, the upper roll is an engraved steel roll and the lower is a cotton- or paper-covered roll. If the calender is a three-roll type, the middle roll is engraved and the others are cotton or paper covered. The cotton-covered rolls are dampened with soap and water, and the calender is run until an impression of the design on the steel roller is made on the cotton roll after which it is dried and made ready for calendering the fabric. The design may be cut away on the roller

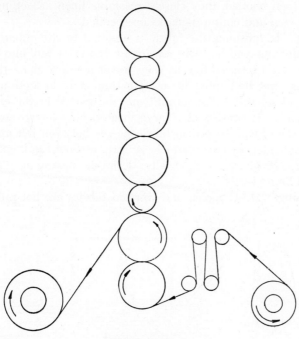

FRICTIONING

Fig. 19.11. Seven-roll calender threaded for frictioning. *Source: Merrill, Macromac, and Mauersberger,* AMERICAN COTTON HANDBOOK, *705.*

and the background pressed lustrous; or the background may be cut away and the design made lustrous by the engraved roll. Embossing is used chiefly on estron, viscose rayons and on cottons to adjust uneven tensions, to give a softer hand, and to produce special textures.

Moiré effects may be produced on ribbed rayons by sewing two layers of fabric together so that ribs are not parallel and then putting them through a calender. Portions of the ribs become flattened and lustrous. This is extensively used on estrons. Such finishes are not very durable.

Schreinering. The schreiner is the most commonly used embossing calender for cotton. It has a series of fine striations, about 250 per inch engraved at an angle of 20 degrees to the weave of the cloth for use on fine sateens, twills, and linings, and about 150 to the inch for heavier fabrics. A spun glass finish is given if friction is also used on the schreiner.

Beetling. Beetling is obtained by wrapping a roll of cloth on a wooden core and pounding it with wooden hammers while the roll revolves.

After a period of 20 to 60 minutes has elapsed, the fabric is rewrapped and beetled again. This may be repeated several times. If cotton fabrics are woven from uneven yarns with thick and thin places, and mercerized, then beetled, they closely resemble linen. Beetling flattens the yarn. Linen and cotton damasks are beetled.

Tentering. In finishing, the fabric is tentered to straighten it and to set it at a definite width. The semimoist fabric is fed into clips arranged on a chain form so that as they travel forward along the chains the fabric is stretched into shape. Heating coils located under the fabric dry and set it. A Palmer-unit may be placed at the end of the tentering frame. It consists of a large, heated cylinder covered with a felt apron. The rayon or cotton fabric passes between felt aprons and receives a calendering effect which is soft, mellow, and without too much luster. It gives an especially desirable appearance to satins, taffetas, and lining twills.

Hot Pressing. Most woolen and worsted fabrics are hot pressed in a

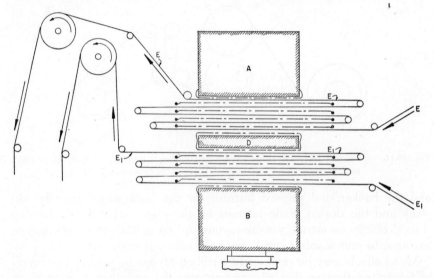

Fig. 19.12. Automatic hotplate pressing machine. *Source: Von Bergen, Werner and Mauersberger,* American Wool Handbook, *868.*

last finishing operation. The fabric is dampened with a fine spray of water while the pressing machines vary the heat, moisture, and pressure in order to give the hand, luster, and appearance desired in the fabric. The old hydraulic paper press used a moderate temperature over a longer time and gave a softer hand and appearance than the rotary and intermittent presses which use higher temperatures and less time.

In the vertical paper press, the fabric is folded and stacked with glazed cardboard paper between the layers and then placed between an upper

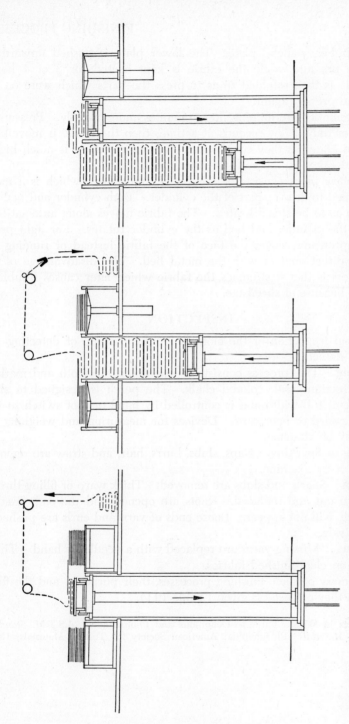

Fig. 19.13. Vertical paper press used in pressing wool fabrics. *Source: Wood,* "Recent Developments in Textile Printing," 576.

and lower heavy metal plate. The lower plate is pushed upward by hydraulic pressure while the fabric is kept heated for 3 or 4 hours. The fabric is then refolded so as to press the parts which were on the edges, and pressed again.

An automatic intermittent press operates more rapidly. Pressure is applied for only a few seconds at a time; then the fabric is moved between the plates as they come apart. The temperature is much higher in this press than in the vertical paper press.

The rotary press consists of a cylinder and a bed, which is a metal plate shaped to fit over part of the cylinder. Both cylinder and bed are hollow so as to be steam heated. The fabric moves along automatically between the cylinder and bed as the cylinder rotates. For light pressing, an apron may cover the face of the fabric instead of running the fabric in direct contact with the metal bed. The disadvantage of the rotary press is that it stretches the fabric which later causes trouble in garments because of shrinkage.

INSPECTION

The final inspection of the cloth is for the purpose of detecting and repairing defects.[2]

Perching. This process consists of examining the cloth and marking all imperfections with colored chalk. The perch is designed to show the fabric at full width and is controlled by hand or foot switch so that it runs forward or backward. Devices for measuring and weighing the fabric may be attached.

Picking or Specking. Naps, slubs, burrs, hair, and straw are removed by hand or by machine.

Burling. Snarls and slubs are removed. Thick warp or filling threads are drawn out and replaced. Knots are opened and the ends fixed so that a hole will not appear. Loose ends of yarn and curls are pushed to the back side.

Mending. Missing yarns are replaced with a needle by hand. This is essential on clear-finished fabrics.

A summary of some finishing processes, their purposes, and the fibers on which they are used is given (Table 19.I).

[2] "Defects in Woven Fabrics—Definitions and Photographs," *A.S.T.M. Standards on Textile Materials* (Philadelphia: American Society for Testing Materials, 1950), 29–34.

TABLE 19.I

SOME FINISHING PROCESSES, THEIR PURPOSES AND THE FIBERS ON WHICH THEY ARE USED

The process	Purpose	Fibers to which applied					
		Cotton	Wool	Rayon	Spun rayon	Linen	Aralac
Beetling	To give lustrous effect and flatten yarns	Cotton				Linen	
Bleaching	To give whiteness	Cotton	Wool	Rayon		Linen	Aralac
Brushing	To remove short ends of fibers and open pile	Cotton	Wool				
Calendering	To remove wrinkles	Cotton		Rayon		Linen	Aralac
Carbonizing	To remove vegetable matters		Wool				
Crabbing	To set the warp and filling threads		Wool		Spun rayon		Aralac
Decating (dry)	To make the luster permanent		Wool				
Decating (wet)	To set the nap and add luster		Wool				
Delustering	To give a softer luster		Wool	Rayon			Aralac
Filling	To shrink and soften the fabric		Wool				
Gigging	To raise and lay down fibers		Wool				
Kier boiling	To scour	Cotton				Linen	
Mercerizing	To give a luster and soft, smooth hand	Cotton					
Moireing	To give a water-marked effect			Rayon	Spun rayon		
Napping	To raise the fibers	Cotton	Wool		Spun rayon		
Scouring	To clean the fabric	Cotton	Wool		Spun rayon		Aralac
Shearing	To cut the surface fiber and yarns ends	Cotton	Wool		Spun rayon		
Singeing	To remove lint and threads by burning	Cotton	Wool		Spun rayon		
Sizing	To add body and crispness	Cotton		Rayon			
Shrinking	To control width and length	Cotton			Spun rayon		
Steaming	To shrink the fabric to shape, to set yarns		Wool			Linen	
Tentering	To straighten and stretch the fabric	Cotton	Wool	Rayon		Linen	

Source: Daily News Record, March 23, 1943, sec. 2, 6, reprinted by permission of Daily News Record.

323

Chapter Twenty

Finishes

MODERN TEXTILE FINISHING ranks with synthetic fibers as one of the two outstanding developments in textiles since the invention of rayon. At present, great progress is being made in the increasing use of continuous-process methods in bleaching, dyeing, and finishing.[1] Technical achievements in modern finishes have paralleled, and in some instances preceded, developments in manufactured fibers. A large share of the fabric finishes has been used on cotton which constitutes about two thirds of the textile market.[2]

Since the first patent law was enacted April 10, 1790, as "an act to promote the progress of useful arts," there has never been a time when so large a proportion of the patents represented progress in fibers and finishes.

FUNCTIONS

The function of a finish is to improve the appearance or the usefulness of the fabric. Some of the service qualities which are imparted to or are improved by the appropriate finish are resistance to: abrasion, destruction by moth or other insects, wrinkling, soiling, shrinkage, fad-

[1] Rabald C. Norris, "Modern Trends in Piece Goods Preparation, Dyeing and Finishing," *American Dyestuff Reporter*, 38-2 (1949), P67.
[2] George S. Buck and Frank A. McCord, "Crush-Resistance and Cotton," *Textile Research Journal*, 19-4 (1949), 216.

ing, and sometimes aging by light, heat, and moisture. It is not only desirable but of economic importance that such functional finishes last the serviceable life of the garment or fabric under conditions of normal use and care. The fabrics should be cleanable by either dry cleaning or laundering, and often, by both processes. Fabrics and finishes used for many purposes should be resistant to hot pressing, either wet or dry. Women's hosiery should be finished or constructed so as to eliminate great losses from snags and runs. More serviceable finishes are needed for window curtains and draperies, outdoor-wear summer clothing, and coat linings. Soft satiny finishes are wanted for bed linens, lingerie, and shirts for men. Finishes are wanted which will not water spot. More fabrics are needed in which the colors, dimensions, and textures do not change when they are washed or dry cleaned. Finishes are needed which impart these desirable qualities but do not at the same time add deteriorating properties.

The order in which specialized finishes were asked for in one study indicated the savings provided by better finishes. Shrink-resistant finishes for wool headed the list. Such finishes would make it possible for many more clothing and household fabrics to be laundered and would reduce the losses from felting and shrinkage. Second on the list of desired finishes was a control for gas-fading or new dyes for cellulose acetate. Next in order were better crease-resistant washable sheers and spot-resisting finishes.[3]

It is of no consequences to tell the consumer buyer the chemical compounds used in finishing her fabrics because 578 textile finishes are reported in use at present (*Daily News Record,* annual summary of textile finishes, September 6, 1951). Demand is growing for labels indicating performance in use of fabric and finish combinations.[4]

PROPERTIES

The properties of a desirable finish are those which

    a) impart desirable hand; e.g., pliable, flexible
    b) are stable to conditions of use; e.g., air, sun, laundry, and dry cleaning
    c) adhere to the fabric and do not reduce the strength
    d) are durable for the purpose for which the fabric is used; e.g., moth proofing
    e) are odorless
    f) are physiologically inert; e.g., should not irritate or poison the skin
    g) meet the requirements of use and care
    h) are themselves clear or colorless and remain so

[3] William G. Dall, "Textile Finishes," *Textile World,* 96-2 (1946), 111.
[4] Jules Labarthe, Jr., "Fabric Facts versus New Names," *Journal of Home Economics,* 44-6 (1952), 419–422.

    i) have no ill effect on dyes or other finishes
    j) are easily available at reasonable cost

STEPS IN FINISHING

The general steps in finishing cloth are

    a) scouring and bleaching
    b) mercerization, often used on cotton
    c) dyeing and printing
    d) some mechanical steps; e.g., calendering; others chemical—e.g., crease
        resistance

Scouring is considered here as preparation for application of finishes and has been discussed previously as were mechanical finishing processes and dyestuffs. Bleaching and mercerization will be discussed here.

Bleaching. Bleaching of cloth was for centuries a slow process which occurred naturally from exposure to the sun during use and washing, or by deliberate exposure of the fabric to moisture and sunlight as was done in the bleaching fields of Ireland. Before the Middle Ages, little was known of the methods used to bleach fabrics. In 1492, brown linen cloth was sent from Scotland to Holland in March and was returned in October. Seven to eight months were necessary to bleach the cloth. A well-bleached white fabric was more prized than a dyed fabric.

Advancements in bleaching and other chemical developments were delayed for 150 years before and during the Industrial Revolution because of the persistence of erroneous chemical theories. The work of such men as Priestley, Lavoisier, Scheele, and Berthollet made possible better controlled and more rapid methods of bleaching plant fibers. At the same time, these men were laying the foundations of modern fabric processing as well as of modern chemistry.

In 1787, chlorine was first used for bleaching fabrics. Soon the bleaching fields were replaced by chemical bleacheries. Today chlorine bleaches and other oxidizing agents are used in various forms and combinations. About 10 years ago, the first continuous bleaching ranges were installed. Cloth may be bleached either in the open width or rope form. After the cloth has been singed, desized, rinsed, and saturated with caustic soda, it goes through squeeze rolls to a J-box where the cloth steeps in the bleach solution for 1 to 1½ hours under steam heat. The cycle is repeated for another 1 to 1½ hours, then washed and pulled into the white bin. Medium- and heavy-weight fabrics can be bleached in a rope range at the rate of 250 to 300 yards per minute.

Special drives make it possible to keep the various parts synchronized in such a range. Labor and time are saved, and a more uniform bleach is secured. Dyeing and finishing plants are both set up in a similar manner.

In the above type of bleaching, it was found to be especially important that the washing be thorough. Mechanical agitation, counterflow of water, water conditioning, needle sprays in open-width washers, and suction plates all help to improve the high speed washing necessary in the modern bleaching processes.[5] One of the factors which makes chlorine hazardous to use is the difficulty of removal by rinsing.[6]
When the chlorine bleaches are used, however, an antichlor should always be used. Cottons and rayons may be bleached at higher temperatures than wool and other protein fibers. Since chlorine was discovered by Scheele, it has been an essential chemical in textile processing.[7]

Mercerization. One of the oldest and most widely used finishing reagents is an alkali. Until the latter part of the eighteenth century, the alkalies were prepared by farmers who collected their weeds and other plant materials and burned them.[8] The ashes were then leached with water to dissolve the alkaline compounds. By 1736, Duhamel had shown that the base of common salt was sodium. Later, Kier, from whom we get the term "Kier boil," had found a means of obtaining sodium from sodium chloride (common table salt) but was unable to make commercial use of the process because of England's high salt duties which were not removed until 1823.

Mercer, an English printer, discovered the benefits of treating cotton fabrics with the alkali, sodium hydroxide. The fabric acquired a soft, full hand and dyed readily to a deep shade. Later, Mercer found that drying the alkali-treated fabric under tension developed a silky luster and increased the strength. The process of swelling in alkali and drying under tension was called mercerization after its discoverer, Mercer. Mercerization is second only to bleaching in age and widespread usefulness as a finishing process, and is older than chlorine bleaching.

FINISHES

The finish on a fabric may be produced by mechanical processes, by chemical reagents, or more often, by both. The finishes achieved by

[5] L. P. Seyb and J. L. Foster, "Bleaching of Cotton, a Proposed Continuous Hypochlorite Process," *American Dyestuff Reporter*, 39-1 (1950), P20–P26.
[6] Joel Lindberg and Nilo Gralen, "Measurement of Friction between Single Fibers: IV, Influence of Various Oxidizing and Reducing Agents on Frictional Properties of Wool Fibers," *Textile Research Journal*, 19-4 (1949), 183–202.
[7] Paul S. Brailler, "Economics of Chlorination Processes," *Industrial and Engineering Chemistry*, 33-2 (1941), 152–155.
[8] Joseph H. Park and Esther Glauberman, "The Importance of Chemical Developments in the Textile Industries during the Industrial Revolution," *Journal of Chemical Education*, 9-7 (1932), 1143–1170.

chemical reagents are by far the more complex and varied. Frequently a finishing agent changes more than one important property of the fabric. Finishes will be discussed from two points of view: first, type of finish, or the property which the finishes are designed to produce; and second, some of the finishing materials themselves in relation to their properties and uses.

Types of Finishes. Sometimes one and the same type of finish may be produced by different processes.

Shrinkage control. One of the most desired finishes in fabrics, shrinkage control, guards against great losses and no end of dissatisfaction because clothing becomes too small, sheets and curtains too short. All fabrics may suffer from relaxation shrinkage. This has been controlled in cottons by a mechanical process of relaxation during finishing. More recently, it has been found that resins and some other finishing materials reduce the yardage loss in finishing. Most fabrics may be made dimensionally stable by either mechanical or chemical treatments. In rayons, estron, some of the synthetics, and wool, the problem is more complex than in cottons.

Shrinkage-resistant finishes for wool fabrics are in the process of development.[9] Felting shrinkage is a result of the characteristic structure of wool fibers. There are differences in elastic properties of the scales and the cortical cells. This causes fibers, which are arranged at random, to stretch under tension or pressure. The scales become interlocked and when tension or pressure is released, the fibers contract.[10] This brings the mass into a more compact form. If fibers swell or are subjected to harsh mechanical action, the opportunities are increased for the scales to become interlocked.

Shrinkage control in wool fabrics is being achieved with some success by variations of the following types of processes: [11]

a) Modification of the structure of the wool fiber by chemical means
b) Modification of the physical properties of the wool fiber by coating or impregnating the fiber with a resin

Chemical modification of wools by one process or another changes the character of the scales in such a manner that felting does not occur to the extent that is otherwise possible.[12]

---

[9] Milton Harris and Alfred E. Brown, "New Developments of Chemical Modification of Wool," *American Dyestuff Reporter*, 36 (1947), P316.

[10] Walton B. Geiger, F. F. Kobayashi, and Milton Harris, "Wool Chemically Modified to Enhance Stability," *Industrial and Engineering Chemistry*, 34-11 (1942), 1398–1402.

[11] National Knitted Outerwear Association, "Progress in Control of Wool Shrinkage," *Rayon and Synthetic Textiles*, 29-10 (1948), 48.

[12] Walton B. Geiger and Milton Harris, *Dependence of the Indigestibility of Wool Protein upon Its Polymeric Structure.* Research Paper 1500, National Bureau of

Recently, it was observed that resin finishes, while generally satisfactory, are sometimes concentrated at the serrated edge of the wool scale and at points of contact of fibers whereas the main surface of the fiber has only a light layer.[13] Even so, fibers treated in the raw or sliver stage do not show good shrinkage control in the finished cloth. It seems that the resin spreads unevenly over the cloth to produce a resin bond at the intersection of the yarns. This aids in shrinkage reduction. Too much resin reduces the flexibility of the fabric and gives it an undesirable hand.

High curing temperatures, unless perfectly controlled, leave wool fabrics harsh, with lowered strength, and possibly yellowed. If the processes are well controlled and the resins well chosen, the resin treatments may well provide the much needed washable wools for clothing and bedding.[14]

Crease resistance. Marketwise a property of great value, crease resistance is described as the property of a fabric that enables it to recover from folding or crushing encountered in ordinary use. The ability to recover is called resilience and is the physical property which is improved by crease-resistant finishes. A crease is a line or mark made by folding a textile fabric.

There seems to be general agreement that the anticrease properties of cotton are produced in proportion to the resin bridges between neighboring cellulose chains.[15] This in turn tends to increase the tensile strength, reduce swelling, and increase abrasion resistance.

A few years ago, the National Cotton Council assembled a list of properties of cotton which it felt could be improved by finishing. Some of the properties considered were draping qualities, elongation, strength, absorbency, luster, resiliency, flex-life, and resistance to: abrasion, water, microorganisms, chemicals, weathering, fire, clinging, and crushing or creasing.

A recent market study on crush resistance showed that even though

Standards, U. S. Department of Commerce (Washington, D. C.: Government Printing Office, 1942), 271–277.

Walton B. Geiger, Wilber S. Patterson, Louise R. Mizell, and Milton Harris, "Nature of the Resistance of Wool to Digestion by Enzymes," *Journal of Research, National Bureau of Standards,* 27 (1941), 459–468.

[13] John M. Gould, "Chemical Control of Wool Shrinkage," *American Dyestuff Reporter,* 38-10 (1949), P407.

C. Maresch and G. L. Royer, "Shrinkage Control of Wool by Melamine Resins," *Textile Research Journal,* 19-8 (1949), 449.

[14] National Knitted Outerwear Association, "Progress in Control of Wool Shrinkage," *Rayon and Synthetic Textiles,* 29-10 (1948), 48.

[15] R. F. Nickerson, "Investigation of Anticrease Treatments for Cotton," *American Dyestuff Reporter,* 39-2 (1950), P46.

D. D. Gagliardi and A. C. Nuessle, "Modification of Fiber and Fabric Properties by Wrinkleproofing and Stabilizing Agents," *American Dyestuff Reporter,* 39-1 (1950), P12–P19.

the value of cotton is greatly enhanced by a crush-resistant finish, less than 1 per cent of the cotton fabrics in 1948 had such a finish.[16] Yet, there are 88 finishes on the market which have crush-resistance properties claimed by their manufacturer.[17] It has been estimated that there are about 2.5 billion square yards of cotton fabrics used each year in clothing and household products in which crease resistance would be desirable. The service, appearance requirements, availability, and cost of suitable competing fabrics will in a measure dictate the extent of demand for and development of crease-resistant finishes on cottons.

Of the factors affecting the crease resistance of fabrics—kinds of fibers, yarn construction, fabric construction, and finish—the kind and quality of fibers are the most important. A good crush-resistant finish improves a number of other qualities, for example, the washability of wool and the wet strength and yarn slippage of rayon fabrics.

There are different types of equipment for measuring the effectiveness of crush-resistant finishes.[18] At present, information on the amount or durability of crush-resistant finishes is scarce on labels for the consumer buyer.

Water repellency. The ability of a fiber, yarn, or fabric to resist wetting is provided by a hydrophobic (water-repelling) surface which does not wet with water. Two general procedures for producing water-repellent fabrics are used. The older method involved coating the fabric with oil or rubber so that it was neither water nor air permeable. These fabrics were rain proof but were uncomfortable to wear because they were nonporous. Frequently, the clothing was wet from perspiration, if not from rain. Today, water repellents are used which do not noticeably lessen the porosity of the fabric. This leaves the wearer more comfortable and produces, if properly styled, a much more versatile garment. Rainwear, children's and adults' snow suits, and lumber jackets are some of the garments which benefit by being given water-repellent finishes. Some finishes are rather easily removed in cleaning procedures, but in some cases it is a relatively inexpensive process to replace the finish.

There are other uses for water-repellent fabrics than for rainwear. Outdoor and indoor uses for nonporous coated fabrics are numerous—kitchen and nursery upholstery purposes, purses, shower curtains, utility bags, and luggage. In the past, oiled and rubberized silks and cottons were widely used. They have been largely replaced by synthetic finishes or extruded, nonwetting films and sheets.

Today, water-repellent fabrics are generally produced by developing

[16] Buck and McCord, "Crush-Resistance and Cotton," 216–247.

[17] Labarthe, "Fabric Facts versus New Names," 419–422.

[18] American Association of Textile Chemists and Colorists, *Technical Manual and Year Book*, 1952, vol. 28, 155.

a nonwetting surface which is also frequently soil resisting. At least one of the popular water-repellent finishes is produced by a substantive (cationic detergent, p. 339). Some of the synthetic fibers have no hydrophilic (water-loving) groups and are therefore ideal for rainwear fabrics. In addition to the above, waxes, resins, and certain water-insoluble soaps are used.

All of the factors involved in water repellency are not clearly understood. There is some evidence to support those who feel that the construction of the fabric is the important factor in water repellency.[19] In general, though, there seems to be need for chemical finishing.

Standard test methods have been developed to measure the resistance of textile fabrics to water, but more should be done about the standards of durability of such finishes.[20] No standard test has been developed as yet to determine the *durability* of a water-resistant finish when washed or dry cleaned.

Absorbency. The reverse of water repellency, absorbency, is important for many uses such as towels, diapers, bed linens, and some undergarments.

Factors affecting the rate and amount of water absorption of fabrics are

a) ease of wetting, type of surface, type of fiber
b) capillary action which is affected by size of fibers, type of yarn, and construction of fabric
c) normal moisture regain of the fiber

It was found that if cotton fabrics had all the waxes and sizings removed, they would absorb about 150 times their weight in water in about 15 seconds.[21] Water absorption of cotton is increased by treatment to produce a derivative of cellulose which absorbs water much more readily than cotton cellulose.[22] Other procedures are also used to increase the moisture absorption of cotton. For moisture regain of fibers see chapter fourteen.

Lacquers and glazes. A much less heavy finish than that found in coatings is implied by lacquers and glazes. In this instance, the structure of the fabric is plainly visible. The finishing substance, frequently a cellulose compound or a synthetic resin, is combined with the fabric in a fairly durable manner.

[19] H. A. Schuyten, J. David Reid, J. W. Weaver, and John G. Frick, "Imparting Water Repellency to Textiles by Chemical Methods, a Review of the Literature," *Textile Research Journal*, 18-7 (1948), 396–415.

[20] American Association of Textile Chemists and Colorists, *Technical Manual and Year Book*, 1952, vol. 28, 136–145.

[21] P. Larose, "Water Absorption by Towels," *American Dyestuff Reporter*, 31 (1942), 105.

[22] Walter W. Scott, "Some Recent Developments in Cotton Research at Southern Regional Laboratory," *Textile Research Journal*, 19-7 (1949), 436–443.

Friction calendering develops the glazed surfaces. The glaze may be produced by allowing one set of calender rolls to operate at a faster rate of speed than the other, or by the calender rolls traveling at one rate of speed and the fabric at another.

Crispness and transparency. In fabrics such as organdies crispness and transparency may be produced by the controlled action of a number of compounds. If the yarns in the fabric are made of cellulose acetate and cotton, the fabric can be treated to fuse the fibers and produce a transparent effect as well as stiffness.

Electrocoating. The fabric is entirely coated with a synthetic resin in electrocoating, or the resin is applied in a design. While the resin is soft, the fabric may be covered with flock, passed through rollers to imbed the flock in the resin, then cured and brushed to remove the

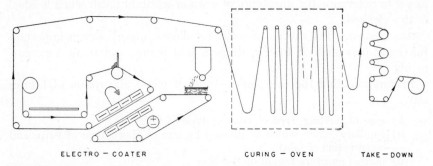

ELECTRO — COATER   CURING — OVEN   TAKE — DOWN

Fig. 20.1. Sketch of electrostatic coating unit. *Source: J. O. Amstutz,* "Electrocoating Fabrics," AMERICAN DYESTUFF REPORTER, *30-19 (1941), P513–P515.*

excess flock. Another method of adding the flock is to pass the fabric between electrodes and have the fibers imbed themselves end first in the resin, which is then set by heat. The latter procedure produces the

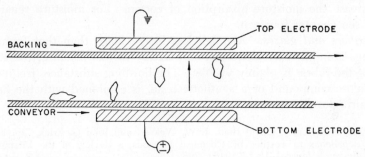

TOP ELECTRODE

BACKING

CONVEYOR

BOTTOM ELECTRODE

Fig. 20.2. Electrocoating: arrangement of electrodes. *Source: Amstutz,* "Electrocoating Fabrics."

more velvet-like surface. Curtain fabrics are frequently flock printed. Some rugs have been produced by imbedding rayon pile in a rubberized back. It is possible to orient on end as many as 275,000 or more fibers per square inch. Both coated fabric and paper have many uses.

Luminescent substances. On textile fabrics either phosphorescent or fluorescent compounds are used. The phosphorescent substances glow in the dark after being exposed to light. They include various salts, especially the sulfides of such metals as zinc, cadmium, calcium, magnesium, strontium, and barium. The brightness of the light varies with the length of exposure. The fluorescent compounds glow while exposed to ultraviolet light. Luminescence may be produced by dyes or pigment which may be applied in the usual manner. The fact that luminescent pigment can scarcely be seen 100 feet away makes it of special value on local guides in theatres and blackouts.

Preservatives. Microorganisms annually destroy great quantities of fabrics made from all the natural fibers and the rayons and azlons among the manufactured fibers. Cotton is especially susceptible to attack by bacteria and molds. Preservatives are usually water soluble. More progress has been made in establishing methods of testing the effectiveness of a particular finish than has been made in developing effective permanent finishes with the desired qualities. This problem has been discussed elsewhere (see chapter twenty-one).

Antiseptic finishes are needed for textile fabrics which would find use in various places from hospital fabrics to fishing nets. If cotton and jute are to continue to compete with synthetics as outdoor fabrics, they will have to be protected from the action of microorganisms.[23] The finish for many uses must be nontoxic for humans. Permanent antisepsis is needed for hosiery, shoe linings, hospital and hotel linens, gauzes, and surgical dressings. Germany has worked on combining dyeing and rot proofing of jute. The United States is interested in developing rot-resistant finishes for cotton.[24]

A secondary benefit from antiseptic finishes is their odor-proof qualities. The decomposition of perspiration on clothing is retarded. Finishing materials for all uses on fabrics have to withstand rigid biological tests before being marketed. Such materials come under the supervision of the Federal Food and Drug Administration.

Insect repellents. Every section of the country needs fabrics which are insect repellent. More permanent finishes are necessary here, also. This topic is discussed in chapter twenty-one.

Fire retardants. It is not essential that all fabrics have the same degree of fire resistance, but fire retardants are of special value on some fabrics in the home as well as in public buildings. Uses and dangers differ. It is thought that when acceptable tests for specified usage are

[23] A. H. Preston, "Preservatives for Textiles," *Textile Colorist*, 63 (1941), 543.
[24] Scott, "Some Recent Developments in Cotton Research at Southern Regional Laboratory," 436–443.

developed, finishes and laws regarding them will follow.[25] A number
of processes for applying fire retardants exists.[26] Fire resistance is difficult to test on pile, tufted, and napped fabrics. At present, there are
no methods of determination of flammability of sufficient accuracy to
enable municipal, state, or federal laws to be generally established. It
is felt at present that for many uses (not clothing) the best procedure
for obtaining fire-resistant fabrics is to use Fiberglas, asbestos, Vinyon,
teflon, or other nonflammable fiber to make the fabric.

Finishing Materials. Information on some of the materials used in
finishes is of importance in understanding the properties and care of
finished fabrics.

Sizings and fillings. These compounds, common among the early
finishing materials, are used to give body, crispness, or softness to fabrics.
Many sheer fabrics have sizing or filling added to facilitate handling and
sewing. In general, these substances do not combine chemically with
the fabric and are quite readily removed in laundry and dry-cleaning
procedures, except when they are held on the fabric by resins or other
coating materials. Starches include corn, rice, potato, wheat, and
tapioca. The starches as well as gums, gelatines, glues, agar, some fats,
oils, soaps, and waxes are used to give stiffness, softness, weight, or
smoothness as the case may be. Metal soaps give weight and act as
delustering agents. Aluminum soaps produce water-retardant finishes
and give a full hand to the fabric. Clays and talcs add weight and
body to the fabric.

There are many uses for fabrics which do not have to be resistant
to laundry and dry-cleaning procedures. Book-binding fabrics, imitation leathers, oil cloth, and window-shade fabrics are examples of
uses of fabrics with fillers. The fabrics may be embossed; dispersed
pigment or pigment printing may add color, and they frequently have
washable resin coatings.

Starches of different kinds have different properties (Table 20.I).[27]
Frequently a mixture of starches is necessary to produce the desired
effect. There are many uses for which sizings are still used; for example, warp sizing for weaving.

In finishing fine wearing apparel, such as men's dress shirts, oils,
waxes, and gums may be used with starches to give a soft, satiny finish.

---

[25] American Association of Textile Chemists and Colorists, *Technical Manual and
Year Book*, 1952, vol. 28, 119–123.

[26] Hugh C. Gulledge and George R. Seidel, "Durable Flame-retarding Cellulosic
Materials," *Industrial and Engineering Chemistry*, 42-3 (1950), 440–444.

[27] R. M. Hixon and G. F. Sprague, "Waxy Starch of Maize and Other Cereals,"
Industrial and Engineering Chemistry, 34-8 (1942), 959–962.

M. S. Furry, *Breaking Strength, Elongation, and Folding Endurance of Films of
Starches and Gelatin Used in Textile Sizing*, United States Agricultural Bulletin 674
(Washington, D. C.: Government Printing Office, 1939).

The gums include tragacanth, arabic, and tragasol. Algenates may be
used. Gelatine and albumen add body and stiffness.

TABLE 20.I

EFFECT OF DIFFERENT STARCHES AS FINISHES

Type	Temperature in F of Gelatinization	Max. viscosity	Effect as a finish on fabric
			Opaque, dry, harsh, boardy
Corn	150	161	Full, mellow hand
Wheat	142	185	Clear translucent, smooth, soft
Potato	136–42	150	Clear translucent, smooth, soft
Tapioca	137	145	Clear satiny and soft
Rice	. . .	. . .	Soft hand
Sweet potato	. . .	. . .	

Source: J. W. Stallings, "Role of Starches in Textiles," *American Dyestuff Reporter,*
    28-1 (1939), 35–37.

Formerly, when starches were generally used to give stiffness to
fabrics, it was customary to add china clay to give weight and other
compounds for hygroscopic qualities. Tallow, olive oil, glycerine, paraffin, and waxes were added to make the cloth softer. All this was followed by one or more of a number of compounds to prevent the development of molds and bacteria.

After World War I, there was considerable redistribution of wealth,
accompanied by drastic changes in fashions.[28] Silks were heavily
weighted with tin, lead, and iron salts. Cottons, linens, and silks were
made to appear more costly by the use of gums, glues, and starches
lubricated with oils and waxes. Most of those finishes, except metallic
weighting, lasted no longer than the first laundering. Today, the
finishing picture has almost completely changed as shown by the large
number of fairly durable finishes on the market.[29]

Cellulose and cellulose derivatives. One of the largest groups of
textile finishing agents, regenerated cellulose (similar to that in the
rayons) and cellulose derivatives (e.g., cellulose acetate) are especially
resistant to washing and dry cleaning when they have been well applied. They provide a full hand, enhance luster, increase strength and
abrasion resistance, and can be applied to gray goods and subsequently
bleached. Some of the limitations of this group of finishing materials
are

  a) require cellulose as a raw material
  b) dust off with use, unless well applied
  c) lose satiny luster after a few washings

The solutions used in finishing fabrics are made from wood pulp or
cotton linters by the same processes as are used in making fibers except

[28] H. H. Mosher, "Evolution of Textile Finishes," *American Dyestuff Reporter,* 29
(1940), 531.
[29] T. H. Thomas, "Present Trends of Textile Finishing," *Dyer and Textile Printer,*
84 (1940), 327.

that shorter cellulose molecules may be used for the finishes. These solutions, when skillfully applied, provide entirely washable and relatively permanent finishes. The fabric is impregnated with the solution which is then coagulated and the fabric washed and dried. After calendering, the finish is usually similar in appearance to a starch finish, but in some instances pigment and a filler are added to the finishing material to produce coatings such as are found on fabrics used as artificial leathers for upholstering.

The derivatives of cellulose are an increasingly useful and growing group of finishes. They are being used as finishes on cottons, rayons, wool, and jute bagging for food packaging. The finish gives a smooth fabric, since all loose, fuzzy fibers are held to the surface of the fabric. They may be applied before bleaching or scouring, during mercerization, or as a final finish. Their properties depend upon the amount and kind or kinds of derivative used.[30] A cellulose acetate surface may be developed on cotton fibers which then behave in part like acetate and in part like cotton. Mercerized cotton may be treated in such a way that the cotton fibers become thermoplastic and, when calendered with a hot roll, the fabric acquires transparency and crispness. Permanent organdy and attractive embossed designs may be produced in this way. Cotton fibers do not dye with ordinary cotton dyes after being immunized.

In general, the cellulose derivatives are especially desirable on wide sheeting, table linens, print cloth, shirtings, back-filled fabrics, collar cloth, window-curtain fabrics, and some underwear. Other finishing materials such as fungicides, colored pigment, fire- and water-resisting compounds may be incorporated into the cellulose finish to decided advantage. Some of the advantages of the cellulose derivatives are that they

  a) allow a range of finished effects
  b) are easy to apply
  c) may be used alone on the face of the fabric or with back-filled finishes
  d) may be used to produce crisp or soft, glazed or dull, finishes
  e) increase strength and abrasion resistance
  f) increase resistance of cotton to alkalies and acids
  g) may be used as basis of printing pastes in textile printing
  h) are comparatively durable

Synthetic materials. In finishing fabrics, two types of synthetic materials are used: thermosetting and thermoplastic. The thermosetting compounds all set or harden with the application of heat. These com-

[30] T. H. Roberts, "Present Trends in Textile Finishing," *American Dyestuff Reporter*, 29 (1940), 396.

pounds are useful as finishing materials but are not used as fibers. The thermoplastic resins soften when heated, and some of these compounds are useful either as fibers or finishes.

The application of resins to fabrics changes physical properties by

    a) improving crease resistance
    b) decreasing yarn slippage
    c) adding stiffness
    d) giving shrinkage and felting control
    e) giving washable glazed fabrics
    f) giving durable embossed effects

Frequently two or more of the above are achieved at one and the same time. Resin finishes have emphasized the necessity for careful control of temperatures, tensions, and time if uniform results are to be

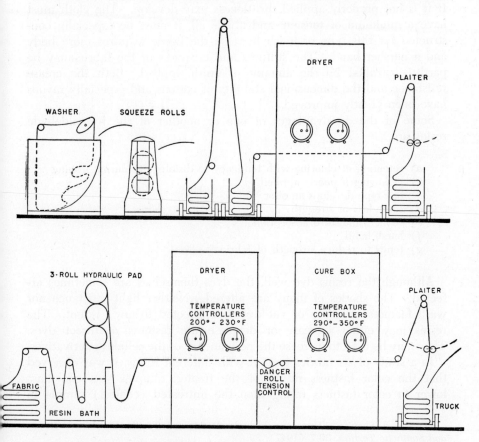

Fig. 20.3. Synthetic resin finishing, a continuous process for application of resin.
Source: AMERICAN FABRICS, 7 (1948), 89.

secured and waste avoided. Various resinous substances are applied with numerous variations to provide finishes which better adapt fabrics to their end uses.[31]

Formaldehyde resins, which are thermosetting low-cost resins, are among the most commonly used finishes. With improvements, they are being used in increasing amounts for crease resistance, shrinkage control, glazed surfaces, and embossing. At present, this type of resin is the most commonly used crease-resistant finish for cotton, wool, linen, or rayons.

The resins may be varied to produce changes in the finish obtained, and may be applied to the scoured, or scoured and dyed, fabric which is then dried, cured, and washed. It is important that the scouring process leave the fibers perfectly clean if the resin is to be evenly distributed. The success of this type of finish depends upon great care. If it is not properly applied, brittleness may develop. The cloth must have a minimum of tension, and above all, it must be especially constructed for this type of finish because the fabric acquires more body and a harsher hand. The stiffness and crispness of the fabric may be partly controlled by the amount of finish applied. Both the crease resistance and the dimensional stability of cottons and especially rayons have been greatly improved.

Some of the disadvantages of one or another of the formaldehyde resins are

a) retention of chlorine with tendency to disintegrate during ironing
b) yellowing if poorly applied
c) one type develops an odor [32]
d) some loss of strength
e) reduces moisture absorption
f) harsh hand
g) tends to reduce strength of fabric

Although the resins dye well, the dyes themselves are sometimes affected. The shades of many are altered. Neither light resistance nor wash fastness of sulfur or vat dyes are affected to any extent. The resins may either increase or decrease the fastness of direct dyes. They may be used to increase the permanence of the cellulose derivatives.

In a study of six fabrics treated with different resins, it was observed that the color fastness rating of the treated samples was one class lower in color fastness rating than the untreated (control) sample in

[31] Leonard Shapiro, "Urea-formaldehyde Resins for Textile Finishing," *Rayon and Synthetic Textiles,* 30-7 (1947), 39.

[32] H. C. Borghetty, "Chemical Aspects of Finishing Fibers and Fabrics," *Rayon and Synthetic Textiles,* 31-1 (1950), 85–87.

the 20-hour and the 80-hour exposures.[33] This seems to indicate an adverse effect of resin finishes on the color fastness to light of some dyestuffs.

The methacrylates resins are used to produce a clear smooth finish such as may be found on chintz or cotton dress fabrics. Such resins may be used for fibers or finishes, as well as for molded objects such as lucite. The finish is remarkably elastic, strong, and clear. It is thermoplastic, stable, and washable. The finish is extremely resistant to alkali and is not destroyed by mercerization.[34]

The vinyl resin finishes are used on raincoat fabrics, shower curtains, and on clothing where acid resistance and water repellency are needed. They act as binders in pigment printing and may be used to produce a fire-resistant finish when combined with suitable materials. Some are suitable for lacquers and bonding fabrics while others are used in shrinkage-resistant finishes for rayons.

One of the resins produces a clear, tough film for sizing threads and fabrics. An important wartime use for the vinyl resins was in finishing fabrics to be used for

- *a*) raincoats for U. S. and Canadian troops (vinyl layer on inside so as not to reflect light when wet)
- *b*) ground sheets coated to provide dry beds when camping
- *c*) top clothes to protect ski troops from wind and snow
- *d*) ski tents coated and light enough to carry in pack
- *e*) desert water bags
- *f*) jungle food bags
- *g*) coated fabric and even films to cover planes and thus serve as portable hangars in order to protect from ice and snow.

The substantive finishes are produced by large, positively charged ions. They behave as a colorless dye and are rapidly applied to cotton, rayon, acetate, nylon, and wool. They have to be cured on the fabric at a comparatively high temperature but are permanent for the practical life of the garment.

The substantive finishes give a soft, full hand to fabrics; some are better than others.[35] If a fabric becomes harsh or stiff because the natural waxes and oils have been removed during the manufacturing processes, it becomes necessary to add softeners to improve the hand.

[33] Dorothy S. Lyle and Marion R. Butler, "Performance of Resin-treated Fabrics in Wet and Dry Cleaning," *Rayon Textile Monthly*, 29-5 (1948), 57.
American Association of Textile Chemists and Colorists, *Technical Manual and Year Book*, 1949, vol. 25.
[34] R. F. Nickerson, "Investigation of Anticrease Treatments for Cotton," P46.
[35] T. H. Thomas, "Present Trends of Textile Finishing," *Dyer and Textile Printer*, 84 (1940), 327.
Borghetty, "Chemical Aspects of Finishing Fibers and Fabrics," 85–87.

Older finishes such as oils, waxes, emulsion, or dispersions of oil with a detergent base are still frequently used, but they furnish food for destructive microorganisms unless preservatives are used.

If the substantive finishes are also to act as water repellents, it is necessary to remove the last traces of soap from the fabric after washing or dry cleaning. The substantives have excellent stability to light and storage but tend to yellow white fabrics. They reduce the light fastness of some dyes and improve it for others. Prior to the introduction of substantives, the printing industry had made little progress for almost a century.

Permanent finishes. There are many finishes which serve quite well the life of the garment or fabric. The cellulose and the synthetic finishes which have just been discussed are, generally speaking, relatively permanent. The use to be made of the fabric should determine how durable the finish needs to be. The finish on a cotton table cloth should probably withstand 100 washings; the finish on an organdy evening dress probably need endure only 10 washings.[36] At the same time, costume tarlatan or holiday bunting may never need be washed. Yet each fabric will serve equally well its purpose.

A number of more serviceable finishes are needed. Fire retardants, insect repellents, and many dyestuffs need to be more permanent than they are. Durable finishes are needed to inhibit deterioration of fabrics by the sun and by action of microorganisms. Wrinkle-resistant finishes are needed which last longer and do not change desirable qualities of fabrics or reduce wearing qualities. Finishes are needed which retard the development of unpleasant odors in fabrics, especially in public buildings as in hotels and in Pullman upholstery and in bedding. Finishes are used to increase the usefulness and beauty of fabrics or to retard one or another of the factors which tend to limit the life or the usefulness of the fabric.

DERMATITIS

From time to time, complaints are made that fibers or finishes cause irritation of the skin.[37] Fibers which have been reported as causing dermatitis are flax, hemp, sisal, jute, silk, wool, and camel's hair. Infected wool may cause anthrax. Fabrics made from spun glass may cause irritation but not dermatitis, unless from a resin finish. The manufactured fibers have not caused dermatitis, but finishing materials on them may. Dyestuffs on fabrics rarely cause dermatitis. When they do, it is usually the result of a faulty dyeing process. The Food and Drug Administration maintains certification services for coal tar colors.

36 John T. Gibbons, "Permanent Finishes," *Textile World*, 86-7 (1936), 88.
37 Louis Schwartz, "Dermatitis among the Public from New Fabrics, Dyes and Finishes," *Chemical and Engineering News*, 27-19 (1949), 1358–1360.

Finishes more frequently cause dermatitis than do fibers or dyestuffs. The new synthetic resins have caused trouble a number of times. Japan and China wax obtained from a tree of the poison ivy family is sometimes used as a water-resistant agent and causes dermatitis. Flame-retarding finishes, delustering agents, and most moth-repellent agents cause no trouble. All finishing agents should be thoroughly tested (and many are) before being applied to fabrics and sold to people.

Synthetic insecticides are usually primary irritants and may be sensitizers. Natural insecticides are sensitizers but are not primary irritants. Mildew preventives are likely to cause trouble.

Dermatitis may also be caused by dry-cleaning chemicals, bleaches, strong washing powders, and detergents which have not been rinsed from the fabric after laundering.

STATIC

Static is not a finish which is applied to fabrics, but it is a condition for which a suitable remedy is needed.[38] Static is the observable effect of the accumulation of electrostatic charges. Lightning is another example. The charge is on the surface of the fabric and is especially noticeable when the mass is small and the surface is great as it is on fibers and fabrics.

The definitions for positive and negative electricity are based upon observations made long ago. A body is said to have a positive charge when it is like that on a glass rod rubbed with silk. A body is said to have a negative charge when it is like that on a rubber rod rubbed with cat's fur. Electrons are negative by definition, because they are the same as the charge on a rubber rod rubbed with cat's fur.

ELECTROSTATIC SERIES

Positive end

Glass	Wool	Paper	Acetate rayon
Human hair	Silk	Ramie	Orlon, acrylic
Nylon yarn	Viscose rayon	Steel	Saran
Nylon polymer	Cotton	Hard rubber	Polythene

Negative end

The electrostatic voltmeter gives a quantitative measure of static on different substances (Table 20.II).

One of the styrene resins is claimed to have pronounced antistatic properties. Such a finish is needed for fabrics to be used in cold, dry regions. The problem of dust on clothing in cold, dry weather is great,

---

[38] D. J. Lehmicke, "Static in Textile Processing," *American Dyestuff Reporter,* 38-24 (1949), P853–P855.

TABLE 20.II

ELECTROSTATIC VOLTAGE OF VARIOUS FIBERS
AGAINST SYNTHETIC RUBBER

Fiber	Voltage
Cotton	50
Viscose rayon	100
Wool	350
Acetate rayon	350
Vinyon N	800
Silk	850
Orlon	900
Nylon	1050

Source: D. J. Lehmicke, "Static in Textile Processing,"
   American Dyestuff Reporter, 38-24 (1949),
   P853–P855.

and so is the problem of cleaning house. The static charge holds the dust on the fabric. However, humidity will cause it to be quickly dissipated.

Chapter Twenty-one

Deterioration of Fabrics

THE CHIEF DETERIORATING FACTORS acting during the life of a fabric may be classed under a few general headings

- *a*) cleaning procedures, wet and dry
- *b*) weathering
- *c*) wear and storage
- *d*) microorganisms and insects

The properties of fabrics, the uses made of fabrics, and the care given them vary so greatly that it is not possible to designate their probable life in terms of time. It is possible, however, to estimate the performance of the fabric in terms of a specific property under a definite set of conditions. For example, color fastness can be expressed in terms of standard Fade-Ometer hours of exposure to a standard light or in terms of hours of standard sunlight.[1] It is then necessary to translate the results of either method of evaluation into average hours of actual sunlight for a specific region for a given time of year. It is obviously impossible for fabrics to carry labels giving the actual hours of wear before fading that is to be expected in every community. It is possible, however, for fabrics to carry labels with performance information which each consumer can quickly learn to evaluate in terms of his own locality and uses.

[1] American Association of Textile Chemists and Colorists, *Technical Manual and Year Book,* 1952, 100–103.

The research necessary to precede this type of information for many fabric properties has already been done. The machinery necessary for putting the information on labels is established in the form of Commercial Standard CS-59 or of Federal Specification CCCT-191a. Either carries test methods which the manufacturer may use to evaluate various service qualities of his fabrics, for example, the fastness to light. When the fabric being purchased carries factual information on light fastness of the color, it is then entirely up to the consumer to select his fabric, use it, and care for it accordingly. If a Class 3 "fastness to light" label is attached, only *fair* fastness to light can be expected, not good or excellent.[2] The consumer must know the *meaning* of information he finds. Color fastness to light is only one of many properties of a fabric and may not be the most essential for many uses; however, it has been used to illustrate some aspects of transferring to the ultimate consumer the information necessary for him intelligently to choose, use, and care for his fabrics.

CLEANING PROCEDURES, WET AND DRY

Cleaning factors involve the behavior of fabrics toward the reagents and the conditions necessary to keep clothing and other fabrics clean. The first requisites for taking care of clothing and household fabrics is to keep them clean, well brushed (if needed), pressed, and properly stored when not in use. The fibers in fabrics suffer from fatigue. Wrinkles become permanently set if left too long. Garments which are kept clean and well pressed wear longer and look new longer than those that are less well taken care of. Frequent brushing helps to keep many fabrics clean, especially wools. Well-swept carpets wear longer than dirty ones.

Cleaning Problems. Cleaning problems are not new. Among the early laundrymen were the Roman fullers. The name *fuller* came from the fact that when fabrics are washed after coming from the loom, they are fulled or shrunk. Later, in England, the Fullers' Guild was formed to establish fair trade practices in the laundry business. Today, in the United States, the National Laundry Owners' Association serves a similar purpose and aids in the improvement of laundry standards. One of the early commercial laundries in the United States was built in California. Until then the '49ers had sent their laundry to Hawaii on a six-month service basis. Today, a very large part of the American laundry is sent to commercial laundries as a matter of necessity or of convenience.

Dry cleaning is used for a large part of the top clothes (suits, coats, dresses, robes) of the American people. The National Cleaners and Dyers Association maintains laboratories to carry on research for the

[2] *Ibid.*, 78.

purpose of improving the standards of service to people and to detect and warn member firms of nonserviceable fabrics and garment constructions which reach the market.

Causes. The causes for cleaning problems have been studied. Laundry and dry-cleaning procedures are frequently blamed because the fabrics fail. The fault may lie in any one of these places

a) fabric or garment construction
b) fabric finish
c) cleaning procedures
d) customer

An analysis of causes for complaint about the laundry on 3,500 cases showed that one third arise from faulty manufacturing, shrinkage, damage from poor sewing, gas fading, chlorine retention by the resin finish, and poor color fastness.[3] Shrinkage and color problems are the two most serious causes for complaint.

Whereas most *fabrics* are washable, not all *garments* are. Any fabric which is to be considered washable without limiting conditions should be both color fast and dimensionally stable within the limits of commercial laundry procedures recognized as acceptable by the National Laundry Owners' Association. Home laundry procedures, like commercial ones, vary with the knowledge, ability, and care of the individual directing or carrying out the process. There is no finish, color, or fabric which is indestructible, but if used and cared for properly most fabrics will give satisfactory service.

It may be difficult to identify the *cause* of damage to a fabric. For example, damage to wool fabrics which appears during dry cleaning or laundry may arise from previous causes

a) action of sunlight on fiber or dye
b) hydrolysis (alkaline or acid) following previous damage
c) shrinkage, felting or relaxation
d) high temperature in the presence of air
e) mechanical damage such as from abrasion
f) microorganisms and moth

Unfortunately, such damages frequently are not found until the garment returns from a cleaning. Finishes often cause dissatisfaction because their nature is not understood or is not taken into consideration. For example, fabrics finished with chlorine-retaining resins should not be cleaned in solutions containing chlorine compounds because color as well as fabric will be somewhat damaged when the fabric is ironed.

[3] Lee G. Johnston, "Consumer Complaints from New Fabric and Finishes," *American Dyestuff Reporter*, 38-2 (1949), 65.

Information on the durability of a finish is rarely given on labels, therefore selection is left to trial and error.

An analytical service provided for the Ohio State Association of Dyers and Cleaners found that damage to fabrics and to wearing apparel during dry cleaning resulted chiefly from comparatively few causes.[6]

The chief causes for complaint of damage to household fabrics were disintegration, dye trouble, and stains. The chief causes for complaint of damage to apparel were from dyestuffs, chemical damage, and stains. The type of solvent used is frequently the cause of color problems in dry cleaning, and the solvent is not infrequently lacking in cleanness. Whites and pastels soon become grayed in many dry-cleaning plants. This problem need not be so prevalent as it is. Measures can be taken to reduce static which causes suspended soil to be redeposited on fabrics. Dry cleaners often encounter complaints about grayed fabrics.

The solvents generally used in dry cleaning are

   a) petroleum distillates which comply with Commercial Standard CS3-40 for Stoddard Solvent, or which have a flash point below 140 F
   b) chlorinated hydrocarbons, such as carbon tetrachloride, usually bought for home use to remove fat-soluble spots

A modification of dry cleaning is called wet-dry cleaning. The process consists of carefully hand washing the fabric in warm water. Fabrics intended for most clothing and general household uses should be dyed with dyes fast to water, because cleaning procedures and use frequently involve contact with water. Many dyes need also to be fast to sunlight and dry cleaning.

Home vs. *commercial cleaning.* The relative merits of home and commercial procedures are frequently discussed. The answer probably lies in the procedures and reagents used in either case, rather than with whether the laundry is done at home or commercially. One comparison of factors involved in home and commercial laundry procedures and the results obtained showed that the soil removal was greater in commercial laundries but that the strength of the fabric was lowered.[4] A comparison of indoor and outdoor drying showed the loss of strength in cotton fabrics was greater if dried outdoors but that the clothes were whiter. The photochemical actions of sunlight on the wet fabrics acted as a bleach and at the same time degraded the cellulose. The conclusions from another study were that rayon degradation in domestic laundry procedures is affected by [5]

[4] Elizabeth Lovell, Jessie Roberts, and Jessie Brodie, "Laundry Processes," *American Dyestuff Reporter,* 31-13 (1942), 301.

[5] Mary H. Graydon, Dorothy M. Lindsley, and Jessie B. Brodie, "Mechanical Degradation of Rayon Fabrics in Domestic Laundry Procedures," *American Dyestuff Reporter,* 36-14 (1947), 397.

[6] Lyle, "Dry Cleaning Problems Brought to Class Rooms," 131.

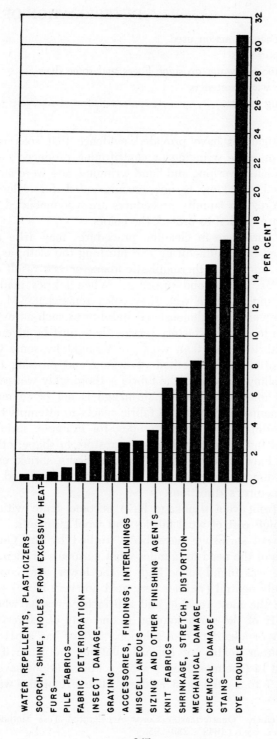

Fig. 21.1. Chief causes for complaint of damage to apparel. *Source: Lyle,* "Dry Cleaning Problems Brought to Class Rooms."

a) the mechanical action used

b) hard-water salts

c) use of too hot water on some fibers and some dyes

d) alkaline water softeners

e) bleaching agents

Other investigations have provided evidence that soaking, machine washing, and machine wringing or centrifuging produced no more degradation than hand washing and hand wringing, and were more efficient in soil removal. Soaking is not recommended for colored rayons. Otherwise, the regular laundry procedures are recommended unless cool temperatures are needed to protect the colors.

Shrinkage. Shrinkage in cleaning procedures may arise as a result of methods used in manufacturing and finishing the cloth, as a result of overheating certain of the thermoplastic fibers, or as a result of methods used in cleaning, drying and pressing. When fabrics made of fibers which absorb moisture are wet, they relax somewhat. Many fabrics, such as some rayons, lack dimensional stability to such an extent that in order for them to give satisfactory service they must be given a stabilizing finish. Fabrics other than wool are thought by some to be more shrinkage sensitive to the method of drying and pressing than to the manner of washing, as long as the fabric is thoroughly wetted. In some instances, the amount of laundry shrinkage is not of so much importance as the manner in which the fabric reacts to attempts to restore it to its original dimensions. Some crepes, for example, shrink considerable when wet but are relatively easy to restore to shape; others cannot be restored. Fabrics from some synthetic fibers shrink even in hot sunlight and cannot be ironed at all. They should be cared for according to manufacturer's directions.

The losses from wool shrinkage have become acute with increasing scarcity and high cost of wool fabrics and wool garments. The factors involved in wool shrinkage have been studied by the Quartermaster Corps because of the need to launder wool garments of men in service.[7] The shrinkage was found to be high at the lower soap concentrations. A comparatively neutral (neither very acid nor very basic) solution was found to give the most reliable and satisfactory results when washing wool. The pH of the wash solution is one way of expressing the degree of acidity or alkalinity of a solution. Water has a pH of 7 which is neutral, neither acidic nor basic. Solutions are basic if the pH is between 7 and 14 (the most basic) while acidic solutions have pH values ranging from 7 to 1 (the most acidic). The pH of the wash solution

[7] Louis I. Weiner, "Quartermaster Corps Accelerated Test Method," *American Dyestuff Reporter,* 38-7 (1949), 289–295.

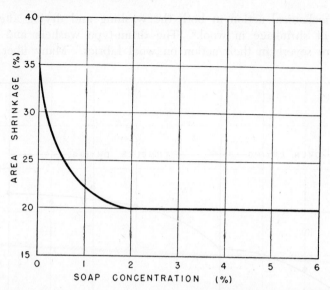

Fig. 21.2.   **The effect of soap concentration on shrinkage of wool.**   *Source: Weiner,* "Quartermaster Corps Accelerated Test Method."

was a definite factor in shrinkage of wool.   Some progress in the understanding of wool and its behavior is being made.[8]

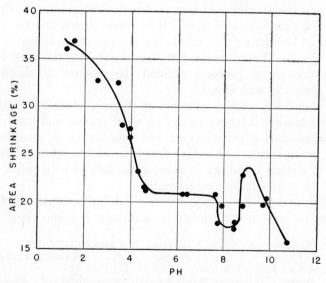

Fig. 21.3.   **Effect of pH on the area shrinkage of wool.**   *Source: Weiner,* "Quartermaster Corps Accelerated Test Method."

[8] Harris and Brown, "New Developments of Chemical Modifications of Wool," 316.

The mechanical action in both the washing and drying affects the amount of shrinkage in wool.[9] The drum-type washers and tumble dryers are severe in their action on wool fabrics. Many fiber blends

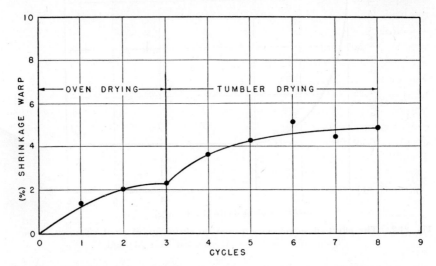

Fig. 21.4. Effect of drying method on shrinkage of warp in wool fabrics. *Source: Weiner,* "Quartermaster Corps Accelerated Test Method."

and resin or other finishes are being used with wool to improve shrinkage and extend the usefulness of wool. It has been shown that the mechanical action of laundering also affects the amount of shrinkage in woven cotton fabrics.[10] The maximum shrinkage came after the third laundering. The manner of pressing affected the amount of shrinkage in fabrics of cotton as well as wool.

Chemical finishes. For a number of reasons, chemical finishes are used on practically all fabrics today: on wool, cotton, and rayon to control shrinkage during dry cleaning and laundering, to provide crush resistance, or to correct some other deficiency of the fabric. The methods used to control shrinkage by coating the fabrics with resins include almost all the resin finishing processes.[11]

Resin finishes will frequently stabilize a fabric so that it retains its dimensions on repeated cleanings or washings.[12] Some resins do not

[9] Weiner, "Quartermaster Corps Accelerated Test Method," 289–295.

[10] Hazel M. Fletcher and Virginia M. Jones, "Shrinkage of Certain Cotton Woven Fabrics," *American Dyestuff Reporter*, 36-25 (1947), 727–729.

[11] D. H. Powers, "Shrinkage, What Are We Doing about It?" *Rayon Textile Monthly*, 27-1 (1946), 97.

Weiner, "Quartermaster Corps Accelerated Test Method," 289–295.

[12] Leo Beer, *Stabilizing Cellulosic Textile Materials against Shrinkage with Glyoxal and a Metal Fluosilicate as a Catalyst*, U. S. Patent 2,521,328, Sept. 5, 1950.

retain chlorine and are thus safe to use. With special finishes, the fibers of napped and pile surfaces do not become "balled" with wear and washing as they do on many untreated fabrics. Unless the resin finishes are properly applied, the fabric may have a harsh hand and lack wearing qualities.

Cellulose and cellulose derivatives often are used on cottons and rayons as glazes or as finishes to prevent yarn slippage and shrinkage.[13] Frequently, the glazed appearance is removed by cleaning processes, wet or dry. Many of the fire, moth, mildew, and other resistant-type finishes are gone with the first cleaning. Other finishes gradually disappear with repeated cleaning. Manufacturers are issuing instructions for care of special finishes. All such instructions should be retained and heeded by the consumer.

Color. In the laundry or dry-cleaning plant, color problems often arise from the following causes:

a) the dye is soluble in the cleaning solvent
b) the dye is mechanically rubbed off the surface of the fabric
c) the spotting or bleaching agents affect the color

Color, as well as other properties of fabrics, gives more satisfactory service when used and cared for with a knowledge of its advantages and shortcomings (see chapter eighteen).

Detergents. One of the problems encountered in cleaning procedures is that of selecting the type of detergent best suited for the purpose. A detergent may be defined as anything added to water or to a dry solvent to increase its effectiveness as a cleaner. Some of the earliest cleaning agents were rubbing stones and washing clays. Today, the number and complexity of the soaps and soapless detergents have become so great that it is not possible for the lay person to choose intelligently the most effective reagents for clothing and household fabrics.[14]

Detergents of one kind or another are of prime importance in cleaning textiles from the time the raw fiber is scoured until the fabric is worn out. Some of the many uses in the manufacturing process may be summarized as follows:

a) scouring, desizing, degreasing, bleaching, and dyeing
b) general finishing agents to modify the physical properties of fibers and improve wearability of the fabrics [15]

[13] Edward C. Pfeffer, Jr. and Jack Epelberg, *Shrinkproofing Regenerated Cellulose,* U. S. Patent 2,530,175, Nov. 14, 1950.
Donald D. Powers and William J. Harrison, *Slip-resistant Textile Products,* U. S. Patent 2,527,329, Oct. 24, 1950.
[14] Harold A. Sweet, "Detergents, Old and New," *American Dyestuff Reporter,* 23 (1934), 198.
[15] H. C. Borghetty, "Auxiliary Products in Dyeing," *American Dyestuff Reporter,* 37-24 (1948), P785.

Detergents are commonly classified in the following way based on the characteristics of the molecule:

- *a*) Anionic detergents include the soaps and soapless detergents commonly used in the home
- *b*) Cationic detergents are substantives used chiefly as germicides, softening agents, and water repellents in finishing textile fabrics (see chapter twenty)
- *c*) Nonionic detergents are neutral compounds, stable in hard water, and improve the efficiency of anionic detergents

Anionic detergents include soaps and many soapless detergents for which the term syndet has been proposed. They may be used alone or together in most textile cleaning processes requiring detergents. There is a multitude of trade names on the market. Selection of the best detergent for a specific purpose is difficult.[16]

Soaps are the salts of high-molecular-weight fatty acids. Since soap is a salt of a weak acid and a strong alkali, the solution in which it is dissolved is alkaline. Solubility of a soap in water depends upon the metallic ions forming the salt. Soluble soaps are detergents, but insoluble soaps have no such action. The ions of sodium and potassium form water-soluble soaps; the divalent ions of calcium and magnesium, and the trivalent ions of aluminum and iron will precipitate soap in the form of soap curd or insoluble soap. Aluminum soaps are used for waterproofing fabrics. Certain ammonium soaps are used in dry cleaning. They are excellent emulsifiers of fats and waxes.

There are three general methods of making soap: boiled, semiboiled, and cold.[17] The American Society for Testing Materials, Committee D-12 has established standards for performing tests for measuring the quality of soaps. One of those tests is the *Titer Test* for identifying and evaluating fats and oils since they influence the properties and applications of the soap. The titer refers specifically to the solidifying temperature of the fatty acids from which the soap is made.

A soapless detergent is a salt of a strong acid and a strong alkali and, therefore, gives a neutral solution. The calcium and magnesium salts of the soapless detergents are soluble; therefore, they do not form soap curds in hard water.

Protein fibers such as wool and silk should be washed at a much lower pH than cellulose fibers such as cotton, preferably between pH 6 and 8. A solution at pH 6 is only slightly acidic; at pH 7 it is truly neutral; and at pH 8 it is only slightly alkaline. Soapless detergents are neutral, or approximately so, and are safe for laundering protein fibers.

[16] H. C. Borghetty, "Detergents in the Textile Industry," *Rayon and Synthetic Textiles*, 30-4 (1949), 110.

[17] H. P. Trevithick, "Soaps and Other Detergents," *American Dyestuff Reporter*, 30-11 (1941), 269.

An increase in alkalinity causes felting of wool and yellowing of both silk and wool.[18]   Apparently, for general home procedures, an approximately neutral solution, a minimum of agitation during washing and drying, and a temperature of about 100 F provide a minimum of shrinkage in wool fabrics and are satisfactory for silk.

The cellulosic fibers, cotton and rayons, are relatively negative when wet and are better cleaned by alkaline solutions than by neutral solutions.   The pH should be kept below 11.4.   Above this, oxidation and breakdown of the cotton and rayon fibers occur rapidly.   Soaps produce alkaline solutions suitable for laundering cottons and rayons.   Often, however, a low temperature and pH are necessary to prevent fading.

It has been shown at the Bureau of Human Nutrition and Home Economics that temperatures of 140 F remove considerably more soil than 104 F and that soaps removed more soil from cotton fabric than did the soapless detergents.[19]   In general, the soapless detergents were also more effective at 140 F than at 104 F.   The soapless detergents were more effective in hard water than were the soaps, especially at concentrations below 0.35 per cent.   In hard water, the soap concentration is lowered as the soap is precipitated by the hard-water ions.   For each detergent there is a critical concentration which produces best results.   The amount of detergent will depend upon the amount of soiling and the type of agitation used.   A high concentration of detergent is most effective on badly soiled fabric.   The horizontal-type washer requires more suds than the vertical-type.   Friction is an important factor in any practical cleaning action.

The removal of fats and oils in the laundry is dependent upon the action of the detergent.   Detergent molecules possess a water-repelling portion and a water-soluble portion.   The differences betwen the two ends of the molecule determine its usefulness.   The water-repellent portion is soluble in fats, oils, and dry solvents such as dry-cleaning agents.   The water-soluble portion of the molecule is attracted to water. This property of being soluble in both fatty substances and water enables detergents to emulsify and remove fats, oils, and greases from fabrics.   Oil can be removed without emulsification, but there is a danger that it will be redeposited.   If the fatty impurity is put into a very fine emulsion, and absorbed into the structure of the fiber, it cannot be eliminated easily.   This sometimes happens in laundry procedures.

Substances, known as protective colloids, stabilize emulsions and prevent flocculation and redeposit of soil in the laundry.   Some detergents for home use have protective colloids added.   One such is a derivative

18 Weiner, "Quartermaster Corps Accelerated Test Method," 289.
19 Margaret S. Furry, Verda I. McLendon, and Mary E. Aler, "An Evaluation of Soaps and Synthetic Detergents," *American Dyestuff Reporter,* 37-23 (1948), P751.

of cellulose itself, CMC. Once soil has been removed from fabrics, it is desirable that it not be redeposited. The solution containing the soil should be well rinsed from the fabric; otherwise, that which is held by any unremoved water, will be redeposited on the fabric as it dries.

Cationic detergents are substantive to cellulosic fibers and provide softening agents and water-repellent finishes (see pages 339 and 340).

Nonionic detergents have neither a positive nor a negative ion, and are miscible with other detergents. They may be used in either a dry solvent or water. They have a low affinity for fibers; hence they rinse well. They are used in wetting, scouring, and bleaching processes. They are valuable in wool processing and are in some consumer products.

Soaps and other detergents may also be classified according to form and alkali type as [20]

    a) industrial bulk soaps
    b) toilet soaps
    c) synthetic or soapless detergents
    d) alkalies or builders

Detergents have been described in a number of ways. Each description should help to explain the valuable part they play in the work of keeping fabrics clean.

Hard Water. Hardness in water is caused by soluble calcium, magnesium, aluminum, and iron salts. Water may be temporarily hard or permanently hard. Calcium bicarbonate causes temporary hardness which is removed when the water is heated and the calcium carbonate precipitated in the form of a scale in kettles, boilers, and water tanks. Certain calcium salts cannot be precipitated by heating, and they give permanent hardness to the water. Such salts have to be removed or "tied up" by chemical means. If this is not done, soap is used to precipitate the "hard" ions.

One of the serious aspects of insoluble soaps is that they collect soil from the wash solution and precipitate, not as a pure white curd or film on clothes during the laundry, but as a more or less gray film which in part accounts for "tattle-tale gray." Insoluble soaps acquired during the laundering procedure do not constitute a desirable finish on clothing and household fabrics.

Water softeners may be used to remove the "hard" ions instead of precipitating them with soap; it is much less expensive and a more satisfactory procedure to use. Sodium carbonate may be used to soften water. Borax and ammonia each removes the objectionable calcium ions but does not remove magnesium ions. Calcium is, however, more prevalent than magnesium. An important method used in both indus-

[20] Trevithick, "Soaps and Other Detergents," 269–273 and 294.

try and homes to remove calcium and magnesium involves an exchange of ions. It is the Permutit or zeolite process. The action of Permutit with calcium and magnesium salts is reversible and for that reason the Permutit may be regenerated by treating the spent substance with a large excess of sodium chloride. Another method of softening water is to form a nonionized compound of the hard-water ion. The phosphates are valuable agents for this purpose.

Measures of cleanness are total light reflectance and bacteriological tests. A clean fabric should be free from both soil and harmful organisms. Efficiency of a detergent in removing soil from white fabrics may be measured by the difference in light reflectance of the unsoiled fabrics which have been washed and that of the fabric which has been soiled and washed.

Two methods are used to increase the apparent whiteness or brightness of fabrics. The increase in whiteness from the use of bluings is only apparent. Bluing reduces the amount of reflected light by graying the yellow or creamy color. Blue pigment such as Prussian blue or blue dyes are generally used as bluings. The bluings which contain iron salts should not be used, since they are a source of iron rust on fabrics. The rust may not be in spots but, more likely, in the form of a uniform yellowing of the fabric. Bluings should not be used on yellow and red fabrics.

The most recent development in bleaching fabrics is the use of so-called optical bleaches which are essentially white dyes which fluoresce blue.[21] In other words, extra light is being reflected from the cloth because fluorescent substances used as bleaches absorb light in the invisible ultraviolet and emit that light in the visible range of the spectrum. They achieve their whitening effect by neutralizing the yellowish discoloration of cloth by the blue color of the fluorescent light emitted under the action of the ultraviolet rays of daylight. These bleaches are said to give a white appearance to the cloth without lowering the strength of the fibers. The process for applying the white dye is rapid in comparison with peroxide bleaching, which requires a slower treatment. Cloth bleached by optical bleaches will not be satisfactory under artificial light but will be in sunlight. Ordinary artificial light is not white light.

Efficiency of a detergent in removing microorganisms may be measured by making cultures of the laundered fabric to determine the extent of removal of control organisms.

Stains and Their Removal. Stains may be defined as unwanted color. Their removal is all too frequently complicated by the stain's being a combination of stain-producing materials, e.g., milk with both protein

[21] Richard Thomas, *Whitening of Textile Materials,* U. S. Patent 2,528,323, Oct. 31, 1950.

and fat; by the dye or finish's being affected by the reagents used to remove the stain; or by the garment's not being considered washable.

The kinds of stains may be classified according to any of the following methods:

 a) according to origin, such as grape juice, tar, or grass stain
 b) according to chemical nature, such as proteins, tannins, or chlorophyll stains
 c) according to the method of removal, such as water-soluble, fat-soluble, or alcohol-soluble stains

The most practical classification of stains for purposes of removal is according to chemical nature.

The protein stains are produced by egg, meat juices, ice cream, milk, and blood. Unless the protein has been coagulated before it comes in contact with the fabric, the fabric may be saturated with the substance. Dry heat as well as hot water will coagulate the protein in and on the fabric. Therefore, cold water should be used to remove as much of the stain as possible before using warm water or soap. In some instances, it may be necessary to follow with a mild bleach. If the protein has been heated or dried, an enzyme may be used to digest the stain, or a laundry bleach may be sufficient. Wash and rinse well.

Plant stains produced by tea, coffee, chocolate, fruit juices, and alcoholic drinks contain tannins which are easily set with metallic ions. The sodium ion in soap solutions help to set many stains of plant origin. These stains should be well rinsed with water before using soap. A solution of equal parts of glycerine and water will usually remove the fresh stain. A mild bleach is sometimes needed. Grass and flower stains are usually easy to remove with an alcohol and water solution.

Ink, bluings, and dyestuff stains, if not water soluble, will need to be bleached. There are many varieties of each of these stains. It is always well to try the mildest method of removal first, cold water.

A miscellaneous group of stains includes sugar stains, water spots, perspiration, urine, mud, and iodine. Water or water and soap should remove all of these, except possibly mud and iodine which may need to be bleached. Iodine may easily be reduced with a dilute solution of sodium thiosulfate.

Mildew stains should first be washed with soap and water. If a stain remains, the fabric should be treated with a mild bleach. Deeply grown mildew may be impossible to remove, because it has permeated the fiber structure. This is especially likely to happen on natural fibers. Mildews can neither feed upon nor penetrate many of the manufactured fibers.

Scorch is the result of a partial decomposition of the fibers by heat. If the scorch is light, the fabric may be laundered or dampened and exposed to the direct sunlight.   Deep scorch cannot be removed because the fibers have been destroyed by burning.   Unless badly burned, it may be possible to remove the burned fibers from the fabric by brushing.

Iron rust, if light, may be removed by applying a solution of oxalic acid.   It is necessary to reduce the ferric iron to ferrous iron and remove by washing the fabric.   Large amounts of iron rust or iron rust that has developed inside the fibers may not be removable without considerable damage to the fibers.

Reagents useful in stain removal may be obtained at a grocery or drug store.   They are

a) Absorbents
   Blotting paper or face tissue
   Corn starch or talcum powder
   A clean cloth
b) Solvents
   Water, cold or hot
   Alcohol
   Carbon tetrachloride
   Hydrocarbons such as naphthalene
   Acetone and amyl acetate
c) Bleaches, dilute solutions
   Hydrogen peroxide, 3% solution
   Sodium hypochlorite
   Oxalic acid, *POISON*
   Commercial color removers, use as directed
   Potassium permanganate
d) Detergents
   Soaps
   Soapless detergents
e) Neutralizing agents, dilute solutions
   Ammonium hydroxide
   Sodium thiosulfate
f) Enzymes—used in dry cleaning plants

Absorbents are mild reagents and are best used at once on moist fresh stains to take up all the stain not already absorbed by the fiber.   Blotting paper, absorbent cotton, talcum powder, chalk, starch, and the like are especially useful in removing fresh stains from nonwashable fabrics and should in no way harm any fabric.   Stains which may be removed, at least partially, by absorbents include fats, oils, and other liquids.

Solvents are of two kinds, wet and dry, and act by dissolving the stain. Water, the most commonly used, is a wet solvent, and will, with care, if used soon enough, remove most fresh, water-soluble stains.   Cold water should be tried first, then warm water, followed by soap if it will not set the stain or fade the color.   Warm water and soap will also remove many of the fat- and oil-soluble stains by emulsifying the fat.   A solution of alcohol and water is the best solvent for grass stains.

Dry solvents are used for removing oils, grease, tar, gum, paints, butter, cream, and lipstick. In many cases, after the stain has been loosened, it is necessary to dry clean or possibly launder in hot soapy water. Sometimes it is necessary to follow with a mild bleach. Dry solvents should cause no damage unless the fabrics are dyed with an oil-soluble dye, but they should be used with care in a well-ventilated room or in an open place. It is wise to use only noninflammable dry solvents such as carbon tetrachloride or trichlorethylene which may be had from drug or grocery stores. These solvents do not wet the fabrics and so may be used on nonwashable fabrics. Kerosene, benzene, naphtha, or gasoline are also dry solvents but are inflammable. Their use in the home is hazardous and is not recommended.

Bleaches are, unless used with care, likely to weaken or destroy the color or fabric, and should be used according to directions provided by the manufacturer. Always rinse the fabric well after using any bleach. Mild bleaches include oxalic acid, hydrogen peroxide, potassium permanganate, and commercial color removers. The most commonly used household bleach is sodium hypochlorite which may be purchased from a grocer under various trade names. It should be used as directed on cottons and rayons but never on wool or silk.

Hydrogen peroxide in a 3 per cent solution may be obtained from a drugstore and may be used on silk or wool if allowed to remain on the fabric only a short time before rinsing. The process may be repeated. If the fabric is not to be laundered, the last rinsing should be done with dilute ammonium hydroxide in order to neutralize the acid used to stabilize the peroxide for storage.

Potassium permanganate may be applied dropwise from a medicine dropper or a glass rod if the stain is small. Allow to remain a few minutes. A brown deposit of manganese dioxide will develop. The brown oxide may then be removed with a dilute solution of oxalic acid. Rinse well with water, then with dilute ammonia, then with water.

Oxalic acid is a POISON. Apply solution to a stain with a medicine dropper or glass rod. Allow to remain for a few minutes (2–5 minutes only). Rinse in clean warm water. Repeat process if necessary, but let the final rinse be in dilute ammonia followed by water

Neutralizing agents frequently need to be used after a bleach. Ammonium hydroxide (a weak base), in 10 per cent solution by volume, may be used to neutralize the acids after using hydrogen peroxide or oxalic acid. A dilute solution of sodium thiosulfate, an antichlor, should be used to stop the action of a chlorine bleach.

Suggestions regarding some of the more common reagents may aid in their satisfactory use. Time is one of the most important factors involved. The more quickly a stain is removed, the easier it is to remove. If possible a liquid stain should not be allowed to penetrate the fibers or the yarns but should be wiped or blotted at once to remove the excess staining material.

It is well to identify the stain and to test the effect of the reagents upon the color by testing a facing, inside seam, or hem, before any attempts are made to remove it. If the stain is unknown, it is necessary to proceed cautiously. Much judgment and experience, as well as information on finish and fiber behavior, are necessary in order successfully to handle stained fabrics. In some instances, the fabric or the color may be destroyed by destroying the stain.

Unless the stain obviously is not water soluble, it is generally well to try to dissolve as much of it as possible with cold water, followed by warm water, then soap and water. If a stain persists and it seems advisable, a mild bleach may be used.

Methods of application as well as the speed of application of reagents are important to successful stain removal.

a) A medicine dropper may be used when only small quantities of reagent are to be applied drop by drop.

b) When stain is to be sponged, place the fabric with the stain down on an absorbent pad of cloth or absorbent tissue, then do the first sponging by tapping lightly. Much of the stain will be removed without passing through the fabric.

c) In using boiling water, as for removing fruit stains from table linen, the boiling water may be poured from a cup or other container held well above the stain stretched over a pan placed in the kitchen sink. The force produced in this way facilitates the removal of the stains. Water coming from a faucet also has pressure which helps in forcing out staining materials.

d) The formation of rings may sometimes be prevented by finishing off the sponging of a spot by working around the outside of the area with the sponging cloth or sponge squeezed almost dry. After drying, the ring may sometimes be rubbed out with finger nails or a dull knife or by rubbing the fabric between the hands. If the garment is soiled, the ring may of course be due to washing the soil into a ring around the sponged area. The garment may need to be cleaned.

The suggestions for stain removal in the home are general and should be followed cautiously, especially on delicate or colored fabrics (Table 21.I). Care should be used to follow a bleach with a neutralizer and thorough rinsing.

TABLE 21.I

STAINS AND SUGGESTIONS FOR REMOVAL

Stain	Washable fabrics	Nonwashable fabrics or garments
Egg, ice cream, milk, cream, blood, meat juices, gravies	Soak in cold water and launder. If a stain from coloring matter remains, bleach.	Sponge with warm water. When dry, remove grease with carbon tetrachloride. If protein is coagulated on the fabric, send to dry cleaner.

Stain	*Washable fabrics*	*Nonwashable fabrics or garments*
Fruit, coffee, chocolate, tea	Pour cold water through the stain. If it remains, follow with boiling water. Alternate method is to rinse stain in warm 50% glycerine solution. If stain persists, bleach.	Spread the stained portion over a pad (towel or blotters) and sponge with warm 50% glycerine solution, then warm water.
Grass and flower	Dissolve stain with alcohol. Launder. If stain persists, bleach.	Sponge the stain with water and alcohol.
Ink, bluing, a dyestuff	Different inks require different treatment. Try one or more of these methods: (1) Launder. (2) Apply chlorine water or commercial ink remover. (3) Apply 3 per cent hydrogen peroxide. (4) Apply dilute oxalic acid solution.	(1) If the stain is moist, apply starch, French chalk, or talcum powder, making fresh applications as they absorb ink. When no more ink can be removed by the dry absorbent, make it into a paste with water and apply. Dry and brush. Sponge with damp cloth.
Sugar stains, water spots, perspiration, mud, iodine	Launder. If a stain remains, bleach. Neutralize.	Sponge with warm water or send to the dry cleaner. Tell the dry cleaner what the stain is if you know.
Mildew	Surface mildew may be removed with dilute solution of potassium permanganate followed by oxalic acid. Deeply grown mildew may be impossible to remove.	Same procedure as for washable fabrics.
Scorch	If scorch is light, launder or dampen and place where sunlight will strike it. Deep scorch cannot be removed.	If scorch is light, apply hydrogen peroxide and follow with dilute ammonium hydroxide.
Iron rust	Apply a solution of oxalic acid. If rust is deep, it may not be removable.	Same procedure as for washable fabrics.
Cod liver oil, lipstick	Launder in hot suds. If a stain remains, bleach.	Sponge with carbon tetrachloride.
Grease or tar, wax	Rub with lard or kerosene. Launder in hot, soapy water.	Sponge with carbon tetrachloride or gasoline.
Gum, adhesive tape	Scrape off as much as possible and sponge with carbon tetrachloride or kerosene. Launder.	Remove as much as possible. Sponge with carbon tetrachloride.
Paint and varnish	Soak in kerosene or turpentine. Rub out as much paint as possible and launder. Varnish may be removed with alcohol.	Sponge with carbon tetrachloride or turpentine.
Nail polish	Sponge with acetone unless the fabric is an acetate, then use amylacetate.	Same as for washable fabrics.

When in doubt as to the effect of the suggested procedure on nonwashable fabric, do not attempt to remove the stain but send to dry cleaner as soon as possible and give him what information you have about the stain. Successful removal of a stain often means the difference between a usable garment or fabric and a nonusable one. Such losses frequently could and should be avoided.

WEATHERING

Weathering of fabrics is the result of a varying combination of factors which have a degrading action on the fibers. The factors, taken in any or all combinations, include wind, heat, rain, microorganisms, sunlight, and corrosive gases. Flags and awnings are not the only fabrics exposed to the weather. If weathering is regarded as outdoor exposure of fabrics, then most clothing fabrics receive weathering. Outdoor work and sports clothes receive a large amount of exposure. Cotton is the fiber most used in fabrics exposed to weathering. Wool is probably next. The Southern Regional Laboratory has studied the degradation of untreated cotton fabrics exposed to weather in a subtropical climate.[22]

The most serious effect of weathering was found to be loss in breaking strength. Unbleached gray print cloth, kier boiled, and bleached print cloth resisted the weather in the order named. The unbleached cloth lost least, and the bleached lost most strength. Since weathering is a composite of many factors, special observations have to be made to know what factor is most detrimental. The fabric which had been most attacked by mildew lost most in strength. Most fibers, except a few such as Orlon and Fiberglas, are weakened by biological decay and sunlight.

Sunlight is generally considered to be the most active cause of deterioration in the weathering of fabrics. The changes caused by the sun are both physical and chemical, but the chemical changes appear to be predominant.[23] Temperature, moisture, air currents, and especially oxygen influence the photochemical decomposition of fibers. The wave length and intensity of the light determine the extent of degradation which occurs in any one kind of fiber (Table 21.II).

TABLE 21.II

COLOR FILTER DATA

Filter	Corning code no.	Transmission % of total sunshine	Degradative index
Corex	9700	95.5	1.0
Ultraviolet	5970	2.5	30.51
Blue	5330	50.0	1.60
Yellow	3482	66.2	0.54
Red	2408	58.9	0.53
Infrared	2540	16.1	1.55

Source: J. P. Flynn, J. E. Sands, and K. S. Campbell, "Cellulose Behavior with Filtered Sunlight," *Textile Research Journal*, 18-6 (1948), 350.

[22] J. D. Dean and R. K. Worner, "Degradation of Untreated Cotton Fabrics Exposed to Weather in a Sub-tropical Climate," *American Dyestuff Reporter*, 36-15 (1947), 405–410 and 423–424.

[23] Dorothy K. Appleby, "Action of Light on Textile Materials," *American Dyestuff Reporter*, 38-4 (1949), 149.

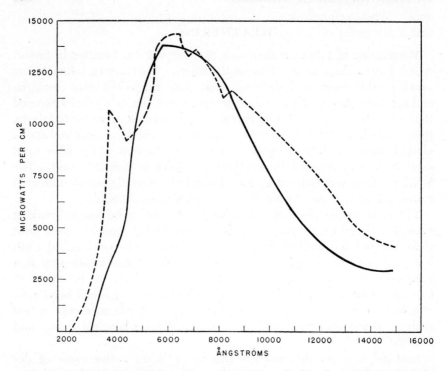

Fig. 21.5. Natural sunlight at the earth's surface (broken line) and the high intensity carbon arc (continuous line). *Source: Appleby,* "Action of Light on Textile Materials."

An especially interesting comparison of results can be made between the effects of sunlight on cotton by the use of the corex filter, which admits 95.5 per cent of total sunshine, and by the use of the ultraviolet filter, which admits only 1 per cent of the sunshine. The degradative index for the corex filter was 1.0, whereas that of the ultraviolet filter was 30.5. In ordinary sunshine, it seems that the longer light rays in some manner neutralize the bad effects of the shorter ultraviolet rays.

Window curtains and draperies are exposed to long hours of sunlight and often to heat.[24]   The rate at which curtains and draperies deteriorate varies with the hours of exposure, the dye (if any), the moisture in the air, and the fiber content.   Light caused a decrease in the strength and elongation of plastics but did not seem to affect the glass fabric (Fiberglas).   Of the fibers tried, glass and cellulose acetate were the most resistant to both heat and light.   Nylon and silk were least resistant in this study, but dull nylon was used.   Bright nylon is highly resistant to sunlight.   In some studies, nylon has ranked with cotton in light resist-

[24] Hazel M. Fletcher, "Fabrics for Glass Curtains and Draperies," *American Dyestuff Reporter,* 38-17 (1949), 603.

ance. When comparisons of fibers are made, it is difficult to be sure that it is a valid comparison.

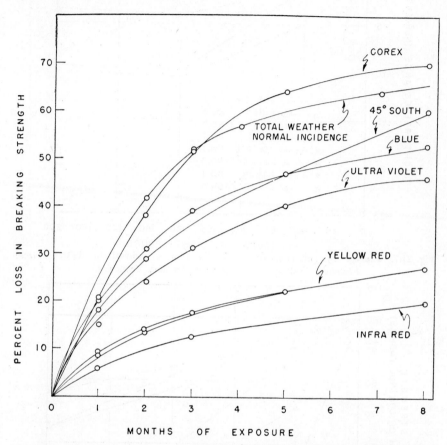

Fig. 21.6. Effect of exposure to different wave lengths of light on breaking strength of a fabric. *Source: Fletcher*, "Fabrics for Glass Curtains and Draperies."

One study has indicated that dyes that are least fast to light on nylon also cause the most degradation.[25]

A summary of the general changes in strength and the changes in color on exposure to sunlight indicates that consideration should be given to the type of fiber chosen for uses involving long hours of exposure to light (Table 21.III). In some cases, finishing processes afford protection from photochemical decomposition. In other cases they accelerate it (see chapter twenty).

Animal fibers are frequently damaged by the sunlight while growing,

[25] G. S. Egerton, "Action of Light on Cellulose Acetate and Nylon," *American Dyestuff Reporter*, 38-17 (1949), 608.

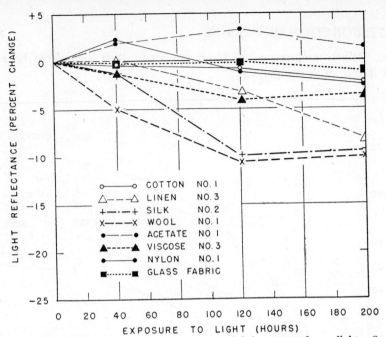

Fig. 21.7. **Change in per cent reflectance of fabrics exposed to light.** *Source: Fletcher, "Fabrics for Glass Curtains and Draperies."*

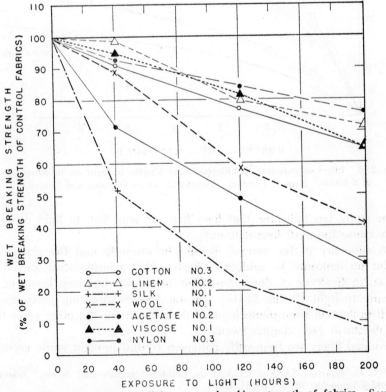

Fig. 21.8. **Effect of exposure to light on wet breaking strength of fabrics.** *Source: Fletcher, "Fabrics for Glass Curtains and Draperies."*

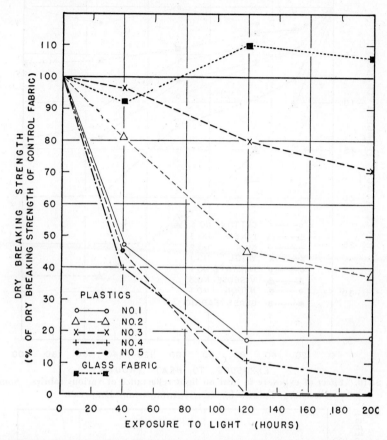

Fig. 21.9. Effect of exposure to light on dry breaking strength of plastics and glass fabrics. *Source: Fletcher,* "Fabrics for Glass Curtains and Draperies."

so that the tips dye darker than the remainder of the fibers. It is a problem for dyers to achieve uniformly dyed fibers when a portion is chemically changed.

Some of the factors which have been shown to increase the photochemical degradation of cottons are found on page 368.

 a) amount of moisture in the air
 b) type of dye, special trouble with orange and vat dyes
 c) alkali, from inefficient rinsing
 d) some pigments used in prints [26]

Cotton is more resistant than linen to sunshine and industrial gases.

[26] G. S. Egerton, "The Action of Light on Dyed and Undyed Cottons," *American Dyestuff Reporter,* 36-20 (1947), 561–570 and 573.

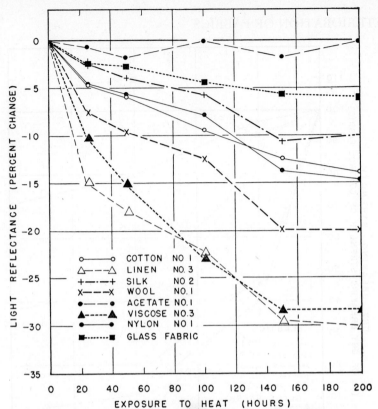

Fig. 21.10. Effect of exposure to heat on light reflectance of various fabrics. *Source: Fletcher,* "Fabrics for Glass Curtains and Draperies."

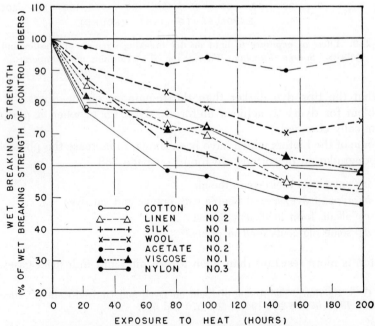

Fig. 21.11. Effect of exposure to heat on wet breaking strength of various fabrics. *Source: Fletcher,* "Fabrics for Glass Curtains and Draperies."

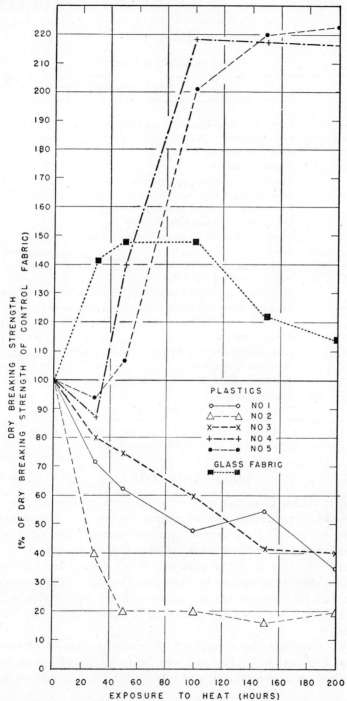

Fig. 21.12. Effect of exposure to heat on dry breaking strength of plastic and glass fabrics. *Source: Fletcher,* "Fabrics for Glass Curtains and Draperies."

TABLE 21.III

ACTION OF LIGHT ON FIBERS

Fibers	Effect of sunlight
Cotton	
unbleached	Less effect than bleached, most resistant of natural fibers
bleached	Loss of strength, yellows, dyeing properties change
Ramie	Similar to cotton
Flax	Similar to cotton
Jute	Much more sensitive to light than cotton
Wool	More resistant than most other fibers, but the cystine linkage may be effected. Dyeing properties changed
Silk	Considered the most light-sensitive fiber
Estron	More sensitive than viscose or cuprammonium rayons
Cellulose nitrate	Sensitive
Viscose rayon	Dull viscose about twice as sensitive as bright viscose or cotton, which are about the same
Casein	Will dye either lighter or darker, depending on type of dye
Peanut	Will dye either lighter or darker, depending on type of dye
Soybean	Will dye either lighter or darker, depending on type of dye
Zein	Slowly weakened
Fiberglas	Little effect, but in time may become brittle
Dynel	Remarkably resistant
Nylon	Resistance depends on type, dull most affected
Dacron	Highly resistant
Vinyon	Some loss of strength and darkening in some types

Source: Dorothy K. Appleby, "Action of Light on Textile Materials," *American Dyestuff Reporter*, 38-4 (1949), 149–156 and 181–192.

WEAR AND STORAGE

A fabric which is in use may be considered as receiving wear. A fabric which is not in use may, in a sense, be considered in storage and receiving no wear. Deterioration progresses at varying rates whether a fabric is in use receiving wear or whether it is in storage and receiving no wear. The rate in either case may be fast enough to destroy the fabric in a short time or may be slow enough under some conditions of storage that the changes are not measurable by ordinary means. For instance, fabrics are carefully preserved in museums so that they last centuries.

Wear. Wear may be considered as a combination of physical and chemical degradation.[27] Physical wear includes the effects of abrasion and stresses (tensile, torsional, and compressional). Resistance to these

[27] Gladys G. Clegg, "A Microscopical Examination of Worn Textile Articles," *Journal of the Textile Institute*, 40-8 (1949), T499–T480.

forces may be measured by such tests as abrasion, compression, breaking strength, and bursting strength tests. The National Bureau of Standards is developing a useful method of evaluating the resistance of fabrics to abrasion.

Breaking strength is defined as the ability of a material to resist rupture by external tension. Bursting strength is defined as the ability of a material to resist rupture by pressure applied in a specified manner. Abrasion may be considered to be the result of friction produced by contact with other surfaces. Fibers suffer a complex set of distorting

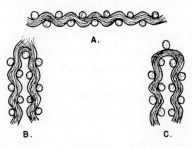

Fig. 21.13. Schematic drawing of a plain woven fabric showing effect of sharp folds; see broken yarn at edge.

forces during folding, creasing, crushing, bending, pressing, and stretching of fabrics during wear. Fiber materials, just as other materials, suffer from fatigue. For that reason, as well as for aesthetic reasons, garments should be kept well pressed and in good shape physically. Otherwise the garment will soon appear old and out of shape. Fiber composition, yarn construction, weave and finish, as well as style and fit of a garment and the care given it, all contribute to the service given by any one garment under any one set of conditions. Different garments fail for different reasons.[28]

a) shirts because of wear at collars, cuffs, elbows, and pockets and because of shrinkage
b) raincoats because of loss of water repellency, or cracks in finish or fabric
c) umbrellas because of cracks at folds
d) curtains because of light tendering
e) velvets and corduroy because of loss of pile

The molecular structures in the fibers are broken down as wear increases. Data, however, indicate that by far the greater number of fabric failures is due to mechanical and not chemical failure. Curtains, draperies, awnings, and blinds are exceptions, since the sun's rays and atmospheric gases cause the chief failures here.

[28] *Ibid.*

According to Pierce, and in keeping with opinions of others, it will not be possible to establish valid accelerated wear tests until there has been a thorough survey of the behavior in actual use of enough different fabrics of known history to determine the nature of causes and effects of deterioration.[29]   At present, more information is needed about the requirements of the various end uses of fibers and fabrics.   More information also is needed concerning which property or properties are the limiting factors in the use of a fabric for specified purposes.   The "weakest link" usually determines the serviceable life of a fabric.   That link may be color, shrinkage, lack of abrasion resistance, loss in strength, loss of desirable properties of hand, loss of water repellency, yarn slippage, or any one of innumerable other properties.   Probably the most profitable procedure for increasing the serviceability of fabrics and garments is, on one hand, in identifying and correcting the weak or limiting features and, on the other hand, in teaching the consumer to select and use fabrics for those purposes for which they are best adapted. Better selections of available fabrics could go far toward increasing the value of the textile dollar.

Storage.   Frequently, storage and care are the factors which eventually destroy a fabric.   The washing and ironing of linen dinner napkins certainly seem to have a more deteriorating effect than the actual use involved.   Fabrics may be affected while in storage by such factors as

  a) finishes and finishing materials which slowly cause chemical change
  b) laundry or dry cleaning procedures which may leave deteriorating chemicals on the fabric
  c) dyes which may decompose to produce deteriorating products [30]
  d) microorganisms under favorable conditions
  e) insects

For long periods of storage, fabrics should be clean and dry and should be stored in a clean, dry, dark place.

MICROORGANISMS AND INSECTS

The losses from damage done to fabrics by microorganisms and insects run into large sums annually.   Some of the problems are well on their way to solution, but as yet losses are serious.

Microorganisms.   The microorganisms include bacteria and molds. The kinds and effects of microorganisms found on textile fibers are of widespread interest.   The areas in the United States in which fabrics are generally vulnerable to mildew attack are well described in Fig.

[29] Dr. F. T. Pierce, "Serviceability of Fabrics in Regard to Wear," *Textile Research,* 7 (1937–38), 381.
[30] D. A. Clibbens and A. H. Little, "Effect of Vat Dyes on the Rate of Oxidation of Cotton by Hypochlorite Solutions," *Journal of the Textile Institute,* 37 (1946), T219.

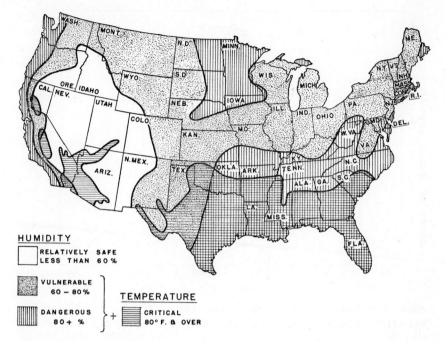

HUMIDITY

☐ RELATIVELY SAFE
 LESS THAN 60 %

▨ VULNERABLE
 60 – 80 %

▥ DANGEROUS
 80+ %

⎫
⎬ +
⎭

TEMPERATURE

▤ CRITICAL
 80° F. & OVER

Fig. 21.14. **Areas of the United States vulnerable to mildew attacks.** *Source: Prepared by Givaudan-Delawanna, Inc.,* AMERICAN DYESTUFF REPORTER, *36-5 (1947), 129.*

21.14. Molds and bacteria are everywhere in the air and in the soil, so that it is possible for mildew to develop in any area or on any fabric which provides the essentials for life—food and water with a favorable temperature and pH.[31]

Enzymes produced by bacteria and molds can rapidly convert cellulose into smaller soluble molecules and in this way destroy or seriously weaken cotton, linen, and viscose rayon fabrics.[32] The word *enzyme* is derived from the Greek and means in (en) yeast (zyme). The enzyme acts as a catalyst to hasten reactions and may be of great assistance when used purposefully in textile manufacturing.

Bacteria are unicellular. They work their way into the fiber wall where the attack is confined only to the point of contact. They digest

[31] P. B. Marsh and K. Bollenbacker, "The Fungi Concerned in Fiber Deterioration: I, Their Occurrence," *Textile Research Journal,* 19-6 (1949), 313–324.

P. B. Marsh, "Mildew and Rot Resistance of Textiles," *Textile Research Journal,* 17-11 (1947), 597–615.

[32] P. J. Wood, "Enzymes in Textile Processing," *American Dyestuff Reporter,* 36-13 (1947), P355–P361.

P. B. Marsh, K. Ballenbecker, M. L. Butler, and K. B. Raper, "The Fungi Concerned in Fiber Deterioration: II, Their Ability to Decompose Cellulose," *Textile Research Journal,* 19-8 (1949), 462–484.

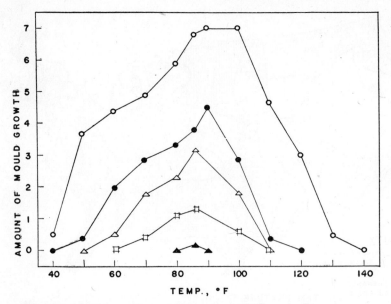

GROWTH RATINGS: NONE TO VERY ABUNDANT - 0 TO 7.
RELATIVE HUMIDITY ▲-70%, ☐-80%, △- 90%, ●-95%,○-100%

Fig. 21.15. Amount of mold growth at various temperatures and relative humidities on a total of 15 substrates. *Source: W. I. Illman and Muriel W. Weatherburn, "Development of Mold on Cotton Fabrics,"* AMERICAN DYESTUFF REPORTER, *36-13 (1947), 343–344, 369–372.*

protein materials found in the lumen of cotton fibers. They absorb only food materials in solution. They favor an alkaline media. Only fabrics that are actually wet are attacked by bacteria to any extent. They may, however, produce acid or other end products favorable to mold growth or other forms of change in the fiber.

Molds are multicellular. They grow on moist surfaces which provide sufficient food and warmth. They prefer an acid media. The mold spores are quite resistant to heat, light, drying, and chemicals, and when transferred to a favorable environment, they germinate and grow. Molds grow over a wide range of temperatures, from a few degrees above freezing to as high as 110 F, with the optimum at 68–104 F.

Although bacteria generally attack cotton from the outside, molds enter the lumen, penetrate the fiber wall and develop until it is difficult or impossible to remove by bleaching without destroying the fiber. The molds in general do the most damage.

Marsh has pointed out that microorganisms are found on fabrics in about the following numbers per square inch of fabric: 32 million on cotton, 35 million on wool, and 2.2 million on silk. Many types of organisms are found on cotton, but few are found on wool. Silk is

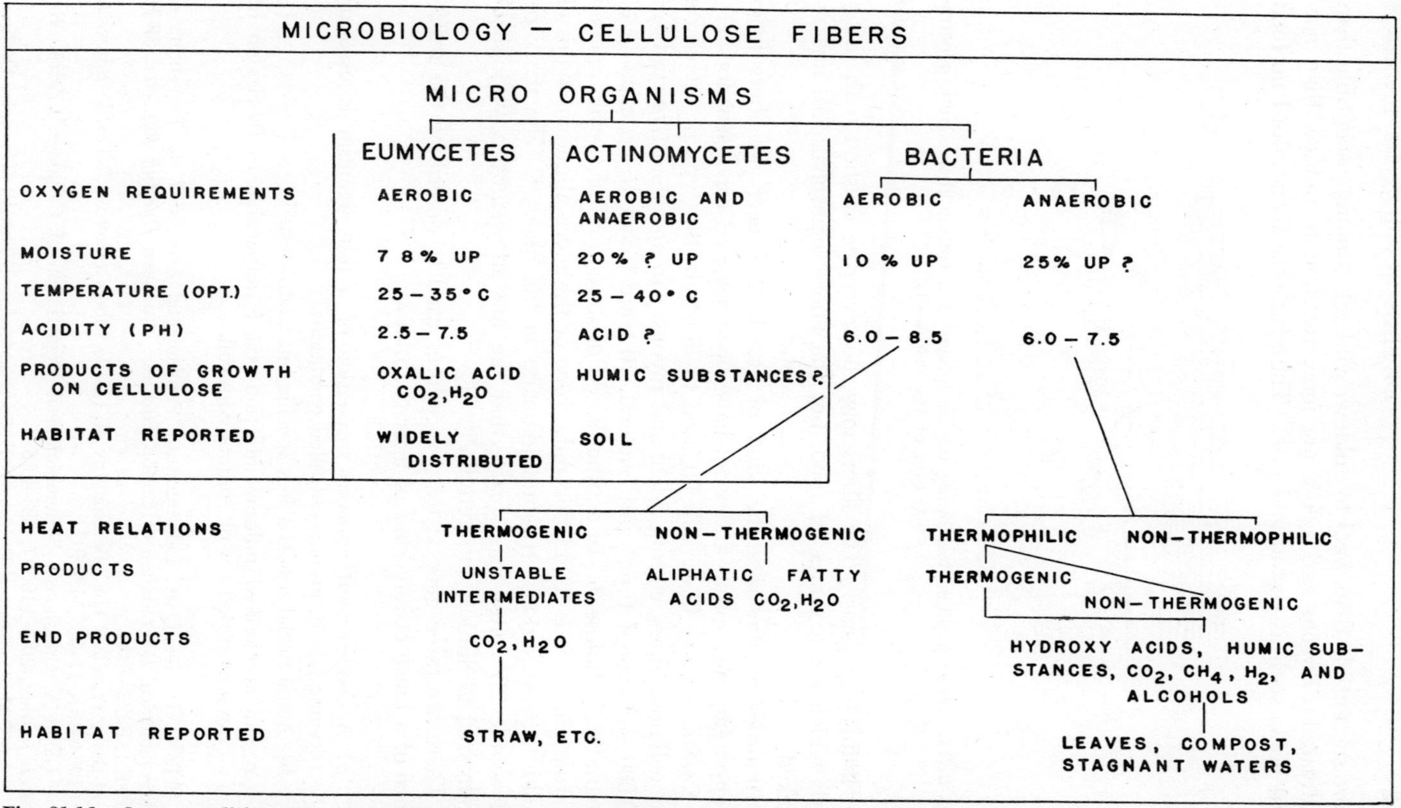

MICROBIOLOGY — CELLULOSE FIBERS

MICRO ORGANISMS

	EUMYCETES	ACTINOMYCETES	BACTERIA	
	AEROBIC	AEROBIC AND ANAEROBIC	AEROBIC	ANAEROBIC
OXYGEN REQUIREMENTS				
MOISTURE	7 8 % UP	20 % ? UP	10 % UP	25 % UP ?
TEMPERATURE (OPT.)	25 – 35° C	25 – 40° C		
ACIDITY (PH)	2.5 – 7.5	ACID ?	6.0 – 8.5	6.0 – 7.5
PRODUCTS OF GROWTH ON CELLULOSE	OXALIC ACID CO_2, H_2O	HUMIC SUBSTANCES ?		
HABITAT REPORTED	WIDELY DISTRIBUTED	SOIL		
HEAT RELATIONS	THERMOGENIC	NON-THERMOGENIC	THERMOPHILIC NON-THERMOPHILIC	THERMOGENIC NON-THERMOGENIC
PRODUCTS	UNSTABLE INTERMEDIATES	ALIPHATIC FATTY ACIDS CO_2, H_2O		
END PRODUCTS	CO_2, H_2O		HYDROXY ACIDS, HUMIC SUBSTANCES, CO_2, CH_4, H_2, AND ALCOHOLS	
HABITAT REPORTED	STRAW, ETC.		LEAVES, COMPOST, STAGNANT WATERS	

Fig. 21.16. Some conditions for microbiological growth on cellulose fibers. *Source: Prindle,* "Microbiology of Textile Fibers (Cotton)."

more susceptible than wool to mildew; wild silk is more susceptible than cultivated.   Rayons and azlons are more resistant to mildew than natural fibers such as cotton and jute.   The synthetic fibers afford no food

Fig. 21.17.   Mold hyphae developing in the lumen of a cotton fiber.   Note penetration of the cell wall.

for living organisms.   The fibers may, however, be finished with materials which are a source of food, but the fibers themselves are not attacked.

In order to illustrate the kind of attack to expect on fibers from microorganisms, cotton and wool have been selected for discussion.

Cotton, a plant fiber, will be used to illustrate the type of attack on the cellulose fibers, cotton, linen, and rayons.   In an exhaustive study of 10,000 cultures of fungi and bacteria, 70 were found to be capable of degrading cellulose.[33]   In another study of stored and of freshly opened cotton bolls, it was found that only three of the more abundant types of molds caused serious structural damage to the fibers.[34]   The work on Stoneville 2B cotton has shown that the loss in weight is very small compared to the loss in strength.[35]

There are three general test procedures used to determine the resistance of a finish or any kind of fiber to mildew.

    a)   A concentrated aqueous suspension of a test organism is used on some fabrics under controlled conditions.[36]

    b)   A soil burial test is a less specific but useful test.[37]

    c)   An accelerated mildew infection test is applicable to fabrics to be used or stored out of contact with soil.

[33] R. G. H. Siu, QMC Laboratories, "Fundamental Aspects of the Prevention of Microbiological Degradation of Cotton Textiles," *American Dyestuff Reporter,* 36-12 (1947), P320–P323.

[34] Bryce Prindle, "The Microbiology of Textile Fibers (Cotton)," *Textile Research,* 5 (1934–35), 11–30, 542–563.

[35] Glenn A. Greathouse, "Microbiological Degradation of Cellulose," *Textile Research Journal,* 20-4 (1950), 227–238.

[36] A.S.T.M. Committee D-13, A.S.T.M., *Standards on Textile Materials,* Designation D-684-45T, 1950, 151.

[37] *Ibid.*

A number of fungi (nonchlorophyll-bearing plants) has been used to test the mildew resistance of fabrics and finishes. All of those used for testing purposes have been found either to discolor the fabric badly or to cause structural damage which may be demonstrated by means of microscopic observations on the rate and amount of staining.

 a) Congo red is a dye which is direct to cotton and other cellulose
  fibers.[38] Spiral splitting of damaged cuticle of cotton may be readily
  observed.
 b) Victoria blue B stains the lumen.

The recommended test organisms are *Chaetomium globosum* and *Aspergillus niger*.[39]

American cottons are the most highly resistant to fungi, and Indian cottons are the least resistant.

Wool will be used to illustrate the action of microorganisms on protein fibers even though wool, of all the natural fibers, is least damaged by bacteria or fungi. The alkaline nature of the sheep's fleece encourages the growth of bacteria rather than molds. Samples of wool were taken from the back and shoulders of sheep in order to study the microbic population of raw wool. Certain types of bacteria and of molds were identified and found to be destructive.[40] Some of the bacteria cause disintegration of the wool fiber but little discoloration. Some of the molds produce both rapid discoloration and loss of strength. It was found that scouring removed or inactivated most of the destructive organisms. One which remained is fortunately not active except at 100 per cent relative humidity, but it is spore bearing and is, under favorable conditions, most active in altering the structure of wool. The scales are removed and the fiber broken down to the spindle or cortical cells. The keratin of the cortical cells does not seem to be attacked. The non-sporulating bacteria generally cause pigmentation of the fiber and loss of scales. Microscopic observation of mildewed wool and hair fibers shows a number of split fibers and free cortical cells which stain more rapidly than undamaged fibers. Prindle found that eight common molds caused discolorations but little structural deterioration.[41] The growth of molds and bacteria on wool causes marked changes in dyeing and structural properties. Visual observation of the fibers or fabric is likely

---

[38] Gladys G. Clegg, "Examination of Damaged Cotton by the Congo Red Test," *Journal of the Textile Institute*, 31-5 (1940), T49.
 [39] Sources of pure cultures:
  a) American Type Culture Collection, Georgetown University School of
   Medicine, 3900 Reservoir Road, N.W., Washington 7, D. C.
  b) United States Department of Agriculture, Plant Industry Station, Belts-
   ville, Maryland.
 [40] Bryce Prindle, "The Microbiology of Textile Fibers: IV, Raw Wool," *Textile Research*, 6-1 (1935–36), 23–43.
 [41] *Ibid.*

to reveal an off color or lack of luster on the areas attacked by bacteria or molds. If such damage occurs before the fabric is dyed, the color will be uneven because the damaged spots do not dye the same shade as the good fabric.

Excessive alkali and chlorination during manufacturing processes leave wool especially susceptible to attack. Soaps, vegetable oils, and wool conditioners all encourage the growth of bacteria.

Moisture encourages and temperature governs the rate of growth of microorganisms. More moisture is needed for bacteria than mold fungi.[42] Molds do not as a rule attack wools unless the humidity is around 97 per cent. Mildew growth generates considerable heat itself after it once becomes established. When wool is saturated with a soap solution as in laundering, it will show a preferential absorption of fatty acids. The fatty acid which is deposited on the fiber enhances mold growth.[43] Neutral solutions of soapless detergents leave a cleaner wool fiber, especially if the water is hard.

Mildew prevention is the number one problem of the textile industry. It continues to be a problem in the home where clothing and household fabrics receive a great deal of service under conditions which provide plenty of food for growth of the organisms which are always present in the air and soil. Clothes which have not been well rinsed when laundered and which have residues of soap, fatty acid, or oils left on them are susceptible to attack by mildew. In addition, acids and alkalies left on fibers cause degradation and thus render the fiber more susceptible to microbic attack by providing food. Remove all impurities by thorough washing and rinsing so that the available food supply is reduced, and the likelihood of growth of microorganisms is also reduced.

Nitrogen is vital to the growth of molds. If soluble nitrogenous material is left on fabrics, the molds become established and secrete enzymes which decompose the fibers to provide more food. It was found experimentally that molds do not generally grow on clean fibers, except at 94 to 100 per cent relative humidity. Fortunately, bacteria grow on fibers only under conditions of actual wetness. In other words, if fibers are kept *clean and dry,* there is small chance for attack by microorganisms. When clothing and household fabrics are stored, they should always be dry and clean.

It is possible to add to fabrics germicides which will last during 30 to 40 washings. An ideal germicide should be nontoxic, have no objectionable odor, have good penetrating power, and be retained by the

    [42] Eric Hardy, "Fungi, Molds and Mildews in Textiles," *Rayon Textile Monthly,* 24-1 (1943), 138.
    [43] B. A. Harold, "Mildew Behavior on Textiles," *American Dyestuff Reporter,* 30-11 (1941), 274–276 and 292–293.

fabric. Salts of silver, copper, thallium, thorium, and mercury have a bacteriostatic effect.

The Quartermaster Corps has studied the prevention of mildew on cotton textiles. After it was observed that the attack of the organism was only at the point of contact, it became possible systematically to develop methods to prevent the development of microorganisms on fabrics. The general methods are

a) physical prevention of contact of organism with fiber, by resin impregnation
b) cell toxicants, fungicides
c) enzyme inhibitors, theoretical at present
d) chemical modification of the cellulose molecule, at present most promising (cellulose acetate is not attacked nor is cotton which has the surface converted to cellulose acetate)

Household fabrics, awnings, sails, tents, and other fabrics which are used where they provide favorable conditions for growth of microorganisms would give much more service if given mildew-resistant finishes.[44]

Insects. Insects which commonly attack fabrics in the United States are numerous.[45]

Common name	Entomological name	Fiber
Webbing clothes moth	Tineola biselliella	wool, fur, feathers
Casemaking clothes moth	Tinea pellionella	wool, fur, feathers
Common carpet beetle	Anthrenus scrophula-riae	wool, fur, feathers, silk
Furniture carpet beetle	Anthrenus varius	wool, fur, feathers, silk
Black carpet beetle	Attagenus piceus	wool, fur, feathers, silk
Silverfish	Lepisma saccharina	any starched and sized
(1) silver gray		fabrics
(2) fire brat		
Grasshopper	Thermobia domestica	rayons
Cricket	Gryllus assimilis	rayons, wool

There are two kinds of clothes moth: the webbing moth, the most common, and the casemaking moth. Interest has grown recently in having all wool fabrics treated so that moths cannot digest the wool. Both moth and carpet beetle damage can be identified by microscopic examination of the bites in the sides of the fibers. It is estimated that the clothes

[44] W. S. March, "Microbiology of Textile Fibers," *American Dyestuff Reporter,* 31-24 (1942), P563–P569.

Margaret S. Furry and Helen M. Robinson, "Mildew Resistant Treatments," *American Dyestuff Reporter,* 30-20 (1941), 504 and 520–524.

[45] Ruth E. Slabaugh, "Testing of Mothproof Materials," *American Dyestuff Reporter,* 30-6 (1941), P142–P146.

moth destroys $100 million annually in clothing, and approximately an equal sum is said to be lost through the work of the carpet beetle which is more difficult to control.

Clothes moths pass through the four stages of all insects in their life history: egg, larva, pupa, and moth. The egg is provided with a serrated shell which enables it to hold to fibrous material. Eggs deposited in clothing by the moths are difficult to eradicate. Hence, the concentration of the chemist's and entomologist's attention upon the insect after hatching. The tiny hair-like grub when hatched is not much longer than the diameter of a period but begins at once to eat voraciously. It is the larva and not the moth that damages wool fabrics. In 6 to 10 weeks it may reach maturity. If agitated or disturbed in any way, it may remain dormant for many weeks. It is very sensitive to light, changes in temperature, humidity, or even noises. The optimal temperature is 80 F. The larva becomes dormant at 60 F. Wool holds enough hygroscopic water to supply the worm. On the Pacific Coast, moth damage is almost unknown in the summer because of the arid condition during July and August.

Mosher has pointed out that air conditioning in homes maintains relatively uniform temperature and humidity through much or all of the year and will probably accelerate larval development.[46] The larva has the opportunity of developing any time of the year. The danger of damage to clothing and household protein fibers is thus greatly increased. The larva stage may last from six weeks to years. When it is grown, it spins a cocoon about itself, and in less than two weeks the moth secretes a fluid to soften the fibers so it can emerge. When the wings are dry, the moth starts on the fourth and last phase of its life history which lasts from 2 to 30 days. The moths mate and lay their eggs. The male flies away to die. Since the female cannot fly because she carries 100 to 150 eggs, she crawls to a suitable place and, in the course of a few days, lays her eggs and dies. The eggs hatch in a few weeks, but the larva—under unfavorable conditions—may lie dormant for varying lengths of time.

The carpet beetle, of which there are three kinds—the common beetle, the furniture beetle, and the tapestry or black beetle—also attack wool and fur. The life cycle of the three species of carpet beetle is similar to that of the moth, and its life habits are similar. The adult emerges in the spring and early summer months. The larva stage may last from a few months to several years. The size of the larva is related to its ability to withstand starvation and toxic foods. If conditions are favorable, the larvae can molt 6 to 10 times and complete a life cycle in 60 to 80 days.

The carpet beetle is much more hardy and less fastidious about food

[46] Hugh H. Mosher, "Moth Proofing Preparations and Identification of Moth Defects," *American Dyestuff Reporter,* 30-13 (1941), P320–P326 and P336.

than the clothes moth.[47]   The larvae seem not to like being exposed during feeding but rather prefer being under cloth or at least under long nap on a fabric. It shuns light but eats incessantly. Wool and mohair are the choice foods, then feathers and furs, or any animal fiber or leather. Silk, glue, casein, and albumin are also eaten. Cottons, rayons, and silks if sized with gelatin may be damaged. Neither the moth nor the beetle larva can digest cellulose or other carbohydrates but will damage such fabrics if they have a protein sizing.

The protein-containing fibers such as those derived from casein, soybeans, and peanuts are also vulnerable to attack. It has been shown that if the insects are entrapped in folds of fabric made of cellulose fibers or silk, they will cut their way out. A loss is incurred, regardless of the cause of the cutting by the insect. Neither the moth nor beetle digests or assimilates much of what it eats. Both are aerobic and do not thrive in closed atmospheres.

There are four general methods of combatting moths and beetles.[48] Cleanliness, exposure to sun and brushing, repellents in air-tight space, and treating fabrics with a suitable reagent will go far toward insuring protection of clothing and household fabrics from damage by moth. Fabrics which are clean do not attract moths so readily. Insects like the dark. Air, brushing, and exposure to the sun check the activity of both moth and carpet beetles. Clean fabrics which are stored in airtight places may be protected with napthalene, camphor, paradichlorobenzene, or other suitable compounds obtainable from a druggist.

Probably the more satisfactory procedure is to treat the fabric in the finishing process with a suitable compound which will act as a stomach poison or will kill by contact. Most such substances are not fast to wet cleaning, some not even to dry cleaning.

The increased selling value of moth-resistant wools and furs has provided incentive for manufacturers to make use of such finishes. In order to test the effectiveness of various finishes, it was necessary to establish standardized test methods.[49] The black carpet beetle and the webbing clothes moth are the most commonly used for laboratory testing of moth-resistant finishes on fabric.

Silverfish are slender, wingless, scale-covered insects. They are about ⅜ of an inch long with three long, tail-like appendages at the rear and two long, slender feelers in front. They are nocturnal in their habits. They hide under objects during the day. There are two species: (a)

[47] *Clothes Moths, Leaflet No. 145*, U. S. Department of Agriculture (Washington, D. C.: Government Printing Office, 1940).

Mosher, "Moth Proofing Preparations and Identification of Moth Defects," P320–P326 and P336.

[48] R. Burgess, "Mothproofing," *Rayon and Synthetic Textiles*, 30-8 (1949), 87.

[49] A.S.T.M. Committee D-13, *A.S.T.M., Standards on Textile Materials*, Designation D582-49T, 1950, 141.

one which is silvery or pearl gray, and (b) the fire brat which has dark markings. Their chief food consists of starchy materials, but they require some protein in their diet. They eat holes in thin fabrics of cellulose, especially rayons, starched clothing, and curtains, as well as any fabric with a protein size.

If clothing and household fabrics are kept clean, dry, and properly stored, the chances of loss from microorganisms and insects are greatly reduced.

Chapter Twenty-two

Textile Standards and Consumer Problems

DIMENSIONAL, PERFORMANCE, AND QUALITY STANDARDS must be developed and described in order to have any reasonable degree of uniformity in textiles and textile products. It is also necessary that test methods be developed to measure specific properties of those same goods in order that dimensions, performance, and quality may be identified for the purchaser. A great many government, trade, and professional agencies contribute to the development and standardization of quality in fabrics and garments. Technical progress of today makes it possible to provide more serviceable and satisfying goods than has been possible in the past.

DEVELOPMENT OF STANDARDS IN TEXTILES

Agencies of Federal Government. The agencies of the Federal Government of the United States which contribute to progress in textiles and textile products are divided into several groups.[1] The work of some of the agencies will be described in some detail.

United States Department of Agriculture. The Department of Agriculture includes among other divisions the Agricultural Research Ad-

[1] U. S. Temporary National Economic Committee, *Investigation of Concentration of Economic Power, Monograph 24, Consumer Standards* (Washington, D. C.: Government Printing Office, 1941).

ministration and the Production and Marketing Administration. The Agricultural Research Administration sponsors textile research (on fibers, fabrics or their utilization) in sections of the bureaus of: Plant Industry;

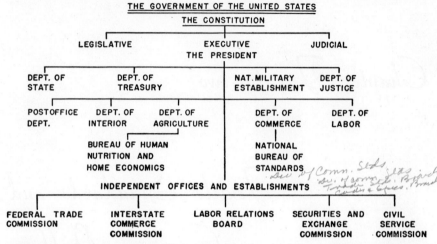

Fig. 22.1. Flow sheet giving relationships of some government agencies which contribute to the improvement and standardization of quality in textiles and apparel. *Source: Adapted from* UNITED STATES GOVERNMENT MANUAL, DIVISION OF FEDERAL REGISTER *(Washington, D. C.: Government Printing Office, 1949), 572.*

Scientific and Agricultural Engineering; Animal Industry; Human Nutrition and Home Economics; and Agricultural and Industrial Chemistry as well as in the Agricultural Experiment Stations. In addition, the four large regional research laboratories[2] are included in the Bureau of Agricultural and Industrial Chemistry.

In the Production and Marketing Administration, studies are made on wool, cotton, testing, standardization, mechanical harvesting of cotton, flax, ramie, and other fibers. The Department of Agriculture aids by improving varieties of fiber-producing plants and breeds of fiber-producing animals. It improves and facilitates marketing procedures. It improves end products by research on quality and serviceability.

A number of bureaus assists with the many aspects of improving the fabrics which are used by all.

The Bureau of Human Nutrition and Home Economics is an outgrowth of the Office of Home Economics which became the Bureau of Home Economics in 1923, to comply with the provisions of the Agriculture Appropriation Act of 1923. In February, 1943, the name was changed to the Bureau of Human Nutrition and Home Economics. A large part of its activities consists of research to meet the demand of the

[2] *United States Government Organization Manual 1950–51* (Washington, D. C.: Government Printing Office, 1950), 211.

American family for scientific facts to aid in the best use of food, clothing, and other agricultural and industrial products in the home, with special suggestions, plans, and methods for more economic procedures for obtaining such products.[3] Considerable effort is expended in order to: (a) determine products for which standards are practicable, (b) carry out research to provide a basis for standards, (c) formulate feasible standards, and (d) promote the use of such standards through identification by labels and by the education of consumers in the use of standards.[4]

In the field of textiles and clothing, consumer standards are based upon detailed studies of physical and chemical properties of fibers and fabrics coupled with studies of design and construction followed by serviceability tests on garments or household articles. Minimum specifications have been recommended for such consumer goods as broadcloth, Turkish (terry) toweling, sheeting, upholstery fabrics, corduroy and blankets.[5]

So far, most of the tests for textiles and clothing "are not closely related to human desire." [6] It would seem that more preference guides, not only need to be developed, but need to be related to physical and chemical data. Johnny Q simply is not happy in a suit, regardless of thread count, breaking strength, or abrasion resistance, if he does not like the lines, fit, color or texture.

The Division of Textiles and Clothing in the Bureau of Human Nutrition and Home Economics has taken an active part in the work of the American Society for Testing Materials in developing standards and specifications for clothing and household textiles. The need for adequate identification of quality and performance increases with the rapidly developing textile industry. Extensive work on service qualities of classes and kinds of fibers used in consumer fabrics should lead to better utilization of resources, both personal and national.

The Division of Textiles and Clothing has been active in studying principles of clothing design. Designs have been developed for functional clothing adapted to different kinds of work. An extensive investigation was carried out to determine the sizes of women and children.[7] These findings have been used to improve the sizing of com-

[3] United States Government Organization Manual 1950–51 (Washington, D. C.: Government Printing Office, 1950), 214.

[4] U. S. Temporary National Economic Committee, Investigation of Concentration of Economic Power, Monograph 24, Consumer Standards (Washington, D. C.: Government Printing Office, 1941).

[5] A.S.T.M. Committee D-13, A.S.T.M. Standards on Textile Materials, 1948.

[6] A. G. Ashcroft, "Interpretation of Laboratory Tests as Quality Indices in Textiles," American Dyestuff Reporter, 33-24 (1944), 486.

[7] Ruth O'Brien, Women's Body Measurements for Sizing Garments and Patterns, U. S. Department of Agriculture (Washington, D. C.: Government Printing Office, 1941).

mercial patterns and of ready to wear. Findings of such magnitude as functional designs and accurate sizings when incorporated into commercial standards and trade practice rules go far toward guiding the manufacturer and simplifying shopping for the consumer buyer. In the meantime, the development of methods for testing the construction and finish of various kinds of fabric and of design and construction of garments is a necessary step toward the formulation of definite standards in clothing.

Studies are made on ways to reduce waste and to more fully utilize textiles by developing mildew-resistant finishes for cotton, chemical finishes to improve cotton yarns, processes for sterilizing wool without damage to the fiber, and by measuring fabric properties.

"Results of all this research are made available through bulletins, press releases, radio talks, and picture material for print and screen. The Bureau also cooperates with other agencies conducting research and educational programs designed to help families to so use their textile resources as to obtain the best returns in health and other elements of satisfactory living." [8]

The Agricultural Extension Service, authorized in 1914 by the Smith-Lever Act, cooperates with the Bureau of Human Nutrition and Home Economics in an effort to translate research information on home and family problems, including those on clothing and household textiles, into a usable form for homemakers. Business and industry are also spending large sums for the same purpose.

The Office of Experiment Stations is another branch of the Department of Agriculture which provides valuable aid to people in every phase of American life. This office administers Federal funds for the support of research in agriculture, the rural home, and rural life by the experiment stations in the several States, Alaska, Hawaii, and Puerto Rico. An important part of their research provides a basis for improving standards in the home. Many of the research problems relate to the improvement and utilization of clothing and household textiles.

The Bureau of Agricultural and Industrial Chemistry was developed in February, 1943, from the Bureau of Agricultural Chemistry and Engineering, an outgrowth since 1901 of the Bureau of Soils and the Bureau of Chemistry. A major portion of the investigations of this bureau is

Ruth O'Brien, Meyer A. Girschick, and Eleanor P. Hunt, *Body Measurements of American Boys and Girls for Garment and Pattern Construction,* U. S. Department of Agriculture, Miscellaneous Publication No. 366 (Washington, D. C.: Government Printing Office, 1941).

Ruth O'Brien and Meyer A. Girshick, *Children's Body Measurements for Sizing Garments and Patterns,* U. S. Department of Agriculture, Miscellaneous Publication No. 365 (Washington, D. C.: Government Printing Office, 1939).

[8] *United States Government Organization Manual 1950–1951* (Washington, D. C.: Government Printing Office, 1950), 215.

carried on in the four regional research laboratories.[9]   These laboratories conduct investigations for the development of new and wider industrial uses of farm products.   A vast research program includes studies being made on the principal crops in each of the four major agricultural areas of the country.   Peoria, Illinois, studies corn, wheat, and other cereal crops, soybeans and other oil seed crops, as well as agricultural residues such as stalks and straws.   In New Orleans, studies are in progress on cotton, peanuts, and sweet potatoes.   Wyndmoor, Pennsylvania, has studies on tobacco, apples, potatoes, and other vegetables, milk products and by-products, hides and skins, tanning materials, and animal fats and oils.   At Albany, California, studies are conducted on wools, fruits, vegetables, wheat, alfalfa, poultry products, and by-products.   Many of these products contribute directly or indirectly to textiles and textile products. The New Orleans laboratory spends more money than all of the others on fibers because of its location in the Cotton Belt.   The work on wool at Albany, California, was greatly stimulated by aid from the Wool Bureau.   Research on natural fibers and fibers made from plant or animal material is of value in each region.

The Office of Fiber Investigation was established in the Department of Agriculture in 1890.[10]   Prior to that, in 1889, fiber investigations had been begun in the Division of Statistics.   The Office of Fiber Investigation collected and disseminated information regarding the cultivation of textile plants, directed experiments in the culture of new and hitherto unused plants, purchased seed and plants for limited distribution for experimental purposes, and investigated the merit of new machines and processes for extracting the fiber and preparing it for manufacturing. The duties of that office have been absorbed by other agencies.

The Bureau of Agricultural Economics was created in 1923 and reorganized in 1939.   Among other things the bureau makes studies of the economic basis of grades and standards and analyzes the effect of particular standards in the marketing process.   An extensive study of consumer preferences of men was recently made.[11]   Preferred products find a ready market.

Part of the work of the bureau deals with the development of new uses for farm products (fiber crops included) and of the economic possibilities of finding new markets for all agricultural products.   At present, this work is largely limited to new markets for cotton.   Three of the studies completed on the utilization of cotton and competing mate-

[9] *United States Government Organization Manual, 1950–1951* (Washington, D. C.: Government Printing Office, 1950), 211.

[10] C. H. Greathouse, "Historical Sketch of the United States Department of Agriculture," revised edition (Washington, D. C.: Government Printing Office, 1898).

[11] *Men's Preferences among Selected Clothing Items,* Miscellaneous Publication No. 706, U. S. Department of Agriculture (Washington, D. C.: Government Printing Office, 1949).

rials dealt with the use of cotton for fertilizer bags, cord, twine, and hosiery.

In 1938, the Post Office Department agreed to make trial use of cotton twine for tying bundles of letters. In the past, jute twine had been used almost exclusively. The bureau is cooperating with the Navy Department in the development of parachute cords of cotton in place of the silk cords now used. This potential use of cotton is not large, but it is obviously important for defense purposes.

United States Department of Commerce, National Bureau of Standards. This bureau was established by an act of Congress on March 3, 1901. It contributes to the improvement of textiles and textile products through numerous divisions.

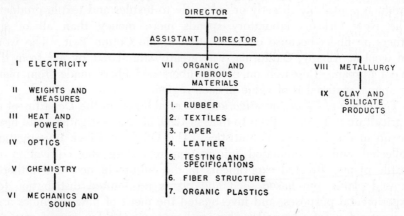

Fig. 22.2. **Divisions of the National Bureau of Standards, Department of Commerce. The Division of Organic and Fibrous Materials studies many aspects of fibers.**

The Division of Organic and Fibrous Materials studies textiles, testing and specifications, and fiber structure. Some of the studies which have been made are on

a) relation of yarn and fabric constructions and finishes to the properties of the finished product
b) carpets and a carpet-testing machine used generally by manufacturers
c) cotton textiles
d) underwear, relative warmth, air permeability, thickness, weight and softness of fabrics made from different fibers, standard sizes for knit and woven goods
e) dry-cleaning solvents
f) dress fabrics
g) gloves
h) hosiery and a hosiery-testing machine
i) water proofing for fabrics

The Division of Commodity Standards was formed by a combination of Simplified Practice and the Division of Commercial Standards and includes the Trade Standards Branch and Codes and Specifications Branch.

The National Bureau of Standards cooperates with industry, business, and education through the branches of the Division of Commodity Standards and thus performs a service to the consumer. The work of eliminating needless variations in sizes and types of manufactured products is carried out by the Division of Commodity Standards. For example, we have not only standard lengths and widths, but also standard types of bed sheets based on yarn count, yarn type, weight, finish, and breaking strength.

Trade Standards Branch aids producers, distributors, and consumers by the establishment of commercial standards for testing, rating, certification, and labeling.[12] Some standards define quality, and some cover methods of measuring quality. These are recorded in standards voluntarily agreed upon by all concerned and thus provide a commonly accepted measure of quality. A trade standard of special importance to fabric consumers is Commercial Standard CS-59 Woven Textile Fabrics, Testing and Reporting, a copy of which may be had from the Government Printing Office, Washington, D. C. If references to this standard on labels are to have meaning to consumers, specific tests and their meaning must be clearly indicated on labels in terms understandable by the consumer.[13] There are also commercial standards covering the standards of construction of many ready-to-wear garments, e.g., work gloves and women's slips.

Such specifications may or may not be practical or valuable for all fabrics for all uses but are of much value for staple fabrics used for household purposes and for the vast ready-to-wear industries.

Codes and Specifications Branch of the National Bureau of Standards, among other things, is concerned with encouraging manufacturers of staple goods to identify their commodities by labels to guarantee compliance with appropriate federal specifications or commercial standards. Federal specifications are prepared for all items purchased by the Director of Procurement for the Federal Government. Such specifications are used to describe the properties which determine the desired qualities of a given item. Specifications are also prepared to describe methods of testing the desired properties of items purchased in order to determine whether or not specifications have been met. Federal Specification CCC-T-191a, Textiles, General Specifications, Test Methods is used for testing woven or knit textile fabrics. Reference is sometimes made on labels to Federal Specification CCC-T-191a as a means of indicating

[12] Henry Miller, "Trade Practice Rules and Test Procedures for Textiles," *American Dyestuff Reporter*, 38-6 (1949), P274–P275 and P280.

[13] American Association of Textile Chemists and Colorists, *Technical Manual and Year Book*, 1949, vol. 25.

to the consumer the performance standard of the fabric in regard to such properties as color fastness and shrinkage. An example of a federal specification suitable for quality labeling of consumer goods is that

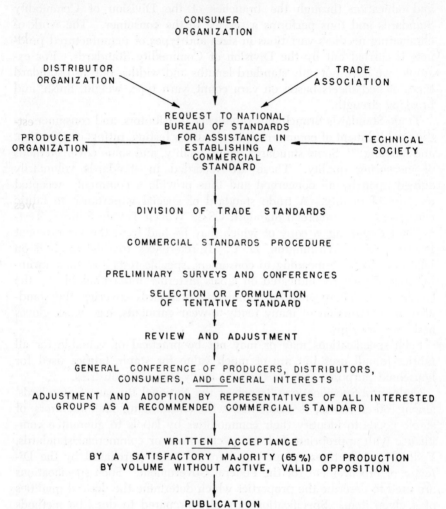

Fig. 22.3. Framework of the procedure by which commercial standards are developed. Commercial standards are voluntary trade standards.

for bleached cotton sheets, Federal Specification DDD-S-281, which covers the kind of material, size, weight, thread count, breaking strength, hems, and stitching.

Of the seventy interdepartmental technical committees on federal specifications, those of special interest in textiles are on

a) color
b) detergents
c) hair for mattresses
d) laundry equipment
e) textiles
f) wearing apparel

Codes and Specifications Branch aids public purchasers in formulating, selecting, and unifying specifications and commodity acceptance testing methods. The division compiles and keeps up to date directories of commercial testing laboratories, college research laboratories, and government testing laboratories (see Appendix). It prepared the National Directory of Commodity Specifications in which are classified and indexed references to all nationally recognized standards and specifications of technical societies and trade associations and several agencies of the Federal Government.

Food and Drug Administration. A constituent organization of the Federal Security Agency, an independent agency of the government, the Food and Drug Administration under other titles has functioned since 1906. Today, it maintains supervision over not only food, drugs, and cosmetics but also certifies dyes and follows up textile finishes which cause irritation to the skin of those who handle or wear the fabric.

Federal Trade Commission. The Federal Trade Commission was established in 1914. The commission as originally established was an agency to protect competitors and not a consumer-protection body. The assumption was that consumers would be protected as a result of fair competition.

From about 1919 to 1937, the commission followed the policy of holding trade-practice conferences in industries where members wished them. As a result of such conferences, a list of fair trade-practice rules was drawn up and submitted to the commission, which then passed on them by disapproving them or by approving and promulgating them.

In 1937, the Federal Trade Commission began issuing rules for trade and industry. The Wheeler-Lea Act of 1938 provided for penalties for violations of trade-practice rules. As a result, the Federal Trade Commission has extensive powers to eliminate unfair trade practices. When consumers are deceived by an act or practice, that act or practice is considered to be an unfair trade practice. False advertising or other misrepresentations which deceive a consumer come under the jurisdiction of the commission. Today the work in consumer protection is significant and was reinforced by the Lanham Trade-Mark Act of 1946 which provides for cancellation of certain undesirable trade-marks.

Trade-practice rules have been set up by the Federal Trade Commission for such industries as rayon in 1937, silk in 1934, fur, dress manufacturing, cotton converting, infants' and children's knit outerwear, linen in 1941, and ribbon. These industries and others through voluntary cooperation, as well as the consumers, benefit by the regulatory activities of the commission.

Many terms used in textiles are defined by the commission; for example, rayon and wool. The Wool Products Labeling Act of 1939 defines the labeling of wool. The act classifies wool according to previous history as new or virgin wool, reused wool, or reprocessed wool (see chapter seven, Wool). It should be kept in mind that rugs, carpets, mats, and upholsteries are excluded from the provisions of the act. When the specialty fibers are used and their presence disclosed, the percentages must be given; otherwise, they are classed as wool.

Department of Defense. The Department of Defense, established in 1949, includes the Department of Air Force, Department of Army, and Department of Navy. The Bureau of Supplies and Accounts is responsible for procurement of all clothing, bedding, towels, and other textile requirements of men and women in military service. Federal specifications cover all government purchases which are priced on a competitive basis and therefore must be adequately described by specifications.

The Research and Development Board of the Department of Defense constantly strives to improve clothing and other fabrics for the use of the military. It was found to be economical to standardize residual shrinkage in cotton sheeting to be used for such things as mattress covers, bed sheeting, and pillow cases. The personnel who work on specifications for the military maintain close contact with the National Bureau of Standards. Each set of specifications is printed separately. There is military representation in the American Society for Testing Materials, of which Committee D-13 is concerned only with textiles. The Standards Council of the American Standards Association also has military representation. Such standards as are developed for military textiles and clothing are of either direct or indirect benefit to the ordinary consumer.

The Textile Foundation, Inc. and Textile Research Institute.[14] The Textile Foundation was created in the Department of Commerce by an act of Congress, June 10, 1930, with a two-million-dollar fund to engage in research for the benefit and development of the textile industry. The fund had come originally from the sale of imported dyestuffs to the textile industry during World War I.

The United States Institute for Textile Research was created in 1930 to help solve the problems of an industry in which rule of thumb rather than scientific information was undermining progress. Later, this or-

[14] *United States Government Organization Manual 1950–51* (Washington, D. C.: Government Printing Office, 1950), 265–266.

ganization became the Textile Research Institute. The objectives of the institute stated briefly are

a) to carry out long-range fundamental research
b) to train textile scientists at the graduate level
c) to disseminate textile research information by publishing *Textile Research Journal*

The work of both the institute and the foundation is now carried on under one director at Princeton, New Jersey. Formerly, the National Bureau of Standards provided space for the research. The projects of the institute include studies of fiber damage, fiber structure, mechanical and chemical behavior of fibers, and effects of moisture as well as static electricity on fibrous materials, and the mechanism of dyeing fibers. Both natural and manufactured fibers are studied.[14] The *Textile Research Journal*, a publication of the Textile Research Institute, is rated as one of the two best textile research journals in the world.[15]

Nonprofit Research Institutes. Not only has the Federal Government been active in establishing standards and specifications, but individual companies and organizations have made great progress. Some of the organizations devote much money and time to research and development of textiles and textile products.

The Institute of Textile Technology. Incorporated in 1944 at Charlottesville, Virginia, the purpose of the institute is twofold: (a) to provide a research center to supplement work of the cotton industry, and (b) to train men at the graduate level for the textile industry. At present, about 20 per cent of the cotton spindles in this country are represented by membership.

Others. Other nonprofit laboratories with interest in textile research are: Southern Research Institute, Mellon Institute, Armour Research Foundation, Mid-West Research Institute, and Massachusetts Institute of Technology. This is not a complete list.

Professional Associations. Professional societies have established standards for raw materials, finished products, processes, construction, and performance of textiles and textile products. Certification systems and identifying labels are encouraged. All of this work is ultimately of value to the consumer.

American Association of Textile Chemists and Colorists. This association was organized in 1921. The purposes of the association are: (a) to promote increased knowledge of the application of dyes and

---

[14] Julius B. Goldberg, "Textile Research and Its Practical Applications in Industry," *Rayon and Synthetic Textiles*, 29-1 (1948), 43.
[15] F. S. Boig and W. J. Fitzpatrick, Jr., "Chemical Periodicals in the Dye and Textile Industry," *Textile Research Journal*, 19-6 (1949), 325–329.

chemicals in the textile industry, (b) to encourage in any way research work or chemical processes and materials of importance to the textile industry, and (c) to establish for members channels by which the interchange of professional knowledge among them may be increased; for example, through meetings and publication of the *American Dyestuff Reporter*.

Even though the activities of this association are closely connected with the manufacturing and distributing branches of the industry, the research committee has tried to give the consumer full consideration when establishing standards.

American Home Economics Association. As early as 1919, the American Home Economics Association started a program to promote the use of informative labels in the marketing of fabrics. There has always been a strong realization of the need for standardization, consumer education, grade labeling, and other means of helping the consumer buyer.

The American Home Economics Association is a charter member of the National Consumer-Retailer Council and has contributed to the cooperation between consumers and retailers on problems of mutual concern.

American Standards Association. The American Standards Association was reorganized in 1928. It expanded its program to include specifically the development of standards for retail goods. One of the standards so far approved for goods to be sold to the consumer is stand-

Fig. 22.4. Standards Council of the American Standards Association develops standards for ultimate consumer goods.

ards for testing woven textile fabrics, Commercial Standard CS-59.

During the 1930's, certain women's organizations showed rising interest in consumer standards within the A.S.A. This led to the organization of an Advisory Committee on Ultimate Consumer Goods to coordinate and direct the work on the standardization of consumer goods. The committee includes representatives of leading national women's organizations, retailers' associations, and interested federal agencies.

Steps have been taken to bring about international standardization of textiles and textile test methods. This country participates through the American Standards Association.

The American Society for Testing Materials. The American Society for Testing Materials promotes knowledge of engineering materials and the standardization of specifications and the methods of testing. Committee D-13 is concerned with methods of testing, specifications, definitions and terms for textiles and related materials.

The A.S.T.M. consists of some 70 committees which now have more than 115 research projects under way. Each committee functions in a prescribed field and under definite regulations to insure adequate representation of producers, consumers, and general interests. The society now has formulated over 1,500 standard specifications and methods of testing, of which a large number is widely used in the textile industries.

The organization has grown from a membership of 70 in 1898 to more than 6,700 individuals and organizations in 1950. Membership is held by persons, corporations, firms, technical and scientific societies, teaching faculties, libraries, and the like. The membership is representative of the United States, South America, Canada, and about 37 other countries.

Trade Organizations. Trade organizations have promoted, in the interests of trade, the development of acceptable standards in textiles.

The American Institute of Laundering. The American Institute of Laundering has led in the effort to establish acceptable laundry procedures and in accumulating performance data on fabrics to aid manufacturers in eliminating nonserviceable fabrics and garments.

Cotton Textile Institute. The Cotton Textile Institute was established for the purpose of promoting cotton. The work of this organization helped to increase the uses made of cotton. Fashion uses were featured. Recently a research program was initiated to support such promotion.

The International Silk Guild. The guild sees that all members adhere to the trade-practice rules for silk set up in 1934 under the auspices of the Federal Trade Commission.

The National Association of Dyers and Cleaners. The National Association of Dyers and Cleaners has been active in improving the standards for dry cleaning fabrics since 1906. This organization is also active and effective in its agitation for better quality in textile fabrics. A garment which will not clean under standard procedures is not serviceable for general wear.

The National Association of Finishers of Textile Fabrics. This association has placed special emphasis upon obtaining satisfactory color fastness on consumer fabrics.

The National Association of Hosiery Manufacturers. The National Association of Hosiery Manufacturers placed a research associate at the National Bureau of Standards in 1922, and now there are two associates and a secretary to study character and performance of materials used by the hosiery industry. Among other things, they have established methods of determining the effects of twist in yarns and have studied service qualities of hosiery.

Textile Color Card Association. The Textile Color Card Association was organized in 1915 to promote the standardization of colors to be used seasonally in fashion goods, such as clothing accessories. The association issues Textile Color Cards to its members twice a year giving selected colors for fall and spring. Various textile manufacturers make up fabrics in the colors each decides to offer. From these fabrics, the color coordinating committee of the National Retail Dry Goods Association, composed of buyers and stylists from different stores and shops, selects fabrics of various colors which in the judgment of the committee will be most generally used during a particular season.

National Chamber of Commerce. The National Chamber of Commerce with the local Chambers of Commerce and Better Business Bureaus afford protection for the consumer by helping to maintain high standards in trade and advertising. Their work applies chiefly to the promotion of honesty in trade practices and advertising of local stores. They often have considerable influence though they have no powers of enforcement except that of good will. Their primary objective is to protect one competitor from another and to insure acceptable standards of business ethics in a given locality.

National Better Business Bureau. The National Better Business Bureau was established in 1911 by the Associated Advertising Clubs of the World, now known as the Advertising Federation of America. The National Better Business Bureau was first known as the National Vigilance Committee of the Associated Advertising Clubs of the World. The name was changed to National Better Business Bureau, Inc., in 1927. Originally, local Better Business Bureaus were sponsored by local advertising clubs, but now they are independent corporations. The purpose of the organization is to protect the public against unfair, misleading, or fraudulent practices in the fields of advertising and selling.

The bureau endeavors to provide the consumer with information which will assist him in buying wisely and obtaining the best service from the goods he owns or purchases, and to encourage the public to "investigate *before* investing."

CONSUMER PROBLEMS IN THE TEXTILE
AND APPAREL MARKETS

Quantities of valuable textile information exist today, some of which is made available to the consumer to aid in selecting clothing and household fabrics. More work, however, needs to be done in translating technical information already available into everyday terms. At present, because of lack of critical, comparable consumer information, the layman has to rely upon window shopping as a basis for comparing values when doing much of his textile buying.

Chance, not coordinated effort, frequently leaves the textile consumer with little of value for his money. The basic difficulty has been aptly stated by Coles. "Few laws and regulations have been set up to protect consumers of clothing and household textiles. The feeling on the part of legislators that only the health of consumers and not their pocket-books needs to be protected is for the most part responsible for the absence of regulations. Since clothing and household textiles are less frequently the source of danger to health and safety than foods and household equipment, fewer minimum standards have been set up for these goods.

"Performance in use, as in other consumers' goods, is very important in clothing and textiles. Relating their composition and construction to performance presents difficult problems which must be solved before we have widespread use of standards and labels for clothing and household textiles." [16]

Even though the consumer buys a fabric for its color and texture, he does not want it to fade or shrink. In other words, it must be beautiful, but serviceable too for the purpose for which it is bought. It will probably be some time before most textile and clothing purchases can be made on the basis of relative merit and not on a hit or miss basis.

Bed sheets are a notable exception. The five types of bleached wide cotton sheeting described in the American Standards for Testing Materials, Committee D-13, Designation D 503-40T are 120, 128, 140, 180, and 200. The type number gives the average number of yarns in one inch of warp plus the average number in one inch of filling. The yarns are designated as either carded or combed according to type. The weight of the cloth is given in pounds or ounces per square yard. The finishing materials cannot exceed a stated amount. The breaking strengths of warp or filling for each type of sheet must not fall below a stated minimum. The length and width are given. The purchaser can weigh the costs (initial and upkeep), service to expect, and differences in texture, then decide upon the type of sheet best suited to his needs and preferences. Shrinkage is usually not given.

Quality standards do not imply that all standards are or should be high. There should be a range of qualities with the performance to expect from each and a means of clearly indicating it. Textiles reach the consumer in the form of finished goods such as yard goods, dresses, coats, suits, hosiery, bed sheets, and other clothing and household products. Information on the performance of these goods and their care

[16] Jessie V. Coles, *Standards and Labels for Consumers' Goods*. (New York: Copyright by the Ronald Press Company, 1950.)

should aid the consumer in making more satisfactory choices and in spending his money to better advantage. Information may be made available to the consumer through

    a) grade labeling
    b) labeling in terms of specific performance
    c) informed sales people to help the customer make his choice
    d) reading about what is available and having the ability to recognize relative qualities

Of these four, the first two are the more practical for the large majority of people. The third emphasizes the need for more and better trained sales people. The fourth may apply to some of the purchases of many people but could not apply to all for any individual consumer.

Information Available. The information found on labels on yard goods and on ready-made garments may be classified as follows:

    a) words and phrases intended only to add appeal or glamor
    b) words and phrases intended to provide information on use and care
    c) words and phrases intended as a measure of quality or performance
    d) trademarks and brand names used for identification
    e) manufacturer's and/or distributor's name

Words and phrases intended only to add appeal or glamor are found chiefly on ready to wear, and then usually on women's clothing. Such statements as "Yes, in every way this dress is personally yours" and "Always young . . . with a flair for lines that define" are sometimes the extent of findings on labels.

On the other hand, words and phrases intended to provide information on use and care of a fabric or garment are found with increasing frequency. Washing instructions found on the label of a dress, junior size, were "To retain brilliancy in color and get maximum wear, be sure to use rich suds of good household soap and lukewarm water. Rinse thoroughly in clear water before drying. DO NOT BOIL, DO NOT USE ANY BLEACHING PREPARATION, DO NOT USE A HOT IRON, Shrinkage not in excess of 2%." Information on a label from a bolt of yard goods read, "Just toss it in the tub . . . will not shrink more than 1%, U. S. Govt. Test CCC-T-191a." Color and finish were not mentioned.

Frequently words and phrases are used as a means of implying quality. Such words as "color fast," "guaranteed," or "washable" are found. No statement is made concerning the conditions under which the color is fast, the kind or amount of washing, amount of sun, perspiration, or other conditions. The term "guaranteed" often does not say under what conditions or even what property is being guaranteed.[17]

---

[17] Jessie V. Coles, *Standards and Labels for Consumers' Goods* (New York: Copyright by the Ronald Press Company, 1950), 28.

Many terms have been defined by the Federal Trade Commission, but the consumer needs to keep himself informed as best he can in order to know that he is buying a quality to fulfill his needs and fit his budget. The fabric *may* have the desired qualities, but labels such as described above are found too frequently and are inadequate for the information-conscious consumer to be sure of his purchase.

Trademarks and brand names, now regulated by the Lanham Trade-Mark Act of the Federal Trade Commission, are the patented property of the user who is usually careful to guard the good quality of his labeled products. Considerable prestige has been attached to this form of labeling, which, of course, had its beginning as a mark of quality, but gives no specific information about the quality of the goods.

Aside from the price tag, frequently the only information found is the manufacturer's and/or distributor's name. Such information is similar to trademarks and brands in that the consumer learns about the properties of the fabric or garment from experience rather than from reading a label, a slow and sometimes expensive process in the extensive markets of today.

A study of information to be found on labels of cotton yard goods and cotton house dresses was made in 1942 and repeated in 1948. Table 22.I gives a brief summary of the findings.

TABLE 22.I

INFORMATION ON LABELS ON COTTON DRESSES AND BOLTS OF YARD GOODS

Key	Information on label	Dresses		Bolts of yard goods	
		1942	1948	1942	1948
1.	Totals observed	6000	2000	6000	1100
		%	%	%	%
2.	Brand and/or manufacturer	52	69	11	72
3.	No labels	16	21	45	29
4.	Labels with information other than brand and/or manufacturer	32	12	8	48
5.	Directions for use and care	3	16	2	38
6.	Shrinkage not to exceed 1 or 2%	0	10	0	23
7.	Offer to replace garment	5	1	2	2
8.	Fiber content given	1	3	1	1
9.	Reference made to Federal Specification CCC-T-191a	1	3	2	5
10.	Reference made to Commercial Standard CS-59 Test	1	1	22	1
11.	Performance claims for which CS-59 tests exist but no reference to tests made	33	9	86	23
12.	Performance claims for which no Commercial Standard CS-59 test exists	1	1	12	0

Source: Elsie Filion Kachulis, *An Evaluation of Commercial Standard CS-59 for Testing and Reporting of Woven Textile Fabrics,* Unpublished thesis, Iowa State College, Ames, Iowa, 1942; and unpublished report of a student problem in Textile Buying, Washington State College, Pullman, Washington, 1948.

Some changes in information found on labels were

a) increase in brand and/or manufacturer's name
b) great increase in use and care directions, including washing and iron-ing directions
c) great increase in shrinkage control, for which standard tests exist
d) great decrease in claims for which Commercial Standard CS-59 tests (covering color fastness to light and washing, shrinkage, strength, yarn count, and many others) exist but no reference to the use of Commer-cial Standard CS-59 for testing
e) decrease in claims for which no CS-59 test exists.

Some standard test methods published by Committee D-13 of the American Society for Testing Materials are listed and would be of greater value if more generally used in labeling of consumer goods.

a) Shrinkage in laundering of woven cotton cloth, A.S.T.M. Designation: D 437-36
b) Color fastness to commercial laundering and to domestic washing of cotton and linen textiles, A.S.T.M. Designation: D 435-42 (A.A.T.C.C. official method)
c) Color fastness of dyed or printed wool, silk, rayon, or estron fabrics to laundering or domestic washing, A.S.T.M. Designation: D 436-37
d) Color fastness of dyed estron to atmospheric fumes, A.S.T.M. Designa-tion: D 682-47T
e) Stretch of hosiery, A.S.T.M. Designation: D 1058-49T
f) Snag resistance of hosiery, A.S.T.M. Designation: D 1115-50T
g) Air permeability of textile fabrics, A.S.T.M. Designation: D 737-36
h) Identification of finishes on fabrics, A.S.T.M. Designation: D 683-42T
i) Fire-retardant properties of treated textile fabrics, A.S.T.M. Designa-tion: D 626-41T
j) Resistance of textile fabrics and yarns to insect pests, A.S.T.M. Designa-tion: D 582-49T
k) Resistance of textile materials to microorganisms, A.S.T.M. Designation: D 684-45T
l) Resistance of pile floor coverings to insect pest damage, A.S.T.M. Designation: D 1116-50T
m) Resistance of textile fabrics to water, A.S.T.M. Designation: D 583-50T
n) Resistance to yarn slippage in silk, rayon, and estron woven fabrics, A.S.T.M. Designation: D 434-42
o) Testing and tolerances for cotton sewing thread, A.S.T.M. Designation: D 204-42

Specifications for some consumer goods have been published by Committee D-13 of the American Society for Testing Materials.

a) All wool, all cotton, and wool and cotton blanketing (household), A.S.T.M. Designation: D 576-40T
b) Bleached cotton broadcloth, A.S.T.M. Designation: D 504-41T

    c) Medium-weight cotton corduroy fabrics, A.S.T.M. Designation: D 625–41T

    d) Bleached wide cotton sheeting, A.S.T.M. Designation: D 503-40T

    e) Terry (Turkish) toweling, A.S.T.M. Designation: D 505-40

    f) Finished, all-cotton, upholstery tapestries, A.S.T.M. Designation: D 678-42T

In order that quality standards such as described above may be of maximum benefit to the consumer buyer, he must be familiar with the relative performance values of the different qualities described. There are five types of bleached wide cotton sheeting: 120, 128, 140, 180 and 200. Type 128 sheet is less expensive but does not give as much wear as the Type 140. Not only initial costs but cost of upkeep should be counted. In comparison with type 200, type 140 costs less to buy but more to keep clean when the laundry is done by the pound, is heavier to handle when the laundry is done at home, but is most durable. Type 120 is the least durable as a bed sheet, too flimsy. Type 200 is made of fine combed yarns and is the most expensive type of cotton sheeting—light weight, easy to iron, well wearing, luxurious in texture and initial price.

When sheets carry the type designation on the label, it is frequently found that no information is given concerning breaking strength, sizing, and weight per square yard. Such facts should be of value in helping the consumer to make his selections wisely. He may not know the significance of the type designation; nor is he likely to have a copy of the specifications for types with him.

Information of Value When Made Available. It would be of value to have wool garments and fabrics carry more specific information on shrinkage, color fastness, cleanability (wash and dry clean), and permanence of moth-resistant or other finishes.

Information is needed about the *quality* of the fibers, natural or manufactured, from which the fabric is made. The manufacturer buys the fibers according to quality. Other factors being equal, the fiber quality makes the difference between good service and poor service from the fabric. Performance in specified end uses need to be establishd for fabrics. This would cover service qualities of fibers.

Shrinkage information would be of much more value if given for the third or sixth washing or dry cleaning rather than the first.

Fabrics with specific limitations should be so labeled, e.g., fabrics which lose their finish, shrink, or fade when dry cleaned or laundered.

Certainly some comparatively simple procedure can be used to indicate to the consumer buyer the relative merits of his purchase in terms of the specific properties desired and performance to expect under specified conditions of use and care.

Consumer Preferences. A national survey has been made of women's and men's preferences in selected items of textile products and clothing.[18] Such market studies are of value to apparel manufacturers, and should result in the manufacture of less unwanted clothing. The Bureau of Human Nutrition and Home Economics sponsored the *Consumer Speaks Program* in which preferences in various items of food, clothing, and household fabrics were expressed. The reports are available.[19] Some of the aesthetic and functional requirements of fabrics for different purposes have been ascertained by means of market studies.

In order that the most progress possible may be made toward providing better and more satisfying clothing and household fabrics, physical and chemical data and standardization need to be related to the aesthetic values and social functions of clothing and household fabrics.

Responsibilities of the Consumer. It should be the responsibility of the consumer buyer to obtain certain information for himself. He can read available labels before making purchases. He can obtain copies of Federal Specifications CCC-T-191a, Commercial Standards CS-59, and others from the Government Printing Office, Washington, D. C., and learn about tests referred to on labels. He can obtain copies of Federal Trade Commission Rulings on various branches of the textile industry and on the use of certain terms. The silk, rayon, and linen industries are among those for which rulings have been handed down. Water resistant, water repellent, and water proof are examples of terms for which the usage on labels has been defined.

Bulletins prepared for the Agricultural Extension Service contain information for the fabric and garment consumer-buyer and may be had from the Superintendent of Documents, Government Printing Office, Washington, D. C.

The slogan, "A man's judgment is no better than his information" is especially true in the fabric and apparel markets.

---

[18] *Women's Preference among Selected Textile Products,* Miscellaneous Publication No. 641, U. S. Department of Agriculture (Washington, D. C.: Government Printing Office, 1947).

Men's Preference among Selected Clothing Items, Miscellaneous Publication No. 706, U. S. Department of Agriculture (Washington, D. C.: Government Printing Office, 1949).

Evelyn Blake, Oris Glisson, and Mildred M. Tate, "A Study of the Preschool Child's Clothing in 100 Families of Radford, Virginia," *Journal of Home Economics,* 45-3 (1953), 179–186.

[19] American Home Economics Association, Washington, D. C.

WOMEN'S WEAR	HAND	RESILIENCY	DYEING IN DARK COLORS	UNIFORMITY IN DYEING	COLOR FASTNESS	FABRIC STRENGTH	CONTROLLED SHRINKAGE	RESISTANCE TO ABRASION DRY	WET
Utility Dresses	●				●	●	●		
Sports Dresses	●	●	●		●				
Fashion Dresses	●	●	●	●					
Suits	●	●	●		●			●	
Washable Suits and Slacks	●				●	●	●		
Linings	●		●	●				●	
Woven Underwear	●			●			●		●
Knitted Underwear	●	●				●			●
MEN'S WEAR									
Suits		●	●		●			●	
Washable Suits and Slacks			●		●	●	●		
Linings	●		●	●	●			●	
Dress Shirts					●	●	●	●	
Sports Shirts	●				●	●	●		●
Woven Underwear	●				●	●	●	●	
Knitted Underwear	●				●	●		●	
MISCELLANEOUS									
Curtains					●	●	●		
Draperies				●	●		●		
Upholsteries: Pile Fabrics	●	●	●		●			●	
Upholsteries: Tapestry				●	●	●		●	
Blankets: Cotton	●					●	●	●	
Blankets: Wool	●	●					●	●	
Floor Coverings		●			●			●	
Sheetings						●	●	●	

Fig. 22.5. Aesthetic and functional requirements for fabric. *Source: Waldemar R. Kuenzel, "Progress in Textile Technology,"* AMERICAN DYESTUFF REPORTER, *36-8 (1947), P212–P214.*

$\mathcal{A}ppendix$

GLOSSARY OF SOME COMMONLY USED
TEXTILE TERMS *

Abacá or Manila hemp—Plant native to Philippines. Fibrous ribbons from the leaf, used for cordage.

Abraded yarns—Continuous filament rayon yarns in which the outer filaments have been set or abraded at intervals, leaving the more centrally located filaments as a continuous core. Usually plied with other yarns before using.

Abrasion—Surface wear, rubbing, friction.

Absorption—A process by which a gas or liquid is held by cohesion or capillary action in the pores of a solid.

Acetylate—To introduce an acetyl radical into an organic compound.

Acid dyes—Cheap bright colors of only moderate fastness.

Adsorption—Condensation of gases, liquids or dissolved substances on the surfaces of solids.

Alizarin dyes—Vegetable dyes, originally obtained from madder root, now produced synthetically.

Alkali cellulose—Cellulose (wood pulp or cotton linters) which has been treated with caustic soda (as in rayon production).

Alpaca—One of the species of llama, a genus allied to the camel (of South America). It produces long, fine fibers.

American Egyptian cotton—Cotton selected and developed from Egyptian cotton seed, grown in the irrigated sections of Southwestern United States (See Pima and SXP).

Angora goat—A variety of goat, yielding mohair fiber.

Angora rabbit hair—Fine, silky hairs from a special breed of rabbit.

Aniline—One of the important intermediates in the manufacture of synthetic dyes.

Aniline black—The fastest and cheapest black cotton dye.

Anticrease finish—A finish for fabrics which enables them to resist and to recover from wrinkling.

Apparel wool—Wool manufactured into cloth for clothing, finer than carpet wool.

Asbestos—Mineral fibers, long, straight, and lustrous—fire proof and acid proof.

---

* This list was assembled in part from "New Words" lists prepared over a period of years by classes in beginning textiles.

Astrakhan—A grade of Karakul lambskins, less lustrous, with longer hair and more open curl than the best grade of Karakuls, which are termed Persian lamb skins. Also applies to imitations made of fabric.

Azlon—A generic term for fibers or filaments manufactured from modified proteins or derivatives thereof, with or without lesser amounts of nonfiber-forming materials—A.S.T.M.

Azoic colors—Colors made on the fiber as an insoluble pigment by diazotizing and coupling. Also called naphthol colors. Give fast colors on vegetable fibers.

Back filling—A system of finishing cloth without finish appearing on the face. A back-filling mangle lays starch or other finish on back side only.

Back cloth—Cloth which, in addition to the face fabric, holds underneath a layer either of extra filling or extra warp. A single-texture cloth with extra backing. The thread of either warp or filling woven so as to show only on the back, principally to add weight.

Bactrian—Asiatic camel which has two humps, the fiber-producing camel.

Bagging—A very heavy, loosely woven fabric used for bags or sacks, woven from heavy, tightly-twisted roving, consisting largely of reworked and waste fibers (principally cotton and jute)—A.S.T.M.

Balanced cloth—A cloth that contains warp and filling yarns of equal size and an approximately equal number per inch in both warp and filling.

Balanced twist—an arrangement of twist in a ply yarn or cord which will not cause twisting on itself when the yarn or cord is held in the form of an open loop—A.S.T.M.

Balbriggan—Medium- or light-weight, plain-stitch knitted cotton fabric for hosiery or underwear, name from Balbriggan, Ireland.

Bale—Compressed package of wool, cotton, or other fiber. The package of raw cotton made at the gin.

Bale breaker—A heavy, hopper-type opening machine which takes the layers of cotton from bales and pulls them apart into small bunches.

Basic dye—Dyes which give bright shades on mordanted cotton and untreated wool and silk. Poor fastness, especially to light.

Bast fibers—Found in inner bark of such plants as flax, jute, ramie.

Batik—Javanese process of resist dyeing on cotton by pouring molten wax on a design, then dyeing cloth, after which wax is removed.

Batten-lay—The moving part of the loom which comprises the reed, lay swords, and shuttle boxes.

Batting—Carded cotton for filling comforters and other stuffing purposes.

Beam—A cylindrical piece of wood or metal on which warp or cloth is wound, part of a loom.

Beating-up—The action of the reed as it drives each pick to the fell of the cloth. One of the three primary motions in weaving.

Beetling—A finishing process which flattens the round-thread yarns in cloth. When beetled, linen damask has a leather-like texture and increased luster. Used to give a linen finish to cotton.

Birdseye—Distinctive weave, small geometric pattern resembling a bird's eye.

Bleaching—Process of treating textile fibers or fabrics to destroy coloring matter and produce white.

Bleeding—Tendency of some dyes to dissolve when the fabric is wet or placed in water and to stain other yarns and fabrics.

Blending—Process of mixing different qualities (or types) of similar materials, in raw fiber or top to form blended yarns and fibers.

Block printing—Printing of fabrics with carved wooden blocks.

Blood—United States system of denoting the fineness of wool as compared with pure merino which is called full blood.

Boarding—Operation in which stockings or other knit garments are drawn over specially shaped, heated, metal forms to dry to a desired shape and size.

Boardy—Fabrics which handle stiff or hard.

Bobbin—A spool for holding thread. Has a head at one or both ends.

Body—The compact, solid, or firm feel of textile stock or fabrics.

Boll—The pod of the cotton plant in which the fibers and seeds grow. When ripe it splits, fiber fluffs up and dries out.

Boll weevil—A species of small beetle which deposits eggs within young cotton bolls. The larvae feed on the developing cotton and so reduce the crop.

Botany—Used in worsted-yarn manufacture to designate yarns made from the soft, medium-length varieties of Australian and South African merino wools. It also is used to signify all fine Australian wool, particularly in Great Britain. Also fine worsted fabrics.

Boucle—Yarn or fabric; curled or looped effects in yarns give an irregular surface to the fabric.

Box loom—Required for weaving fabric containing two or more kinds or colors of filling yarns. A loom fitted with box motions.

Box motion—Raising and lowering the various shuttle boxes on each side of the box loom.

Bradford or English system—Method of spinning worsted yarn originated in Bradford, England. Suitable for wools above 2½ inches in length, combed on Noble or Lister combs with addition of 3 or more per cent of oil, drawn by addition of twist, and spun on cap, flyers, and ring frames.

Braid—A narrow tubular or flat fabric produced by intertwining a single set of yarns according to a definite pattern—A.S.T.M.

Bright yarn—Lustrous rayon or nylon yarns made from fibers or filament without pigment, not delustered.

Bristle—A very coarse stiff hair or fiber, as used for brushes.

Broken twill—Twill weaves in which the direction of the twill line runs part way to the left and part way to the right in short lines to produce a pattern.

Burling—Taking knots, loose threads, stubs, and burrs from cloth, thus improving its appearance.

Cable twist—A cord, rope, or twine construction in which each successive twist is in the opposite direction to the preceding twist: S/Z/S on Z/S/Z.

Calendering—Finishing process for cloth, the cloth is made smooth by passing under pressure between heated rollers.

Camel hair—The tan-colored fibers shed by the Bactrian camel, the two-humped Asiatic camel.

Cap spinning—Spinning by means of a steel cap placed mouth downward over the spindle, instead of a flyer. This system is used for worsted yarns, for English system, and for the fine counts.

Caracul—Native Bokhara sheep of central Asia; also Karakul, fur from the lamb of this sheep. Persian lamb is the best grade of Karakul lamb skin.

Carbon disulfide—A compound of carbon and sulfur which reacts with alkali-cellulose to produce cellulose xanthate in viscose-rayon production.

Carbonizing—Process of destroying the vegetable matter in wool, noils, wastes, rags, etc. with acid and heat.

Card—Machine that does the carding of fibers. Has surfaces covered with many wire points.

Card clothing—Covering of card cylinders.

Carded yarn—Yarns made of fibers which have been carded but not combed, used for ordinary-quality fabrics.

Cardigan—A sweater or coat open down the front.

Cardigan stitch, knitting—Based on rib stitch, half and full.

Carding—Operation which opens the wool, separates the individual fibers, and delivers them in slivers or rope.

Carding wools—Those particularly adapted for woolen manufacture because of short lengths, below 1¼ inches.

Carpet wool—Wool from sheep that have had no attention paid to breeding. Wool is coarse, harsh, and strong, more suitable for carpets than apparel. Some of finer carpet wools are used to make tweeds or rough sports clothing.

Casein—Protein from skim milk.

Cashmere goat—Native goat of Tibet, northern India, Russian Turkestan, and China.

Cashmere wool—Fine wool from Cashmere goat.

Cellophane—Thin, transparent sheets of varying thicknesses made from cellulose by the viscose process. Strips of cellophane are used for hats, braids, woven and knitted cloths.

Cellulose—A constituent of all vegetable matter, e.g., cotton. A carbohydrate of complex molecular structure, a constituent of plant cells and walls.

Cellulose acetate rayon—The acetic acid ester of cellulose, now known as estron.

Cellulose xanthate—The viscous mass resulting from the reaction of carbon disulfide with alkali cellulose crumbs during the production of viscose rayon.

Chenille—Fringed thread used in rugs, curtains, coverlets. A soft, velvety cord of any fiber. A yarn with a cut pile protruding from all sides at right angles to length of yarn. Used for filling in cloth and for fringes, tassels, and cordage.

China grass—Ramie which has not been degummed.

Chlorinated wool—Wool treated with a chlorination process to prevent excessive shrinkage or felting.

Circular knit—Fabric or garment made in a tubular form on a circular knitting machine, shaped by shrinking, stretching, or tightening of stitches but not by variation in needles.

Cloth—Pliable fabric formed by weaving, knitting, felting or other suitable process.

Cochineal—Red dye derived from dried bodies of insects native to Central America.

Cohesive—Sticking together of like or unlike substances.

Coir—Coarse brown fibers obtained from the fibrous outer covering of the coconut, used for mats, cordage.

Color fast—Term applied to dyed and printed fabrics to indicate that their colors are fast to light and washing.

Comb—Process of straightening fibers in yarn production, laying fibers parallel and eliminating the noils or short fibers.

Combed—Yarns or fabrics made from combed fibers.

Combing wool—Wool which is strong and strictly of combing length, 2-inches or more—A.S.T.M.

Condition—Process in which the moisture content of textile materials is brought to a desired amount. Standard conditions require 70 F. and 65 per cent relative humidity.

Cone—Yarn holder of conical shape used as a core for a yarn package. The yarn package obtained when yarn is wound upon a cone.

Converter—Finisher of textile fabrics who buys gray goods and sells them in a finished state to retailers, cutters, and the like.

Cop—Yarn package wound on a paper tube.

Cord—Product formed by twisting together two or more ply yarns, cable and hawser.

Cortex—Principal body of the mammalian hair fibers made up of elongated cells—A.S.T.M.

Cortical cells—Elongated fibrous cells forming the main body of the wool fiber.

Cotton lint—Long fibrous down covering the seed of a particular plant, genus *Gossypium*.

Cotton linters—Short, fine fibers which cling to the cotton seed after lint, the longer fibers, has been removed.

Count—Number of warp yarns (ends) or filling yarns (picks) per square inch of cloth.

Course—In knitted fabrics, a series of adjoining loops of any one yarn lying crosswise.

Crabbing—Setting worsted goods in finishing, a mild shrinkage process.

Creel—Framework for holding bobbins, cones, or tops, and various packages from which material is drawn to supply a given machine—roving, spinning, winding, twisting, warping, slacking, knitting.

Crepe—Fabric with crinkly surface character produced by suitable use of S and Z hard-twist yarns.

Crepe yarn—Hard-twisted yarn of special construction.

Crimp—a) Waviness in a fiber or yarn. The tiny undulation or wave seen in locks of fine wool. Long, coarse wools usually are waved rather than crimped.

　　　　　b) Percentage decrease in the length of a yarn caused by weaving, based on the length of the cloth.

Crocking—Transfer of color from a dyed to a white fabric by rubbing.

Cross dyed—Cloth containing fibers of different nature or characteristics dyed in different shades according to affinity of the fibers for the particular dye used.

Cross dyeing—Dyeing of union goods in which one kind of fiber is dyed and another kind is not.

Cuprammonium rayon—Rayon made by the cuprammonium process, commonly called Bemberg.

Cut—Yarn-numbering system. The number of 100-yard lengths per pound of asbestos yarn or glass yarn, or the number of 300-yard lengths per pound of woolen yarn.

Cuticle—Outer covering, or layer of plant or animal tissue, e.g., cuticle of cotton fiber.

Damask—Firm, lustrous fabric woven with more or less elaborate Jacquard designs, commonly with warp face background and filling faced design.

Decating—Finishing process applied to woolen and worsted fabrics to set the nap and develop the luster of the material. Wet decating uses hot water. Dry decating uses steam.

Deformation—Alteration of form or shape.

Deliquescence—Property of absorbing water from the atmosphere to dissolve.

Delustering—Addition of white pigment to a spinning solution to produce a dull filament.

Denier—A unit of weight used to express the yarn number of silk, rayon, and other continuous filament yarns. Conveniently expressed as the number of grams per 9,000 meters.

Discharge—Method of printing used for dark-colored cloth to produce white or light designs. Cloth is piece dyed, and color is discharged or bleached in spots, leaving white or colored design.

Doubling—Operation in yarn manufacturing designed to average and even the character of the resulting product. It consists of feeding a number of laps, slivers, or rovings; drafting the required amount; and delivering one lap, sliver, roving, or yarn.

Drape—To cover or adorn with folds of cloth, manner of folding or hanging.

Durability—Lasting quality or quality of permanence.

Dyestuff—Material used to dye or color fabric.

Elasticity—Property of a material by virtue of which it tends to recover original size and shape immediately after removal of the stress producing the deformation.

Embossing—Calendering process for imparting moire effects or ornamental designs to a cloth. Specially engraved steel rolls are used, and the design is impressed on the cloth by means of heat and pressure.

Ends—*a*) Loosely, an individual strand of sliver, roving, or yarn.

b) Short length of fabric; remnant.

c) Warp yarns.

Estron—Generic name for esters of cellulose, e.g., cellulose acetate.

Extrusion—Molding procedure for extended shapes of uniform cross section, whereby a heat-softened substance is forced through an orifice, e.g., fibers and rods.

Fatigue—Deterioration resulting from long, continued, or frequently repeated stress.

Felting—Tendency of wool fibers to tangle and mat when moisture, heat, and pressure are applied. One type of wool shrinkage.

Fiber—Fundamental unit used in making yarns and fabrics.

Fiberglas—Filaments made from refined molten glass by drawing.

Filament—Single, natural strand of silk or variety of fiber characterized by great length.

Filling—Same as weft, woof, or picks, also refers to fabric finishing materials such as starch, china clay; also to weighting of silk.

Flax—Bast fibers from the stalk of the fiber flax plant. Yarns and fabrics made from this fiber are called linen.

Fleece—Entire coat of wool as sheared from the animal.

Floats—*a*) Flaws in cloth made by loose yarn floating on surface.

b) Yarns not bound for some distance in weaving for purpose of forming certain designs and textures.

Fulling—Controlled shrinkage of woolen fabrics in preparation for finishing, such as napping and polishing.

Gauge (or gage)—*a*) Hosiery—A measure of fineness expressing the number of needles per 1.5 inches on the needlebar.

b) Knitted fabrics—A measure of fineness expressing the number of needles per unit length (across the wales).

Gingham—Yarn-dyed fabric woven in checks, plaids, stripes, or plain color.

Ginning—Process of separating the lint from the cotton seed.

Glaze—Finish on a cloth giving a smooth, highly polished surface as in chintz.

Gray goods—Woven or knitted fabrics which have received no bleaching, dyeing, or finishing treatment. A.S.T.M.

Gums—Various plant materials, glutinous when moist, but hard when dry.

Hackling—Process whereby scutched flax is drawn through the metal combs of a hackling machine in order to separate, grade, and parallel the fibers.

Hank—Standard measure of yarn length used in calculating the weight or count of yarn. The term is also used to mean a skein of yarn.

Hard fibers—Fibers obtained from the vascular system of leaves of certain plants.

Harness—Part of a loom with attached heddles, by which the warp threads are raised and lowered to form the desired pattern.

Hawser twist—Twine, cord, or rope construction in which the first and second twists are in the same direction while the third twist is in the opposite direction, e.g., S/S/Z or Z/Z/S.

Heddle—Cord or wire containing an eye through which a warp yarn is drawn, a number of which makes up the harness of a loom.

Hemp—Bast fiber obtained from the stalk of the plant *Cannabis sativa,* very strong, easily bleached.

Hull—The outer, hard shell of cotton or other seeds.

Humidity—Moisture in the atmosphere.

Hygroscopic—Readily absorbs and retains moisture, a property of most fibers.

Impregnated fabrics—Fabric treated so that the interstices between the yarns are completely filled, from face to back, with the impregnating compound.

Indanthrene—An anthraquinone vat dye; fast to bleaching.

Inorganic—Does not contain carbon.

Jacquard—Jacquard machine is a shedding mechanism attached to a loom to facilitate weaving intricate (Jacquard) patterns.

Jute—Soft, yellow fibers from the inner bark of the jute plants.

Kapok—Silky fiber obtained from the seeds of the Kapok tree grown in Java. Used as a filling for mattresses; also life preservers.

Karakul—See Caracul.

Knit fabrics—A fabric formed by looping and interlacing yarn or thread by means of needles.

Koroseal—Trade name for a synthetic resin used in coating fabrics to make them water proof and air resistant.

Lambs' wool—First clip, usually eight months old. Short but soft.

Lamination—Process for joining layers of cloth permanently together so that they form a unit.

Leaf fibers—Hard fibers from the leaves of various plants. Fibers are generally long, coarse, and stiff.

Leno—Fabric of open construction in which the warp yarns cross from one side to another of designated filling yarns. All-over type is commonly called gauze or marquisette.

Line—Long flax fibers. Short fibers are known as tow.

Lint—Spinnable cotton fiber used in the manufacture of yarns and fabrics.

Linters—Short, fuzz-like fibers remaining on cotton seeds after the lint has been removed.

Loom—Weaving machine.

Lumen—Canal or cavity which runs longitudinally in cotton fibers.

Madras—First made in Madras, India, for sailors' headdresses.

a) Curtain madras. Thin drapery fabric of cotton or rayon. Dobby- or Jacquard-woven design in marquisette; float yarns clipped for dots or figures. Shaggy effect on one side due to ends of cut yarns. Width: 36″, 50″.

b) Shirting. Soft cotton fabric, white or yarn-dyed, usually mercerized. May contain rayon. Plain, stripe, or figure weave in white or colors, many variations in pattern and texture. White filling, dyed warp called chambray.

c) Heavy-grade madras for foundation garments such as corset fabric.

Maturity—State or condition of becoming mature (to become ripe or fully developed).

Medulla—Pith of a hair fiber.

Mercerization—Process of treating cotton yarn or cloth with caustic soda to produce luster, named after discoverer, John Mercer, a calico printer in Lancashire, England.

Methyl methacrylate—Synthetic resin used on fabrics to produce crush-resistance and glazed surfaces.

Microorganism—Microscopic organism such as bacteria and molds.

Milanese—Variety of warp-knit fabric in which the threads run diagonally and are interknitted at every course. These cloths are characterized by a fine rib on the face and a faint diagonal or diamond effect on the back, and if well made are run resistant. Milanese fabrics do not have the variety of pattern found in tricot cloth.

Mildew—*a*) Growth of parasitic fungi on various form of organic matter.

b) Popularly, any discoloration caused by fungi or bacteria on cloth, leather, or any other substance.

Moiré—*a*) Finish on rayon, silk, or cotton fabrics, a ribbed or corded, rippling, or wavy effect. Produced by plain or engraved rollers, heat, and heavy pressure.

b) Fabric with such a finish.

c) Defect which sometimes develops in dyeing fabrics, particularly on a jig.

Mold—Superficial growth, often wooly, produced by fungi.

Mordant dyes—Dyes which do not have a direct affinity for any of the fibers but require the use of a mordant in their application. Often called chrome colors because potassium bichromate is the usual mordant.

Napping—Finishing process which raises a nap on the surface of cloth.

Nitrocellulose—Original type of rayon as produced by Chardonnet, but is no longer in commercial production in the United States.

Noils—Short fibers removed in combing. Applied particularly to wool, but also to other fibers such as cotton, silk, and rayon. A.S.T.M.

Organic compounds—All compounds containing the element carbon.

Organzine—Type of silk yarn produced by the throwster; generally used as warp, consists of two or more twisted singles.

Oxidizing agent—Compound which can take on electrons from other compounds and is itself reduced in the process.

Pick—Filling yarn, either before weaving or in the cloth.

Picking—*a*) Operation of harvesting the bolls of cotton from the plant.

b) Removing hairs, kemps, straws, and other foreign matter from the face of woolen fabrics.

c) In weaving terms, the second of the three basic motions used in weaving.

Piece dyed—Term used to indicate that color has been applied to the cloth after it has been woven, not printed.

Pigment—*a*) Powdered coloring matter used in printing pastes to impart color to fabrics.

    b) Powder used to subdue the luster of rayon and nylon, titanium dioxide is commonly used.

Pile—Raised loops or tufts (cut loops) that form all or part of the surface of a fabric. A.S.T.M.

Plain weave—Fabric pattern in which each yarn of the filling passes alternately over and under a yarn of the warp and each yarn of the warp passes alternately over and under a filling. A.S.T.M. It is loosely referred to by such terms as one up and one down, calico, taffeta, tabby, and cotton weaves.

Plastic—Capable of being molded, pliable.

Pliability—Capable of being bent and twisted with ease. Easily yielding to influence of pressure.

Plissé crepe—Puckered or creped effect produced by the shrinking action of caustic soda on cotton. Usually applied to fabrics such as print cloth, lawn, or organdy. The pattern is in the form of stripes—termed plissé or of spots—called blister crepe.

Ply—*a*) Number of single yarns twisted together to form ply yarn; also number of ply yarns to form a cord.

    b) Individual yarn in a ply yarn or cord.

    c) One of several layers of fabric. A.S.T.M.

Polymerization—Reaction in which molecules of the same or related substances combine to form a compound.

Printing—Process of producing designs of one or more colors on a fabric. There are several methods, such as roller, block, screen, and several styles, such as direct, discharge, and resist.

Protein—Nitrogenous organic compounds found in all living cells. All proteins contain the elements carbon, hydrogen, oxygen, and nitrogen. Some also contain sulfur and phosphorus.

Pulled wool—Wool removed from the pelts of slaughtered sheep by use of lime, sweating, or depilatory process.

Pyroxylin—Mixture of one or more cellulose nitrates soluble in organic solvents and used in making artificial leather, plastics, and lacquers.

Racking—Operation in knitting to produce a modification of the stitch, usually used in rib stitch. It consists in moving one set of needles by the other between courses. It causes the loops to be distorted to the right or left and produces either a zigzag series of wales or wales which incline to the right or left.

Ramie—A soft fiber obtained from the bark of the ramie plant, *Boehmeria nivea*, belonging to the nettle family.

Rayon—Generic term for man-made fibers, monofilaments, and continuous filament yarns composed of regenerated cellulose with or without lesser amounts of nonfiber-forming materials. A.S.T.M.

Reducing agent—Any substance that is readily oxidized (loses valence electron), and thereby reduces another substance (which gains valence electron). Some common reducing agents are sulfurous acid, stannous chloride, and ferrous chloride.

Reeding—Operation of drawing the warp thread through the holes in a reed.

Reeling—Process of unwinding yarn from bobbins or spools into a hank or skein. A silk term describing the unwinding of silk filament from the cocoon.

Regain (moisture) standard—Regain of moisture in textile materials when brought from lower moisture content into equilibrium with standard atmosphere expressed as percentage of the oven-dry weight.

Regenerated cellulose—Cellulose which has been changed physically but not chemically. Viscose and cuprammonium rayons are of this type.

Relative humidity—Ratio of pressure of water vapor present to the pressure of saturated water vapor at the same temperature, usually expressed as a percentage.

Repeat—Number of warp or filling necessary to complete a pattern in weaving, design unit.

Resiliency—Ability to recover from deformation over a period of time.

Resins—Natural or synthetic products made by polymerization or other complex chemical processes. Not soluble in water.

Resist printing—Style of printing in which a dye-resisting substance is printed on the cloth, after which the cloth is piece dyed, leaving the printed portions undyed.

Retting—Process of soaking fiber forming stalks in water containing bacteria to decompose connective tissue of the bark in order that fibers may be obtained from stems.

Rippling—Process of removing seeds from plant in flax production with a toothed instrument called a ripple.

Roving—Continuous, slightly twisted strand of fibers in yarn production—the product of a roving machine.

Sanforizing—Mechanically controlled shrinkage process.

Saponification—Chemically, hydrolysis of a fat (ester) by alkali, with the formation of a soap.

Scales—Outer protective cells arranged in an overlapping scale-like fashion around wool fibers, the epidermal cells.

Schreinerizing—Physical means of improving the natural luster of a fabric by a method of embossing, will not withstand washing.

Scouring—Washing process for removing grease and dirt from raw fibers or from gray goods.

Scroop—Peculiar rustling or crunching sound noted in certain rayon and silk fabrics, usually developed by special finishes.

Scutching—Process for separating flax fiber from woody portion of stem, may be done by hand or machinery.

Seed hairs—Single-celled fibers such as cotton or kapok.

Selvage or selvedge—Lengthwise woven edge of a fabric. To impart additional strength and firmness, the ends in the selvage are often of coarser count, with more yarns per inch, than in the body of the cloth.

Sericin—Natural, gummy substance on the surface of silk filaments, is boiled off previous to finishing cloth.

Sericulture—Raising of silkworms.

Sewing thread—Plied or cabled yarns made in a variety of diameters, used in hand and machine sewing.

Shed—Opening formed in weaving when some warp threads are raised by their harnesses while others are left down.

Shedding—Separation of the warp threads into two groups during weaving to form a shed to allow the filling to pass between them.

Shrinking—Finishing process using water or steam to remove tendency of fabric to shrink by relaxation.

Silicate—Any salt derived from silicic acid.

Silk—Fiber produced by the silkworm to form its cocoon.

Silk throwing—Twisting of silk threads to make stronger and thicker yarn.

Singeing—Finishing process in which the projecting fuzz-like fibers are removed from the face of the cloth by passing it over gas flames or over red-hot plates or rollers.

Single—Composed of fibers twisted or laid together to form single strand suitable for use in forming fabrics.

Sizing—*a*) Process of coating warp yarns with solution (called a size) to lay and hold projecting fibers to protect yarns from strain of weaving.

b) Addition of size to produce more weight, gloss or stiffness in cloth.

Skein—Continous strand of yarn or cord wound in collapsible coil.

Sliver—Continous strand of loosely assembled fibers that is approximately uniform in cross-sectional area and without twist. A.S.T.M.

Slub—Soft, thick, uneven place in a yarn, may be a defect or produced intentionally.

Solubility—Extent to which a substance mixes with a liquid to produce a homogeneous system.

Spinneret—Cap (nozzle), made of precious metal, base metal, glass or rubies, and perforated with minute holes through which the spinning solution is forced to produce fibers.

Spinning—Process of making yarns or cordage from fibers, tow or liquid materials. A.S.T.M.

Spun-rayon yarn—Yarn made from staple rayon.

Staple rayon—Rayon fibers of spinnable length manufactured directly or by cutting continous filaments. A.S.T.M.

Starch—White, granular, or powdery, complex carbohydrate taken from corn, potatoes, wheat, rice, for commercial use, an important compound used in sizing and finishing processes.

Steaming—*a*) After-treatment given to certain printed or dyed fabrics to fix the colors on the cloth, also to set fabrics.

b) Treatment of yarns with steam to eliminate liveliness and snarled conditions.

Stoving—*a*) Bleaching of wool or silk by exposing it to sulfur dioxide fumes formed by burning sulfur.

b) Killing of chrysalis inside a silk cocoon by subjecting it to heat.

Strand—Fibers twisted together to form a single (yarn) in a ply thread, rope, or cable, also a single filament.

Stress—Force or load exerted upon a sample. Breaking strength of fabric refers to amount of force being exerted at the time the fabric breaks.

Suint—Excretions from the sweat glands of sheep, principally potash salts. A.S.T.M.

Surface contour—The divergence of a surface from planeness. A.S.T.M.

Synthetic—Term applied to man-made fibers produced from small beginning units.

Tearing strength—Force required to start or continue a tear in a fabric under specified conditions. A.S.T.M.

Tenacity—Breaking strength of a sample (fabric or yarn) expressed in force per unit of yarn number, as grams per denier or strength count product (breaking constant). A.S.T.M.

Tensile strength—Breaking strength of a material expressed in force per unit cross sectional area of the original specimen.

Tentering—Continuous process for drying cloth while it is held under tension to remove wrinkles and give a smooth surface.

Textiles—General term for fibers, yarn intermediates, yarns, fabrics, and products made from fabrics which retain more or less completely the strength, flexibility and other typical properties of the original fibers or filaments. A.S.T.M.

Texture—Surface effect to the hand or eye of cloth as dull, lustrous, wooly, stiff, soft, sheer, heavy. Hand and appearance depend largely upon fiber, weave, color, and finishing processes.

Thermoplastic—Materials of this type soften when heated, e.g., estron, nylon, Vinyon.

Thermosetting—Materials of this type harden when heated, e.g., some crush-resistant finishes for fabrics.

Top—Continous untwisted strand of fibers from which the shorter fibers or noils have been removed by combing.

Tow—*a*) In bast fibers, the short fibers removed by hackling.

    b) In rayon fibers, a multifilament strand suitable for cutting into staple or spinning directly to a spun rayon yarn. A.S.T.M.

Tricot—French term for certain warp knitted fabrics.

Tube—Wooden or paper core upon which yarn is wound.

Twill—Weave characterized by diagonal lines produced by a series of staggered floats, may be warp or filling faced.

Twine—Ply yarn made of medium twist single yarn with ply twist in the opposite direction. A.S.T.M.

Twist—Turns about its axis, per unit of length, observed in a fiber, yarn, or cord. Twist is expressed (1) as turns per inch, (2) as turns per meter, or (3) by helix angle in a structure of known diameter. A.S.T.M.

Twist, balanced—Arrangement of twist in a ply yarn or cord which will not cause twisting on itself when the yarn or cord is held in the form of an open loop. A.S.T.M.

Twist, direction of—Yarn or cord has an S twist if, when held in a vertical position, the spirals conform in direction of slope to the central portion of the letter S; and Z twist if the spirals conform in direction of slope to the central portion of the letter Z. A.S.T.M.

Typp—Yarn number, the number of thousands of yards per pound.

Vat dyes—Dyes developed by oxidation; originally made in vats.

Viscose—Third method (historically) of producing rayon. The product of this method is a regenerated cellulose, which has been coagulated or solidified from a solution of cellulose xanthate.

Warp—Yarn running lengthwise of a woven fabric, parallel with the selvage, also called ends.

Waste—Material removed, rejected, or otherwise disposed of in various yarn- or fabric-manufacturing processes. Classified as soft or hard waste, according to origin.

Waterproof—Fabric so treated that water and air does not penetrate.

Water repellency (textile)—Ability of a textile fiber, yarn or fabric to resist wetting (American Association of Textile Chemists and Colorists).

Water resistance (fabric)—General term denoting ability of a fabric to resist wetting and penetration of water (American Association of Textile Chemists and Colorists).

Weaving—Interlacing of two or more sets of yarns at right angles to form a fabric.

Weft—Filling threads in a woven fabric.

Weighting—Process of adding weight to a yarn or fabric by loading it with certain substances, e.g., chemical methods, as in weighting silk with metallic salts; or mechanical methods using starch, China clay.

Wool—Wool Products Labeling Act defines wool as the fiber from the fleece of the sheep, or lamb, and hair from the Angora or Cashmere goat (may include such specialty fibers as the hair of the camel, alpaca, llama, and vicuna) which has never been reclaimed from a woven or felted product.

Woolen yarn—Yarn spun from wool fibers which have been carded but not combed or gilled. A.S.T.M.

Worsted yarn—Yarns spun from wool fibers which have been carded and either gilled or combed, or both. A.S.T.M.

Yarn—A generic term for an assemblage of fibers or filaments, either natural or manufactured, twisted or laid together to form a continuous strand suitable for use in weaving, knitting, or otherwise intertwining to form textile fabrics. A.S.T.M.

Yarn number—A measure of linear density. Two systems are in current use, (1) based on the number of fixed lengths per standard weight, and (2) based on the number of fixed weights per standard length.

INDEXES COMMONLY USED IN LIBRARY REFERENCE WORK

Title	Dates covered	Contents
Agricultural Index	1916 to date	Subject index to agricultural products and allied subjects—periodicals, books, bulletins, pamphlets, reports
Art Index	1929 to date	General—magazines and museum publications
Bibliographic Index	1937 to date	Bibliographies included in books and pamphlets or as parts of books, pamphlets, and periodicals
Book Review Digest	1905 to date	Selected list of books
Cumulative Book Index	1898 to date	World list of books in English language from all countries
Education Index	1929 to date	Leading educational periodicals and books of U. S. and other countries
Engineering Index	1884 to date	Textile industry included
Industrial Arts Index	1913 to date	Covers 200 periodicals on engineering, science, industry (textile and others), economics, business; technical, scientific, and business information
International Index to Periodicals, Library Card Catalog	1908 to date	Educational and other periodicals, books by author, title, subject
Readers Guide to Periodical Literature	1890 to date	General periodicals
U. S. Office of Experiment Stations—Experiment Station Record	1889–1946	Scientific articles and reports—in foreign and English language
United States Superintendent of Documents—Catalog of the Public Documents of Congress and All Departments of Government of the United States (U.S. Document Catalog—common usage)	1893–1940	Complete catalog of all government publications
United States Superintendent of Documents—Monthly Catalog of United States Government Publications	1895 to date	All government publications
Vertical File—Pamphlets	. . . .	General pamphlets placed in arranged file in library

SELECTED BOOKS ON TEXTILES

Title	Author	Type	Date published	Publisher
A Comprehensive Dictionary of Textile Terms	Higgins and LaVault	Dictionary	1948	Dover Press Fall River, Mass.
American Cotton Handbook	Merrill, Macromac, and Mauersberger	Reference	1949	Textile Book Publishers, Inc. 303 Fifth Avenue New York 16, N. Y.
American Wool Handbook	Von Berger and Mauersberger	Reference	1949	Textile Book Publishers, Inc. 303 Fifth Avenue New York 16, N. Y.
America's Fabrics	Bendure and Pfeiffer	Reference	1946	The Macmillan Company 60 Fifth Ave. New York, N. Y.
Applied Textiles	Linton and Pizzuto	Textbook	1948	Lifetime Editions, Inc. 120 E. 25th St. New York, N. Y.
Calloway Textile Dictionary	Carmichael, Linton, and Price	Dictionary	1947	Calloway Mills La Grange, Georgia
Fiber to Fabric	Potter	Textbook	1945	The Gregg Publishing Co. 330 W. 42nd St. New York, N. Y.
Handbook of Industrial Fabrics	Haven	Reference	1938	Wellington Sears Company 65 Worth Street New York, N. Y.
Rayon Handbook	Schwarz and Mauersberger	Reference	1939	Rayon Handbook Company 303 Fifth Avenue New York, N. Y.
Staple Cotton Fabrics	Hoye	Reference	1942	McGraw-Hill Book Company 330 W. 42nd St. New York, N. Y.

Title	Author	Type	Date published	Publisher
Staple Cotton Fabrics Swatch Book	Hoye	Reference	1943	Hoye Publishing Company 5341–64th St. Maspeth, L. I., N. Y.
Textile Brand Names Dictionary	by publisher	Dictionary	1947	Textile Book Publishers, Inc. 303 Fifth Avenue New York, N. Y.
Textile Chemistry and Dyeing	Olney	Reference	1942	Planograph Printed by Spaulding Mose Company Boston, Massachusetts
Textile Fabrics and Their Selection	Wingate	Reference	1942	Prentice-Hall, Inc. 70 Fifth Avenue New York, N. Y.
Textile Fiber Atlas	Von Bergen	Reference on microscopic structure of fibers	1942	American Wool Handbook Company 303 Fifth Avenue New York, N. Y.
Textile Fibers and Their Use	Hess	Textbook	1948	J. B. Lippincott Co. 333 West Lake St. Chicago, Ill.
Textiles	Denny	Dictionary	1947	J. B. Lippincott Co. 333 West Lake St. Chicago, Ill.
Textiles	Woolman and McGowan	Textbook	1943	The Macmillan Company 60 Fifth Ave. New York, N. Y.
Textile Testing	Skinkle	Reference	1949	Chemical Publishing Co, Inc. 26 Court Street Brooklyn 2, N. Y.
The New Fibers	Sherman and Sherman	Reference	1946	D. Van Nostrand Company, Inc. 250 Fourth Avenue New York, N. Y.

JOURNALS AND MAGAZINES OF VALUE IN TEXTILES

Title	Customary abbreviation	Country	Address of publisher
American Dyestuff Reporter	Am. Dyestuff Reptr.	United States	1 Madison Avenue New York 10, N. Y.
American Fabrics		United States	Reporter Publications, Inc. Empire State Building New York 1, N. Y.
A.S.T.M. Standards on Textile Materials (annual)	A.S.T.M.	United States	American Society for Testing Materials 1916 Race St. Philadelphia 3, Pa.
American Wool and Cotton Reporter	Am. Wool and Cotton Reptr.	United States	530 Atlantic Ave. Boston 10, Mass.
Canadian Textile Journal	Can. Text. J.	Canada	1434 St. Catherine St. W. Montreal, Quebec Canada
Indian Textile Journal	Indian Text. J.	India	Surya Mahal Military Square Fort Bombay, India
Industrial and Engineering Chemistry	Ind. Eng. Chem.	United States	American Chemical Society Easton, Pennsylvania
Journal of the Chemical Society of Japan	J. Chem. Soc.	Japan	Editorial Office 1155–16th St. N.W. Washington, D. C.
Journal of the Society of Dyers and Colourists	J. Soc. Dyers and Colourists	England	The University Leeds, England
Journal of the Textile Institute	J. Text. Inst.	England	16 St. Mary's Parsonage Manchester 3, England
Melliand Textilberichte (2 editions,–1 English and 1 German)	Melliand Textilber.	Germany	Heidelberg, Germany

Title	Customary abbreviation	Country	Address of publisher
Modern Plastics Encyclopedia (annual)		United States	122 E. 42nd St. New York 17, N. Y.
Papers of the American Association of Textile Technologists	Papers of A.A.T.T.	United States	7 East 12th Street New York 3, N. Y.
Rayon and Synthetic Textiles (formerly Rayon Textile Monthly)	Rayon and Syn. Tex. (Rayon Text. Mo.)	United States	Rayon Publishing Corporation 303 Fifth Ave. New York 16, N. Y.
Teintex	Teintex	France	Paris, France
Textile Age	Textile Age	United States	381–4th Ave. New York 16, N. Y.
Textile Bulletin	Tex. Bul.	United States	Clark Publishing Co. P.O. Box 1225 Charlotte 1, N. C.
Textile Industries (formerly Cotton)	Textile Inds.	United States	W. R. C. Smith Publishing Co. 806 Peachtree St., N.E. Atlanta, Georgia
Textile Journal of Australia	Text. J. Australia	Australia	19–47 Jeffcott St. Melbourne, Victoria Australia
Textile Recorder	Textile Recorder	England	Old Colony House S. King St. Manchester 2, England
Textile Research Journal	Tex. Res. J.	United States	10 E. 40th St. New York 16, N. Y.
Textile Technology Digest	Tex. Tech. Digest	United States	Institute of Textile Technology Charlottesville, Virginia

Title	Customary abbreviation	Country	Address of publisher
Textile World	Textile World	United States	330 W. 42nd St. New York 18, N. Y.
Textil-Rundschau (new)	Textil-Rundschau	Switzerland	St. Gallen, Switzerland
Transactions of the Faraday Society		England	Gurney and Jackson 98 Great Russell St. London, England

Note: The magazines in this list include the first nineteen in a rating list of the world's most important textile magazines. An idea of the relative importance of textiles in the different countries may be obtained from the number of textile magazines published in each country.

The first nineteen magazines in the rating list:

8 in United States
4 in England
1 each in:
  India
  Canada
  Switzerland
  Australia
  France
  Japan
  Germany

ABSTRACTS FOR SPEED IN REFERENCE WORK

Title	Dates	Types of abstracts	Publisher
Abstract Service—Resins, Rubbers, Plastics	1942– to date	Technical	Interscience Publishers, Inc. 250 Fifth Ave. New York, N. Y.
Chemical Abstracts	1907– to date decennial for 1907–1916 1917–1926 1927–1936	Technical	American Chemical Society Easton, Pennsylvania Editorial office: Ohio State University, Columbus 10, Ohio
Textile Technology Digest	1914– to date	Technical—textile chemistry, physics, machinery, processes, management	Institute of Textile Technology Charlottesville, Virginia

Each copy of the following magazines has a section devoted to abstracts and book reviews:

	Vol. no. for 1949		
American Dyestuff Reporter	38	Technical— periodicals books	Howes Publishing Co., Inc. 44 E. 23rd St. New York 10, N. Y.
Journal of Home Economics	41	Technical and general— periodicals books	American Home Economics Association 700 Victor Building, Washington 1, D. C.
Journal of the Textile Institute	40	Technical— periodicals books	The Textile Institute 16 St. Mary's Parsonage Manchester 3, England

Title	Dates	Types of abstracts	Publisher
Rayon and Synthetic Textiles	29	Technical and general— periodicals books	Rayon Publishing Corp. 303 Fifth Ave. New York 16, N. Y.
Textile Research Journal	19	Technical— periodicals	Textile Research Institute, Inc. and Textile Foundation 10 E. 40th St. New York 16, N. Y.
Textile World	99	Trade and Industrial book reviews	McGraw-Hill Publishing Co. 330 W. 42 St. New York 36, N. Y.

INVENTORY OF RESOURCES OF UNITED STATES OF AMERICA FOR TEXTILE RESEARCH, DEVELOPMENT, EDUCATION, AND TESTING *

a) Textile schools and colleges giving degrees in textiles
  (1) Bradford-Durfee Technical Institute, Fall River, Mass.
  (2) School of Textiles, Clemson Agricultural College, Clemson, S. C.
  (3) A. French Textile School, Georgia Institute of Technology, Atlanta, Ga.
  (4) Lowell Textile Institute, Lowell, Mass.
  (5) New Bedford Textile Institute, New Bedford, Mass.
  (6) School of Textiles, North Carolina State College, Raleigh, N. C.
  (7) Philadelphia Textile Institute, Philadelphia, Pa.
  (8) Rhode Island School of Design, Textile School, Providence, R. I.
  (9) Texas Technological College, Lubbock, Tex.
  (10) School of Textile Technology, Alabama Polytechnic Institute, Auburn, Ala.

b) Educational institutions giving graduate courses leading to a master's or doctor's degree in science, engineering, or research directed toward textiles
  (1) The Clemson Agricultural College, Clemson, S. C.
  (2) Georgia Institute of Technology, Atlanta, Ga.
  (3) Institute of Textile Technology, Charlottesville, Va.
  (4) Lowell Textile Institute, Lowell, Mass.
  (5) Massachusetts Institute of Technology, Cambridge, Mass.
  (6) Princeton University in cooperation with Textile Research Institute, Inc. and the Textile Foundation, Princeton, N. J.

c) Colleges, universities, and trade schools giving courses in textiles
  A large number of schools give courses in textiles, especially in home economics and retailing departments, not leading to degrees in textiles. For names of schools including such courses in their curricula write Office of Education, Washington, D. C.

d) Textile foundations and research institutes
  (1) The Textile Foundation, Princeton, N. J., and Washington, D. C., devoted to textile research. (Publication offices: Kent, Conn.)
  (2) The Textile Research Institute, Princeton, N. J., and New York, N. Y.
  (3) The Institute of Textile Technology, Charlottesville, Va. Chartered by the state of Virginia as a graduate school, authorized to grant master's and doctor's degrees.
  (4) New England Textile Foundation, offering support to the four New England Textile Schools, 68 South Main St., Providence, R. I.
  (5) North Carolina Textile Foundation, offering support to School of Textiles of North Carolina State College, Raleigh, N. C.
  (6) Philadelphia Textile Institute Foundation, Land Title Building, Philadelphia, Pa., offering support to the Philadelphia Textile Institute.

* *Inventory of the Resources of the U. S. of America for Textile Research, Development, Education and Testing* (New York: New York Board of Trade, Textile Section, 1949).

(7) J. E. Sirrine Textile Foundation, offering support to the School of Textiles, Clemson Agricultural College, Clemson, S. C.

(8) The Textile Education Foundation, Inc., offering support to the A. French Textile School of The Georgia Institute of Technology, Atlanta, Ga.

e) United States Government agencies contributing to textile development

    (1) National Bureau of Standards, Department of Commerce, Washington 25, D. C.

    (2) United States Department of Agriculture:

        (a) Southern Regional Research Laboratory, New Orleans, La. Cotton, peanut proteins

        (b) Northern Regional Research Laboratory, Peoria, Ill. Soybean, amyloseacetate, zein, proteins

        (c) Eastern Regional Research Laboratory, Wyndmoor, Pa. Casein

        (d) Western Regional Research Laboratory, Albany, Cal. Chicken feather (keratin), egg albumin, wheat protein

        (e) Bureau of Human Nutrition & Home Economics, 14th and Independence Avenue, S.W., Washington, D. C.

        (f) Research & Testing Division, Cotton Branch, Agricultural Marketing Administration, Washington, D. C.

            Field Laboratories:

                Clemson, S. C.

                College Station, Tex.

                Stoneville, Miss.

    (3) United States Army:

        (a) Quartermaster General, Research & Development Branch, Washington 25, D. C.

        (b) Research & Development Laboratory, Quartermaster Depot, Philadelphia, Pa.

        (c) Ordnance Department, Washington, D. C.

    (4) United States Air Force:

        (a) Material Command, Wright-Patterson Air Base, Dayton, Ohio.

    (5) United States Navy:

        (a) Bureau of Ordnance, Washington, D. C.

        (b) Bureau of Naval Supplies, Washington, D. C.

        (c) Bureau of Aeronautics, Washington, D. C.

    (6) Federal Trade Commission, Washington, D. C.

    (7) National Research Council, Washington, D. C.

f) Technical associations and societies contributing to textile research and standardization

    (1) American Society for Testing Materials, Committee D-13 on Textile Materials

    (2) American Association of Textile Chemists & Colorists

    (3) American Association of Textile Technologists

    (4) The Fiber Society

    (5) Textile Section of the American Society of Mechanical Engineers

    (6) Textile Section of New York Board of Trade

    (7) American Standards Association, Inc., Committee D-14 Textiles

g) Independent laboratories specializing in textile testing

See "Directory of Textile Testing Laboratories, Commercial and Educational," published by The Textile Foundation, Kent, Conn., 1943. Free upon application. Fifty-eight commercial laboratories are listed.

h) Educational laboratories equipped to make textile tests
See the "Directory of Textile Testing Laboratories, Commercial and Educational." Thirty-five educational textile testing laboratories are listed.

i) Other laboratories, some of which conduct textile research and make textile tests

(1) Directory of the American Council of Commercial Laboratories, 1949 (no charge), obtainable from

> Dr. Harold M. Dudley, Executive Secretary
> 1507 M Street, N. W.
> Washington 5, D. C.

(2) Directory of Commercial and College Laboratories, 1947 (Miscellaneous Publication M 187), National Bureau of Standards, Washington, D. C., Government Printing Office, Washington 25, D. C.—30 cents.

(3) Industrial Research Laboratories of the United States (eighth edition), 1946; Bulletin 113, 414 pages—$5.00; National Research Council, 2101 Constitution Avenue, Washington 25, D. C.

CONVERSION TABLE, LENGTH, VOLUME, WEIGHT

Length:

1 angstrom (Å) = (10^{-10}) meters = 0.000,000,000,1 meters
1 millimicron = 10^{-9} meters = 0.000,000,001 meters
1 micron (mu) = 0.000,001 meter
1 millimeter (mm) = 0.001 meter
1 centimeter (cm) = 0.01 meter
1 decimeter (dm) = 0.1 meter
1 kilometer (km) = 1000 meters
1 meter = 100 cm = 1000 mm = 0.001 kilometer = 39.37 inches
1 centimeter = 0.3937 inches = 10,000 microns
1 inch   = 2.54 cm
1 foot = 12 in.   = 30.48 cm = 0.305 meters
1 yard = 36 in. = 3 ft = .914 meters

Fig. Ap.1. Centimeter-inch rule (to scale).

Volume:

1 cubic centimeter (cc) = 0.061 cubic inch
1 cubic meter   = 35.314 cubic feet
1 cubic meter   = 1.308 cubic yards

Volume:

    1 cubic inch =   16.387 cubic centimeters

    1 cubic foot =   0.0283 cubic meters

    1 cubic yard =   0.765 cubic meters

Weight:

    1,000 milligrams = 1 gram (gm)

    1,000 grams = 1 kilogram (kg) =   2.2 pounds

    1,000 kilograms = 1 metric ton = 2,204.6 pounds

    16 ounces = 1 pound = 453.25 grams

    2,000 pounds = 1 ton = 907.185 kilograms

COMPARISONS OF MAGNIFICATIONS

Instrument	Focal length mm	Useful magnification, diameter	Depth of focus	Limit of resolution
Eye	..	1	..	100–200
Hand lens	25	5–20	40	10
Binocular microscope	32	80	25	2.5
Research microscope	16	200	4	1.0
Research microscope	8	400	0.9	0.5
Research microscope	4	700	0.2	0.3
Research microscope	4	800	0.08	0.26
Oil immersion objective 4200Å	3	1,400	0.06	0.15
Ultraviolet objective 2700Å ..	3	2,000	0.04	0.10
Electron microscope	4	50,000	10	0.004

Source: Charles J. Burton, R. Bowling Barnes, and T. G. Rochow, "The Electron Microscope," *Industrial and Engineering Chemistry* (Reprinted by permission), 34-12 (1942), 1429–1436.

Index

Abacá, 6, 7, 14, 66
Absorbency, finishes for, 331
Africa, fibers from, 83, 84
Alaska, musk ox, 127, 128
Aleppo wool, 102
Algenates, 157–158
Alkalis, effect on wool, 106–107
Alpaca, 123–125, 301
Aluminum fiber, 4, 185
American Home Economics Association, 392
American Society for Testing Materials, 153, 184, 383, 390, 393
American Standards Association, 153, 157, 392
Aralac, 160–162
Ardil, 163
Argentina:
  jute industry, 74
  wool, 91, 92
Arkwright, Richard, 44, 87
Asbestos, 4, 8, 183, 184
Atlas cloth, 268
Australia:
  rabbit hair, 129
  ramie, 61
  wool production, 8, 91, 94, 95, 96–97
Azlons, 154–167
  definition, 159
  stabilization of molecular chains, 159–160

Bag industry:
  jute, 73, 74, 78–79, 81, 83
Bast fibers, 84, 188
  jute, 72, 83
  physical characteristics of, 53, 191
  properties, 51–57
  ramie, 60–66
  retting methods, 50
Batik, 298
Beetling, 319–320

Belgium, flax, 45, 58
Bemberg rayon, 147, 148, 151, 152, 154, 155, 156
Bengal, 14
  jute, 74
Bleaching, 326–327, 358
Blends, fibers used for:
  casein, 162
  peanut fiber, 163
  rayon and wool, 153
  ramie used in, 66
  redwood bark fibers, 83
  vicara for, 165
Bobbin winding, 242
Bonded fabrics, 275–276
  properties and uses, 276
Boston, Mass., wool market, 96–97
Braiding, 277
Brazil, textile industry, 61, 74, 76, 136
Breaking strength:
  definition, 369
  effect of light on, 361–368
Bristles:
  cabbage palmetto for, 83
  casein for, 162
  Orlon, 176
British Empire, wool industry, 92
Bureau of Human Nutrition and Home Economics, 35, 382–384, 400
Burlap bags, 13, 73, 74, 78–79, 81, 83
Burling, 322
By-products:
  cotton, 27, 28
  fibers from agricultural, 166
  flax, 58

Cabbage palmetto, 83
Cables, hemp for, 68, 71
Calcutta, 14
  jute industry, 73
Calendering, finishing processes, 316–318
Camelidae, 121–123